HELICOPTERS

MODERN CIVIL AND MILITARY ROTORCRAFT

HELICOPTERS

MODERN CIVIL AND MILITARY ROTORCRAFT

GENERAL EDITOR: ROBERT JACKSON

BARNES & NOBLE

NEW YORK

This edition published by Barnes & Noble, Inc.,
by arrangement with Amber Books Ltd
2006 Barnes & Noble Books

Editorial and design by
Amber Books Ltd
Bradley's Close
74–77 White Lion Street
London N1 9PF
United Kingdom

Barnes & Noble Publishing
122 Fifth Avenue
New York 10011

ISBN-13: 978-0-7607-8167-8
ISBN-10: 0-7607-8167-2

Printed in Singapore

M 10 9 8 7 6 5 4 3 2 1

Project Editor: Sarah Uttridge
Design: Hawes Design

PICTURE CREDITS:
All photographs and illustrations provided by Art-Tech/Aerospace Publishing.

Contents

Introduction

On the night of 16/17 January 1991, several hours before the start of Operation Desert Storm – the Allied offensive against Iraq – eight McDonnell Douglas AH-64 Apache helicopters of the US 101st Airborne Division flew northward at low level into the desert darkness. The helicopters were heavily laden with extra fuel tanks, Hellfire air-to-surface missiles, 70mm (2.75-in) rockets and 30mm (1.2-in) ammunition. Accompanying them, for navigational purposes, was a USAF special operations CH-53. The Apaches' mission was to penetrate deep inside Iraq and destroy two key radar sites, opening a corridor for the Allied strike aircraft assigned to key targets in the Baghdad area.

The mission involved a round trip of 950 nautical miles, and was flawless. The Apaches split into two attack groups in the target area, popping up to 100 feet at the last moment to launch a total of fifteen laser-guided Hellfires, all of which hit the two radar sites. The helicopter teams also launched 100 70mm (2.75-in) rockets and strafed the targets with 4000 rounds of 30mm (1.2-in) ammunition before leaving the area. The attack had lasted less than two minutes.

This incident serves to demonstrate the awesome power of the attack helicopter, a concept first devised by the Germans in World War II. At that time the Germans enjoyed an undisputed lead in helicopter development, the two companies at the forefront being Focke-Achgelis and Flettner. They first pioneered the operational use of the helicopter, both as a weapons platform and a transport vehicle.

On the Allied side, one name quickly came to the forefront of helicopter design: that of Igor Sikorsky. It is a name that still stands at the forefront of medium and heavy helicopter design today. Another American firm, Bell helicopters, dominated the post-war market for lighter machines, ranging from utility to fast attack helicopters.

In the Soviet Union, Igor Sikorsky's opposite number was Artem I. Mil, whose design bureau was responsible for a range of massive heavy-lift helicopters. By the beginning of the 21st century, more than 30,000 Mil helicopters had been built, with many of these rugged machines remaining in service worldwide.

Today, helicopters are applied to so many different tasks that it is difficult to list them all. They are the most versatile flying machines in existence, and they enable the pilot to operate in three dimensions in a way that no fixed-wing aircraft can – except, of course, VSTOL machines like the Harrier, which are restricted to a specific role and which are by no means as prolific.

The helicopter, for all that it is expensive to operate, has become an indispensable tool of modern aviation. New technology, in particular the use of advanced composite materials of far greater strength and lightness than anything previously available, has given designers the means to enter a new phase of development that combines greater speeds with lower operating costs.

This book gives an in-depth insight into helicopters of all kinds, civilian, military and naval, combining expert text with splendid artworks to provide an excellent work of reference.

The awesome power of the modern military helicopter is epitomised in this dramatic shot of a Sikorsky MH-53J Pave Low III, in service with the special operations squadrons of the United States Air Force.

For a demonstration tour of the People's Republic of China in 1987, this Boeing 234 Chinook was painted in the colours of the Chinese National Airline, CAAC.

Civil Helicopters

Aérospatiale SA 365 Dauphin family

Despite its limited early sales, Aérospatiale's Dauphin series later emerged as one of the most successful helicopters ever produced. Characterised by its fenestron tail rotor, the Dauphin found particular favour as a fast executive transport.

France entered the helicopter business soon after World War II and went on to produce the Alouette series of machines, which remained in production until 1985. By the late 1960s Sud-Aviation, which had been created on 1 March 1957, and was itself succeeded by Aérospatiale on 1 January 1970, was working on a single-engined successor. Designated the SA 360 Dauphin, the new model made its first flight on 2 June 1972, but was not seen in public until the Paris Air Show in June the following year.

The first prototype (F-WSQL) was powered by the 730-kW

Above: Intended as a replacement for the widely-used Alouette series, the prototype Dauphin F-WSQL was highly praised by pilots for its exceptional visibility from the cockpit, although many pilots complained that the helicopter was under-powered.

Top: Prominent on the early Dauphin variants were the small outrigger and tail-mounted wheels. This ski equipped single-engined SA 360C is seen demonstrating its high altitude ability.

(980-shp) Turboméca Astazou XVI turboshaft engine, and had a four-bladed main rotor, using Alouette blades, and a fully-

In the commercial market the SA 360 was able to carry up to nine passengers in a number of alternative cabin layouts. Also offered was a medevac-configured model able to accommodate four stretcher cases plus an attendant.

glazed front fuselage section. But its most notable feature was the new fenestron shrouded fan in place of the conventional tail rotor, though this had already flown on the Gazelle light military utility helicopter. After 180 flights the prototype was fitted with the more powerful 782-kW (1,050-shp) Astazou XVIIIA along with new plastic rotor blades, and further modified to reduce

SPECIFICATION

Aérospatiale SA365C Dauphin
Type: Utility helicopter
Powerplant: two 680-hp (505-kW)
Turbomèca Arriel turboshafts
Performance: max cruising speed 260
km/h (166 mph); initial climb rate 504
m (1,653 ft) per minute; hovering
ceiling 4572 m (15,000 ft); range 545
km (339 miles)

Weights: empty 1806 kg (3,980 lb),
maximum takeoff 3400 kg (7,495lb)
Dimensions: main rotor diameter
11.68 m (38 ft 4 in); length overall
13.32 m (43 ft 9 in); fuselage length
10.98 m (37 ft 7 in).
Payload: maximum seating for 14
people

Already flown on the earlier and popular Gazelle helicopter, the fenestron was to be retained throughout the Dauphin series. Later models would also be fitted with a retractable nosewheel undercarriage.

vibration and eliminate ground resonance. It flew again in its modified form on 4 March 1973 and went on to establish several closed-circuit speed records in its early career.

Production of the commercial 11-seat SA 360C Dauphin began in 1974. The French airworthiness certification was awarded on 18 December 1975, followed by American Federal Aviation Administration (FAA) certification on 31 March 1976.

Double power
The big but under-powered Dauphin proved of limited appeal in the marketplace and only 28 were built, including a single SA 360A for evaluation by France's Aéronavale. Three SA 360Cs were also converted to SA 361 models with Astazou XX turboshafts and Starflex rotor hubs, adapted as standard on later models. The prototype (F-ZWVF) for this improved variant flew for the first time on 12 July 1976. Development for military use meanwhile continued on an experimental basis, and produced the SA 361H/HCL (Hélicoptère de Combat Léger) anti-tank prototype (F-WZAK), equipped with FLIR and eight HOT missiles.

However, Aérospatiale quickly realised that the way forward was to produce a twin-engined version and this prototype, SA 365C Dauphin 2 (F-WVKE) made its maiden flight on 24 January 1975, introducing

twin Arriel 1A turboshaft engines, each delivering 485 kW (650 shp) take-off power. This was followed two days later by the SA 366, which differed only in having two 507-kW (680-shp) Lycoming LTS 101 engines to appeal to the American market. The first civil production model was designated SA 365C and entered service in 1978. Slight improvements in powerplants and transmissions produced the SA 365C1, with 497-kW (667-shp) Arriel 1A1 turbo-shafts, and the SA 365C2, with 499-kW (670-shp) Arriel 1A2s.

Chinese take-away
On 2 July 1980 Aérospatiale signed an agreement with China National Aero-Technology Import & Export Corporation (CATIC) for licence-production of the Dauphin 2 by the Harbin Aircraft

Manufacturing Company (HAMC). The first (French-built) example made its initial acceptance flight in China on 6 February 1982. Chinese parts manufacture began in 1986 and the last of an initial batch of 50 assembled aircraft was delivered in January 1992.

The first units were designated Z-9 Haitun (Dolphin), but later aircraft were updated to AS 365N1 standard as Z-9As, and also incorporated an increased portion of locally-produced components.

A second batch of 50 is currently believed to be under construction, designated Z-9A-100, with further increases in local production, amounting

to 72.2 per cent of the airframe and 91 per cent of the engine. The Z-9A-100 made its first flight on 16 January 1992 and received type approval on 30 December 1992, after a test programme of 200 hours in 408 flights.

Its engine is the Arriel 1C1 turboshaft, produced in China by SMPMC as the WZA8A. Most of the Haituns built are believed to be operated by China's Aviation of the People's Navy and Army Aviation Corps on utility and transport support duties. An armed anti-tank version has also reportedly been developed, although though the capabilities of this machine have yet to become clear.

With the local name Z-9 Haitun, the Eurocopter AS 365N is built under licence by Harbin for both civil users and all three Chinese air arms. The first production batch was of 50 aircraft. The current version is the Z-9A-100, which is thought to be an anti-tank variant.

Dependable Dauphin

Having established itself an enviable reputation in the four-tonne commercial helicopter field, Eurocopter eagerly sought new roles for its highly capable Dauphin. Whether operating as a corporate taxi or rescuing sailors at sea, the Dauphin has proved to be a most dependable helicopter.

No fewer than 96 examples of the HH-65A Dolphin have been purchased by the US Coast Guard for applications in short-range recovery operations.

At the 1979 Paris Air Show, Aérospatiale won its most prestigious contract, when the US Coast Guard announced that the SA 366G had beaten the Bell 222 and Sikorsky S-76 in fulfilling its SRR (short-range recovery) requirement for

operation from 18 shore bases, cutters and icebreakers. Under the Buy American Act, 51 per cent of the value of each machine had to come from the US aviation industry. What emerged was a truly Franco-US helicopter with Collins avionics, Lycoming LTS101-750 engines,

and a hoist on an outrigger to the right of the cabin, able to lift up to 1600 kg (3,500 lb). The airframe also had to be extensively modified, with a new fenestron which was 20 per cent more efficient than a conventional tail rotor, and offered improved handling in a crosswind. Another benefit of the enclosed tail fan was that, if

it failed, the pilot could perform a running landing at 60 kt (111 km/h; 69 mph); in most other helicopters, the pilot would have to have resorted to an emergency autorotation. Pop-out flotation bags, a roof-opening to ease the passage of casualties, and internal stretcher fittings, were other specifics demanded by the USCG.

The SA 366G, known by the USCG as the HH-65A Dolphin, flew for the first time on 23 July 1980, before being shipped to the Aérospatiale Helicopter Corporation (AHC) in Texas for the installation of avionics and flight-testing for FAA certification. A total of four development aircraft was built, before delivery of the first operational aircraft with enlarged fenestron, designated SA 366G1, was made in 1984. Over

Three SA 365Fs were acquired by the French navy for plane guard duties aboard the Jeanne d'Arc, Foch and Clemenceau. The Aéronavale may buy a further 40 examples.

Right: Although the Dauphin was targeted at the corporate and air taxi markets, it has been operated by offshore operations and law enforcement agencies. Civilian variants are flown in a number of countries, including Angola, France, India, Malaysia (illustrated), South Africa, Sweden, the UK and the US.

the next five years, 96 Dolphins were purchased by the Coast Guard. The Dolphin was also the catalyst for an Israeli Defence Force order for seven AS 565SA ASW/ASUW variants with Elbit search radar and navigation suite, to be known as Atalef (Bat).

Extending the capability

The type has been continually improved, first with the reinforced gearbox and servo controls of the AS 365N2, which allowed an increase in all-up weight from 4060 kg (8,950 lb) to 4250 kg (9,369 lb). This was followed by the installation of a cockpit voice recorder and flight data recorder, NVG-compatible light sources and an air collision avoidance system (ACAS). Other planned modifications include increasing the engine power by 10 per cent with the LTS.101-750-132 turboshaft with FADEC, and replacing the fuel tanks.

Some 80 Dolphins are in continuous service from 18 different bases, as far apart as Alaska and Hawaii, on missions ranging from sea rescues to the pursuit of drug traffickers; during the latter operations, the Dolphins operate alongside the USCG's HC-130Hs. The Dolphins are not limited to operating from land bases. Recently, shipborne operations have seen the helicopters accompany expeditions to the Arctic and Antarctic for environmental research purposes where, despite the harsh conditions, the helicopters have performed well.

Although the Dolphin has been a success, there were complaints that it lacked power, especially in the hot conditions around the coastlines of California and Florida in the summer. Re-engining the helicopter was considered, but rejected as being too costly.

Right: Seen during a training exercise, an HH-65A Dolphin approaches the USCG cutter Matagorda, lowering a transfer basket towards the stern of the vessel. The Dolphin is mainly restricted to inshore operations due to its lack of range.

HH-65A Dolphin

The HH-65A is based on a three-seat version of the AS 365N. The HH-65A makes extensive use of composite materials giving the helicopter the nickname of 'plastic puppy'.

High conspicuity
The entire HH-65A fleet has now adopted an overall red paint scheme, primarily to enhance its conspicuity when flying from icebreakers. The single-colour paint scheme also saves about three man-days per helicopter during overhauls.

Flight characteristics
Instead of a traditional tail rotor, the Dolphin has a shrouded fan know as a fenestron, which gives the pilot better crosswind control and uses less power when in the hover.

Cockpit configuration
The crew of the Dolphin consists of a pilot, co-pilot and flight engineer. The flight engineer's seat moves from one side of the cabin to the other by means of rails in the floor. The large glazed area provides excellent visibility for the crew.

Shipboard operations
HH-65As embarked on icebreakers are now fitted with skis in addition to their standard undercarriage, giving them more stability in snow and ice operations.

Aérospatiale

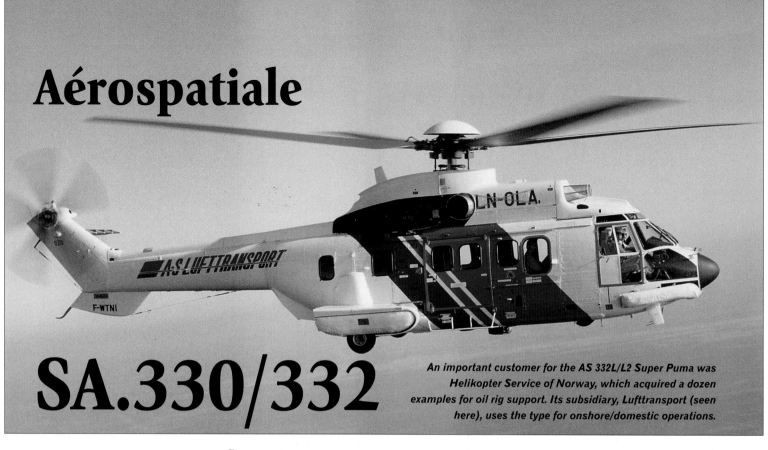

SA.330/332

An important customer for the AS 332L/L2 Super Puma was Helikopter Service of Norway, which acquired a dozen examples for oil rig support. Its subsidiary, Lufttransport (seen here), uses the type for onshore/domestic operations.

Puma/Super Puma
Offshore 'cats'

Civilian versions of the Puma/Super Puma family have been used as passenger and cargo transports. The aircraft has also gained a reputation as the world's leading oil rig support helicopter.

The Puma originated in the Anglo-French Helicopter Agreement of 1967, under which Britain and France co-operated in the design, development and manufacture of the British-led Lynx and French-led Gazelle and Puma. The Puma was designed principally as a military support/assault helicopter to replace RAF Whirlwinds and Belvederes and French ALAT-operated Sikorsky S-58s.

The original specification called for an all-weather, day/night helicopter though, in the event, it was to be some years before the type had a suitable radar (and sufficient power reserves) to meet the requirement. Early versions were, however, fast, reliable, and agile, and marked a

dramatic improvement over the helicopter types which they replaced. Using the same basic configuration as the larger Super Frelon, the Puma was of lighter, more modern, construction. It introduced a counter-clockwise tail rotor to starboard, and had a semi-retractable undercarriage, with the main and nose gear retracting into open bays in the lower fuselage and sponsons. The type also featured huge sliding cabin doors on both sides, allowing for rapid ingress and egress. Provision was made for a central external load hook, for carrying underslung cargo.

The first of eight prototype and pre-production SA 330s made its maiden flight at Marignane on 15 April 1965, and the type entered military service in 1970.

Originally optimised for

From the beginning, the key market for the Puma/Super Puma was the oil company support sector. This Italian registered, float-equipped SA 330J was operated by Shell (Malta) Ltd.

military use, what was then known as the Sud Aviation SA 330 had obvious potential for several civilian roles, and soon spawned a number of civil variants. The first of these was the SA 330F, which was broadly equivalent to the original ALAT SA 330C and RAF SA 330E (Puma HC.Mk 1), with two 984-kW (1,320-shp) Turmo IIIC4 engines and capable of a top speed of 151 kt (280 km/h; 174mph). The basic Puma enjoyed only modest sales

success on the civil market, despite offering good performance and relatively low operating costs. Fortunately, the next generation would be more successful.

The Puma had always had considerable development potential, and this was exploited with the launch of the AS 332B and civil AS 332C Super Puma. These versions retained the basic cabin dimensions of the standard Puma, but had more powerful 1327-kW (1,780 shp)

Tyrolean Airways operated this AS 332C Super Puma in the early 1980s. The aircraft's versatility was utilised to undertake many different tasks such as erecting ski lift pylons, as seen here.

Makila 1A turboshaft engines. Associated with the new engines were prominent intake filters (also fitted to some standard Puma versions) and a noticeable ventral fin below the rear part of the tailboom. Intended primarily for the civil market, the Super Puma also had a new nose profile, with provision for a Bendix/King RDR 1400 or Honeywell Primus 500 weather radar.

With more power available, Aérospatiale next stretched the aircraft by 76 cm (30 in), adding 1.9 m³ (67 cu ft) to the cabin volume and allowing up to 21 passengers (usually 20) to be carried. In this stretched form the aircraft was designated as the AS 332M or (civil) AS 332L Super Puma. The first stretched Super Puma was certificated in 1983, and the type rapidly proved popular with civil operators, particularly in the North Sea oil rig support role. About 70 were delivered.

Bristow Helicopters procured large numbers of Super Pumas (some 31 aircraft), and modified them to meet their North Sea support requirements, renaming the aircraft the Tiger. The aircraft, often confusingly referred to as 'Super Tigers', feature a proprietary passenger interior with a hard floor and folding seats – to allow the carriage of passengers and/or freight – automatic cabin door jettison, large-capacity liferafts, and North Sea navaids. The aircraft have a full IFR instrument fit, a flight management system, and ice protection on the tailplane, main and tail rotor blades and main rotor droop stops. They also have external access to the baggage compartment.

Indonesian production
A small number of civil AS 332s was built in Indonesia by IPTN as NAS 332L1s, seven of which were sold to Iran in 1996 for offshore oil rig support duties.

Military Super Puma variants were redesignated in 1990, gaining 532-series mark numbers and the name Cougar, but civil variants continued to use the AS 332 designation and the original Super Puma name. The basic Super Puma/Cougar was further developed to produce the AS 332L2 Super Puma Mk II, first delivered in 1993. This, the current production version, is built only in 'long-fuselage' form, although this is longer than the original AS 332L1, with a 55-cm (1-ft 9½-in) composite plug in the rear cabin making space for an extra row of seats and with the tail rotor shifted further aft. This also gives the new version a less obvious step between the cabin and the tail rotor pylon, with a gentler, less inclined slope up to the tailboom. The new variant makes increased use of composite materials, and has

A total of 27 AS 332L Tigers remains in service with Bristow Helicopters, servicing the oil rig routes in the North Sea.

Spheriflex main and tail rotor heads, longer, parabolic-tipped main rotor blades, a four-axis AFCS (automatic flight-control system), built-in HUMS (health and usage monitoring system) and a digital EFIS flight deck. This is supplied by Sextant Avionique, and consists of four integrated LCD display screens. The introduction of the AS 332L2 saw the original AS 332L re-designated as the AS 332M, and the Super Puma Mk 1 name was retrospectively applied to these older aircraft.

The standard AS 332L2 has an airline-type interior with seating for 24 passengers and a flight attendant, or for 19 passengers over longer ranges, with increased seat pitch. Customers for the type have included Helikopter Service of Norway, which ordered four in May 1992, followed by four more in June 1997. Bond Helicopters ordered two in 1998.

A more austere configuration could use the military interior, which can seat 28 troops plus a loadmaster. There is also an ambulance version holding 12 stretchers and seating four 'walking wounded', plus an attendant. The AS 332L2 Super Puma Mk II VIP seats between eight and 15 passengers, with a two four-seat lounge arrangement in the least intensive configuration. The aircraft also has a fully-equipped galley and toilet, and is rather more luxuriously appointed. The only known civil customer for the VIP Super Puma is the Korean electronics firm, Samsung.

New variant
Production of the Super Puma (and the military Cougar) continues, while further developments are planned to compete with newer entrants to the market like the EH 101 and the Sikorsky S-92. In 1998, Eurocopter announced a proposed Super Puma Mk III, specifically tailored to the offshore/oil-rig support role, with a further 25 per cent increase in cabin volume. Eurocopter optimistically expects to sell 200 examples of the new version.

SPECIFICATION	
Aérospatiale SA 330L Puma **Type:** medium transport helicopter **Powerplant:** two 1175-kW (1575-hp) Turboméca Turmo IVC turboshafts **Performance:** maximum speed 294km/h (182mph); range 572 km (355 miles); service ceiling 6000 m (19,700 ft)	**Weights:** Empty 36156 kg (7,953 lb); max takeoff 7400 kg (16,280 lb) **Dimensions:** Rotor diameter 15 m (49ft 3in), length overall 18.15m (59 ft 6in); height 5.14m (16ft 10in). Main rotor disc area 176.7m2 (1901 sq ft) **Payload:** up to 20 fully equipped troops or 3200 kg (7,000 lb) of cargo

SA 332 Super Puma/AS 532 Cougar

The Icelandic Coast Guard operates a single AS 332L2 Super Puma from Reykjavik airport for search and rescue (SAR), air ambulance and fisheries patrol work.

The Puma led, almost inevitably, to the Super Puma – a larger transport helicopter that has been built in a bewildering range of variants. Since 1990 the military aircraft have been known as the Eurocopter AS 532 Cougar family and are in front-line service around the world.

While the original SA 330 Puma was a popular, and successful design, plans for a replacement began early. By 1974 Aérospatiale had already drawn up proposals for a 'super Puma', which would answer customer calls for more power and more lift capacity. The design that emerged was the SA 332 Super Puma, which shared the uncluttered lines of its predecessor, but was subtly

different. From the beginning the Super Puma used the glass-fibre composite rotor blade technology that had been introduced on the late-model SA 330s. The most obvious change to the SA 332 was the addition of a nose radome to house a weather radar (typically either a Bendix/King RDR 1400 or a Honeywell Primus 500). Under the skin the Super Puma was completely re-engined with a pair of more powerful

Turboméca Makila 1A turboshafts, replacing the original Turmo engines. Unlike the Puma, the Super Puma was aimed squarely at the civil market, though Aérospatiale did not ignore its military potential. The design incorporated several military survivability features such as a gearbox that could run without lubricants (if hit by small arms fire) and main rotors that were ballistically tolerant to up to 40 12.7-mm (0.5-in) calibre hits.

First flight

The first Super Puma took to the air on 13 September 1978. Six prototypes were built and deliveries began in 1981. The initial production aircraft, the military AS 332B and the civil AS 332C, were no larger than the original Puma and could carry up to 21 passengers or 12–18 equipped troops. A stretched

The Super Puma incorporates four glassfibre rotor blades with titanium leading edges and de-icing equipment. The blades are lighter and aerodynamically more efficient than the Puma's original blades.

Super Puma was on the way, however, and in 1979 Aérospatiale introduced the AS 332M (military) and AS 332L (civil) models. These aircraft had a 76-cm (30-in) increase in length and could carry four extra passengers. The stretched Super Puma was certified in 1983, and cleared for operations in known icing conditions – a vital capability for offshore work and SAR missions. In 1986 the Super Puma family was up-engined with the Makila 1A1 turboshaft, and a '1' was added to all aircraft thus modified (the AS 332B becoming the AS 332B1, for example). Aérospatiale also began to introduce more specialised military variants, including the AS 332F/F1, a naval warfare variant that could be armed with two AM39 anti-ship missiles.

The maze of Super Puma designations then started to become even more complex. In the late 1980s, the basic military Super Puma was split along two lines, the AS 332M1 Super Puma Mk I and the AS 332M2 Super Puma Mk II. The Mk I was an AS 332M (stretched AS 332B) fitted with the Makila

1A1 engines. The Mk II was stretched again, this time by a further 0.76 m (2 ft 6 in), adding enough space in the cabin for an additional row of seats. It was also powered by the Makila 1A2 engine. The same process was applied to the civil AS 332L1/L2.

In 1990, the military line was completely reorganised once more. A new designation was adopted, the AS 532, along with a new name, the Cougar. A range of versions appeared, to which Aérospatiale (soon to become Eurocopter France) assigned designation suffixes in the form of: U, unarmed military utility; A, armed; S, anti-ship/anti-submarine; C, *court* (short) fuselage, military transport; L, long fuselage military (and civil). The basic aircraft became the AS 532UC (formerly the AS 332B1) Cougar, a short-fuselage transport version. The AS 532UL (formerly the AS 332M1) was the basic military transport model, derived from the stretched Mk I. The AS 532AC was the armed version of the AS 532UC, while the AS 532AL was the armed version of the AS 532UL. A specialised naval version of the long-fuselage AS 332F1 was developed as the AS 532SC, with the Royal Saudi Navy as its launch customer. This version could be armed with a pair of AM39 Exocet AShMs

The AS 532U2 (formerly the AS 322M2) was the stretched, up-engined military transport version, while the AS 532A2 was its armed derivative. The AS 532A2 is the basic airframe used for the French air force's new RESCO Combat Search and Rescue (C-SAR) helicopter. The RESCO Cougars are fitted with an inflight refuelling probe, FLIR, GPS-based navigation system, a personnel locator system, a sophisticated self-defence system and provision for cabin and pylon-mounted weapons. Development of the RESCO aircraft began in 1995

and the first RESCO Cougars were handed over to the French air force in 1999. Transport AS 532U2s are currently in service with the air forces of France, the Netherlands, Saudi Arabia and Thailand. The final (basic) Cougar variant was developed in 1997. This was the AS 532UB Cougar 100, a simplified 'low-cost' basic transport version without the external sponsons, with revised main undercarriage struts and a new systems fit. An armed version was designated the AS 532AB.

Licence production

The AS 332/532 family has been built under licence by IPTN in Indonesia (as the NAS 332), CASA in Spain and F+W in Switzerland. Some air forces have given their Super Pumas/Cougars local designations, including Spain (HD.21 SAR and HT.21 VIP transport) and Sweden (Hkp 10).

The AS 332F1 Super Puma is a navalised version which incorporates a folding tailboom for shipboard operations, and can be armed with AM39 Exocet missiles, as seen here.

SPECIFICATION	
Aérospatiale AS 332L-1 Super Puma	**Weights:** empty 4460 kg (9,812 lb);
Type: twin-engined transport/support helicopter	maximum take-off 8600 kg (18,920 lb)
Powerplant: two 1184-kW (1,590 lb) (continuous rating) Turbomeca Makila 1A1 turboshafts	**Dimensions:** rotor diameter 15.60 m (15 ft 2in); length 16.29 m (53 ft 5 in); height 4.92 m (16 ft 2 in); main rotor disc area 191.10 m² (2,056 sq ft)
Performance: cruising speed 266 km/h (165 mph); initial climb rate 486 m (1,600 ft) per minute; service ceiling 4600 m (15,100 ft); range 870 km (539 miles)	**Payload:** up to 24 passengers

Right: The AS 532UC retains the original Puma cabin volume. However, a hatch in the floor below the centreline of the main rotor is provided for carrying loads of up to 4500 kg (9,920 lb) in an external cargo sling.

Below: Along with UH-1s, AB 212s and Chinooks, Spanish Army Aviation operates AS 532 Super Pumas/Cougars in the crucial battlefield mobility role.

The JetRanger name has become synonymous with civilian helicopter operations. Most of the major radio and news companies in the USA have operated the type at some time for traffic reports/news-gathering.

Bell 206 JetRanger family

Civilian variants

The JetRanger is one of the most widely recognised aircraft of all time. Having made countless cinema and TV appearances, Bell's Model 206 was the first practical light transport and business helicopter. Even though more modern designs are now available, the JetRanger is still in production, alongside its larger sibling, the Model 206L LongRanger.

In the early 1960s Bell took the reliable turbine powerplant and teetering rotor layout that it had embraced in the Model 204/205/UH-1 Huey family, and built a smaller, lighter, sleeker helicopter around them. This was the Model 206, designed to meet the US Army's requirement for a four-seat, light observation helicopter (LOH).

In the event, Bell was beaten by Hughes's superlative Model 369, which became the OH-6 (though the military Model 206 later staged a major comeback). Undaunted by this initial failure, Bell moved quickly to adapt the Model 206 for the commercial market, where there was a growing niche for a modern utility transport helicopter.

Bell's JetRanger is utilised in a wide variety of tasks. Here, a JetRanger I, carrying a bucket full of agricultural chemicals, demonstrates the type's crop-spraying potential.

The result was the Model 206A JetRanger, which became the blueprint for every light transport helicopter that followed over the next 40 years.

The Model 206A was redesigned from the initial military proposal with a deeper five-seat fuselage, a sharply pointed nose with high stepped windscreen, and streamlined undercarriage skids. The JetRanger, which used conventional materials and was built largely from aluminium, used Bell's trademark twin-bladed, gimballed 'see-saw' main rotor, driven by a 236-kW (317-hp) Allison 250-C18 turboshaft. The main rotor blades had a bonded aluminium skin and aluminium honeycomb core. The tail unit was slightly more exotic, being made from magnesium alloy – a lightweight material, but also a fire hazard if exposed to high temperatures; the use of magnesium was thus limited to the extremities of the aircraft. The housing around the

Joe Ronald Bower established the eastbound round-the-world speed record for rotary-wing aircraft from 28 June to 22 July 1994. Flying a JetRanger III, the journey took 24 days 4 hours 36 minutes. The record still stands today.

engine and pylon was formed from honeycomb glass-fibre. A special extended high-clearance skid option was available, as were large fixed pontoon floats or emergency flotation gear for overwater operations.

The prototype flew on 10 January 1966. FAA type certification was awarded on 20 October and the Model 206 became an instant hit in a notoriously conservative market. In fact, the JetRanger would pioneer the use of the helicopter as a serious business aircraft and was also widely adopted for police and even overwater use. By mid-1967 over 100 had been sold and Bell had brokered a licence-production deal with Agusta in Italy, for the AB 206. By December 1970 Bell alone had built 600 commercial JetRangers, and had had renewed success in building military versions of the Model 206 for the US Army, US Navy and for export.

In early 1971 Bell introduced the more powerful Model 206B JetRanger II, which quickly became the standard production model. This version was powered by a 298-kW (400-hp) Allison 250-C20 turboshaft, for improved 'hot-and-high' performance. Conversion kits were made available to bring earlier aircraft up to JetRanger II standard. By January 1975 Bell and its licensees had produced over 4,000 JetRangers and the type had been adopted by several military users (quite apart from the dedicated military versions). The largest civil JetRanger operator during this period was US-based Petroleum Helicopters Inc., which had a fleet of 125 aircraft. So great was the demand that Bell outsourced airframe production to Beech Aircraft during the 1960s and 1970s.

JetRanger II production ceased at 1,619 aircraft, with the introduction of the further improved Model 206B-3

JetRanger III. The first of the new breed was delivered in mid-1977. The JetRanger III incorporated the Allison 250-C20B turboshaft of the larger LongRanger, providing improved power margins at power-limited airspeeds in high-altitude/temperature conditions. By January 1980 Bell had delivered over 3,300 JetRangers to commercial customers, and over 6,000 military and civil versions. Three years later this total had climbed to over 7,000 helicopters, with an increasing proportion of commercial customers. Between 5 August 1982 and 22 July 1983 Australian businessman and pilot Dick Smith completed the first solo round-the-world helicopter flight in his JetRanger III, *Australian Explorer*. The distance covered was 30,618 nm (56665 km/35,211 miles), equivalent to one-and-a-half times around the globe at the equator.

Canadian production

On 7 October 1983 Bell reached agreement with the Canadian government to set up a major production facility in Canada, to which several entire product lines were moved. By 1987, the new plant at Montreal-Mirabel had taken over all JetRanger and LongRanger production. By 1989 production of the JetRanger III was continuing at a rate of seven aircraft per month. Today, despite the advent of more modern alternatives, such as Bell's own Models 407/427, the Jetranger III remains in production. Over 7,700 aircraft have been built in total, including 4,400 commercial versions and a further 900 from the Agusta production line. Deliveries from the Bell Helicopter Textron Canada facility continue at about 40-50 per year.

Building on the success of the Model 206A/B JetRanger, Bell developed the stretched, seven-seat Model 206L LongRanger, to fill the gap in its product line

SPECIFICATION

Bell 206B-3 JetRanger III
Type: light general-purpose helicopter
Powerplant: one 313-kW (420-hp) Allison 250-C20J turboshaft, flat-rated to 236 kW (316 hp)
Performance: maximum cruise speed 216 km/h at 1525 m (134 mph at 5,000 ft); service ceiling 4115 m (13,500ft); range 730 km (450 miles)

Weights: empty 737 kg (1,620 lb); loaded 1520 kg (3,345 lb) with external load
Dimensions: main rotor diameter 10.16 m (33 ft 4 in); length 11.82 m (38 ft 9 in); height 2.91 m (9 ft 6 in); rotor area 81.10 m² (873 sq ft)
Payload: three passengers; provision for medical attendant, litter, and up to 600 kg (1,320 lb) of ambulance equipment

between the Model 206 and the 15-seat Model 205A-1. The LongRanger was announced in September 1973, and was based on the JetRanger II airframe. The fuselage was lengthened by 0.64 m (2 ft 1 in) and an uprated 313-kW (420-hp) Allison 250-C20B was fitted. From the outset the LongRanger used Bell's patented Noda-Matic transmission suspension system, which gave a substantial reduction in airframe vibration and isolated structure-borne noise from the cabin. The Noda-Matic rotor system had been introduced on the JetRanger II. The prototype Model 206L made its maiden flight on 11 September 1974 and production deliveries commenced in 1975. The LongRanger featured a third side window, between the cockpit and the main cabin window. Double doors were added to the port side, allowing the easy loading of cargo, or stretchers in the emergency medical role.

The LongRanger followed the JetRanger's path of improvement with the arrival of the Model 206L-1 LongRanger II in 1978. This developed version was

certified on 17 May that year and introduced a 373-kW (500-hp) Allison 250-C28B turboshaft. The LongRanger II had several other detail changes, including a slightly roomier cabin. In 1978 a modified Model 206L-M served as a testbed for the Bell 412's four-bladed rotor and, later, the OH-58D's rotor system. By 1979 Bell was building 170 LongRangers per year and had delivered over 600 aircraft by the end of 1980. In all, a total of 787 Model 206L and 206L-1s was built.

In 1981 the Model 206L-3 LongRanger III became the standard production variant. A total of 612 LongRanger IIIs was built before production switched to the latest version, the Model 206L-4 LongRanger IV, which remains in production with Bell Helicopter Textron Canada. Announced in March 1992, the LongRanger IV is an increased gross-weight version, with an uprated transmission to handle the extra load. A twin-engined version of the LongRanger, the Model 206LT TwinRanger, was developed by Bell to counter the commercial threat from the Tridair Gemini ST upgrade.

The Bell 206L-4 is the current production version of the LongRanger. The aircraft has the greatest lifting capacity of all the single-engined Bell 206 variants.

▶

Canada's 74 COH-58As were delivered from 1971 onwards, and were taken from a batch ordered by the US Army. The type was redesignated CH-136 in Canadian service. The latest CH-139 JetRangers are operated by the Basic Helicopter School, and are leased from the CAF.

Kiowa, Creek and military 206s

Bell's Model 206 began life as a military design, but was quickly re-invented for the commercial market. When a second shot came at military service, the JetRanger was to enjoy important sales success.

When the US Army issued its LOH (Light Observation Helicopter) specification in 1960, Bell submitted its YHO-4 (OH-4A) design, as the Model 206. The Bell submission was beaten by the Hughes Model 369 (YOH-6A), which was a smaller, lighter, faster aircraft – that came in at a bargain basement price. The Hughes aircraft went on to win immortality in Vietnam as the OH-6 Cayuse (better known as the 'Loach'), while Bell took its Model 206 and transformed it into the Model 206A JetRanger.

The first JetRangers appeared on the market in early 1967, but Bell had not given up its plans for military variants. Bell campaigned vigorously behind the scenes to win political support for its aircraft and the company scored an important early victory in January 1968 when it won an order for new training helicopters for the US Navy. A total of 40 TH-57A SeaRangers was acquired for Naval Air Training Command, to replace existing Bell TH-13Ms (Model 47s). The TH-57A was essentially the same as the Allison 250-C18A-powered Model 206A, with naval avionics and communications fitted. The aircraft had dual controls as standard. The TH-57A was an important sales success, and improved versions are still in regular USN service today, but at that time Bell had its eyes on a much bigger prize.

Kiowa emerges

After some spectacular backroom manoeuvring, the US Army re-opened its LOH requirement and the Bell OH-58A Kiowa was selected as the winner. Based on the Model 206A airframe, there were differences between the Kiowa and the JetRanger – the former had an increased rotor diameter, a 236-kW (317-hp) Allison T63-A-700 engine and several equipment and avionics changes – but outwardly they were almost indistinguishable. The US Army announced that it would acquire up to 2,200 of the new helicopters and by 1970 it had placed firm orders for 1,800 aircraft. The first OH-58A was delivered to the Army on 23 May 1969 and by the end of that year aircraft were operational in Vietnam. The role of the Kiowa was as an unarmed scout and light transport. It never won the same reputation for ruggedness and reliability as the 'Loach', and was never used for the same diversity of roles, but was valued for its larger size.

As soon as the US Kiowa deal was done, foreign interest was translated into orders. In May 1970 Canada announced an order for COH-58As (later CH-136). In 1981 a batch of 14 new-build JetRanger IIIs (CH-139s) was acquired to supplement the first batch of CH-136s in the training role.

Kiowa in combat, 1970–88

Not originally ordered by the military following the OH-6's LOH success, the OH-58A made its combat debut with the US Army over Vietnam in 1970, after it had been taken into service as a less costly alternative to the Cayuse. In Southeast Asian combat, the OH-58 could be equipped with the XM27 kit, incorporating a 7.62-mm (0.30-in) Minigun (pictured).

In October 1983 the Kiowa returned to war, when US Army OH-58Cs deployed troops and evacuated casualties during the assault on Grenada. The Honduras-based 101st Aviation Batallion was involved in the support of CIA and Contra activities in Nicaragua in the 1980s, and one of its OH-58As was forced down on the border of Nicaragua on 11 January 1984; although the pilot was shot dead on the ground, two sabotage experts on board escaped unharmed. During the latter stages of the first Gulf War in 1988, the US Army flew OH-58Ds in support of SEAL-manned oil support barges in the Persian Gulf, surveying and defending against IRGC (Islamic Revolutionary Guards Corps) reprisal attacks.

Australia signed a co-production deal for up to 75 OH-58As to equip its Army Aviation element. In the event, the Commonwealth Aircraft Corporation built 56 Kiowas to Model 206B-1 standard, all delivered by 1976, under the local designation CA-32 Kalkadoon. Bell had already had some success in selling the civil JetRanger to military customers. One example of this was the Brazilian navy which adopted four armed aircraft, as OH-4s, equipped with a pylon-mounted 70-mm (2.75-in) rocket pod and a 12.7-mm (0.5-in) machine-gun.

The OH-58B designation was applied to 12 Kiowas built for Austria in 1976, but the next variant, the OH-58C, marked the first major development of the basic design. In June 1976 the US Army awarded Bell a contract to improve the Kiowa through the addition of an uprated 313-kW (420-hp) T63-A-720 turboshaft, a flat glass canopy to reduce glint and provision for IR-suppressing shrouds around the engine exhausts. The OH-58C was roughly equivalent to the civil JetRanger III and two OH-58As were modified to act as testbeds. The OH-58C incorporated new systems, navigation equipment and mission avionics. The role of the improved aircraft was to act as a scout aircraft for US Army Aviation AH-1 Cobra units, the so-called 'scout/gun teams'. As US Army doctrine called for units to be able to mount 24-hour combat, particularly on the Central European Front, the OH-58C was fitted with an NVG-compatible cockpit. It could also be armed with the M27 gun kit which added a 7.62-mm (0.3-in) Minigun on a short cabin pylon.

By March 1978 Bell had been awarded a contract to upgrade 275 OH-58As to OH-58C standard, at its Amarillo, Texas, facility. By 1985 a total of 435 aircraft had been redelivered to the US, and IAI undertook an additional 150 conversions for the US Army in Germany. The OH-58C still serves with US Army Reserve and National Guard units, but its place in the front-line force has now been taken by the OH-58D. In 1981 the US Army launched a major upgrade and modification programme for its Kiowas under the AHIP (Army Helicopter Improvement Programme). AHIP led to the up-engined OH-58D Kiowa Warrior, fitted with a new four-bladed main rotor, a mast-mounted sight and Hellfire missile capability. The Model 406 Kiowa Warrior, and similar Model 406 Combat Scout, are very different beasts to the earlier OH-58s.

In October 1980 Bell announced that it was developing a multi-purpose military variant of the Model 206L LongRanger – the Model 206 Texas Ranger. The Texas Ranger had a strengthened airframe and a 485-kW (650-hp) Allison 250-C30P engine (though the demonstrator was fitted with a 373-kW/500-hp -C28B engine). Bell undertook successful TOW missile firings with its single testbed, using a palletised launcher that could be fitted in the rear cabin. The aircraft could be rapidly reconfigured for attack/ armed reconnaissance, troop/ utility transport, medevac, SAR and command and control missions. The Texas Ranger was aimed squarely at the export market but did not meet with any sales success.

Chilean gunship
In Chile during the late 1980s and early 1990s, Industria Cardoen attempted to develop a more ambitious military modification of the LongRanger, the CB 206L-III gunship. This aircraft featured a revised, narrower forward fuselage, with a squared-off nose and flat-panel cockpit transparencies. The CB 206L-III could be armed with missiles, rockets or gun pods. The project was halted after US suspicions of Iraqi involvement in its development were raised.

Pleased with the performance of its TH-57As, which remained in active service into the 1980s, the US Navy ordered the follow-on TH-57B Sea Ranger – a similar 'off-the-shelf' purchase, based on the JetRanger III. The TH-57B featured many detail changes to improve overall safety and reliability and a total of 21 was delivered by December 1984. These were accompanied by the further improved TH-57C, fitted out with an expanded instrument panel for full IFR training. TH-57Cs were delivered in parallel with the TH-57Bs, and 76 were handed over by the end of 1984.

The latest military development of the JetRanger family is another dedicated training version, the US Army's TH-67 Creek. The TH-67 has full provision for VFR and IFR flight training. A total of 137 aircraft was ordered, split between dedicated VFR (102) and IFR (35) versions, and all were in service by the end of 1995.

Both Bell and Agusta have delivered substantial numbers of civil-standard Model 206s to military customers, from Brunei to Venezuela. The same is true of the LongRanger, which is in service with several international operators.

Above: Replacing the TH-55 and UH-1 at the US Army's Aviation School at Ft Rucker, Alabama, the TH-67A Creek was the winner of the Army's March 1993 NTH (New Training Helicopter) competition. The TH-67A is based on the Model 206B-3 JetRanger III.

Below: The IDF/AF operates both the Model 206L and the Agusta-built AB 206B (pictured) for liaison and training. The helicopters are based at Sde Dov (125 Tayeset) and Hatzerim (130 Tayeset).

Left: Frontier Helicopters of Canada operates two Bell 212s converted by Conair for firefighting duties in British Colombia and the Yukon Territory. The water, mixed with fire-retardant chemicals, is dropped from a specially-developed detachable tank beneath the main cabin.

Bell **212/214/412**

Civil 'Hueys'

With the Model 205 – better known as the UH-1 'Huey' – firmly established as the world's leading military assault/transport helicopter, Bell took steps to improve on that design and translate its success into the civil world. The result was the Model 212, which would itself go on to bigger and better things in the shape of today's Model 412.

The development of the twin-engined Model 212 was spurred by Canadian interest in such a (proposed) aircraft that would be powered by a pair of Pratt & Whitney Canada PT6T turboshafts. On 1 May 1968 Bell announced that a Canadian Armed Forces order for 50 aircraft had formally launched the new project and major orders from the US military, and others, soon followed. The twin-engined UH-1 was known as the UH-1N and deliveries began in 1970. At the same time, Bell developed a civil version, dubbed the Twin Two-Twelve, which received initial FAA type certification in October 1970 and full Category A transportation certification on 30 June 1971.

The Model 212 featured an all-metal fuselage and Bell's trademark twin-bladed, all-metal, semi-rigid 'teetering' main rotor. Compared to the Model 205, it had an elongated nose and an expanded 7.02-m³ (248-cu ft) main cabin, capable of carrying up to 14 passengers. Two doors were fitted on each side – one forward-hinged, one rear-sliding. Power was provided by a PT6T-3 Turbo Twin Pac engine, which coupled two PT6 turboshafts to a single combining gearbox and rotor drive shaft. The Turbo Twin Pac

was flat-rated at 962 kW (1,290 shp), but had a maximum power output of 1342 kW (1,800 shp). The Model 212 had an even higher payload than the military UH-1N and could carry an underslung load of up to 2268 kg (5,000 lb).

The Twin Two-Twelve was certified for IFR operations in January 1973, making it an even more attractive proposition to

Above: Redhill, UK-based Bristow helicopters operates the Bell 212 in Nigeria, and (pictured) Trinidad. The 212 is also available in a float-equipped version, and is cleared for single-pilot IFR operations.

potential operators. Customers, such as logging firms and off-shore support companies, needed a reliable aircraft that could continue to work in bad weather, and with the Model 212 that is just what they got. In June 1977 the Model 212 became the first helicopter certified for single-pilot IFR

The Bell 412 is in service with police and security forces around the world. This example, operated by the US Park Police, can be fitted with a searchlight, tannoy system and infra-red cameras.

Similar in basic form to its American counterpart, the Model 212 entered production with Agusta in Italy under the designation AB 212. Agusta has, in addition, developed its own anti-submarine and -ship version known as the AB 212ASW.

operations over water, with fixed floats. Another notable milestone came in February 1979, when nine 212s were ordered by China for energy and natural resources development support. These were the first US helicopters ever exported to China.

Lifting ability

Many Model 212 operators used their aircraft to haul underslung loads and always craved more lifting power. In January 1974 Bell announced the Model 214B BigLifter, which would have the greatest load-carrying ability of any helicopter in its class. The Model 214B inherited several of the features developed for the Imperial Iranian Army's specialist Model 214A Isfahans. It was powered by the same 1678 kW (2,250 shp) Lycoming T5508D turboshaft and used the same revised, uprated rotor drive and transmission. The redesigned main rotor blades had swept tips and the hub used Elastomeric bearings. In 1978 a glassfibre main rotor was certified for the Model 214B, the first such rotor to be built in the USA, which could be refitted to existing aircraft. The BigLifter came with an automatic flight control system, twin hydraulic systems, improved maintenance access,

an engine fire extinguisher and push-pull emergency windows.

The basic Model 214B, which was certified on 27 January 1976, could carry an external load close to 3629 kg (8,000 lb). With an internal load of 1814 kg (4,000 lb), it could cruise at 259 km/h (161 mph) and could carry up to 14 passengers. The subsequent Model 214B-1 was recertified to carry a huge external load of 5670 kg (12,500 lb).

Military Model

The military Model 214A, developed by Bell and Iranian Helicopter Industry, also led to another twin-engined commercial helicopter, the Model 214ST. This began life as the 'Stretched Twin' but was rechristened the SuperTransport (or SuperTrans). The Model 214ST looked very different to the Model 212 and 214B. Its sharply upswept tail boom was faired into the engine exhaust housings and its redesigned nose was routinely fitted with a weather radar. The Model 214ST was powered by a new 1286 kW (1,725 shp) General Electric CT7-2A turboshaft, driving an advanced-technology glassfibre twin-bladed main rotor. The prototype first flew in February 1977 and production began in

November 1979. The 214ST was certified for two-pilot IFR operations in 1982 and could carry up to 17 passengers. It became a popular type with offshore oil support operators – one such early user was British Caledonian Helicopters, which acquired 214STs for its North Sea operations.

Four-bladed version

In September 1978 Bell announced that it was going to develop an improved version of the Model 212, with an all-new four-bladed main rotor. The resultant Model 412 became the first Bell helicopter to be fitted with such a rotor, which improved overall performance while reducing noise.

The Model 412 used blades similar to those of the 214ST. These have a glassfibre spar, with a Nomex honeycomb core and a wrapped glassfibre skin.

The steel and light alloy rotor head uses Elastomeric bearings and, unlike the Model 212, the main blades can be folded.

Indonesia's IPTN had a licence to build 100 aircraft as the NBell 412. Production commenced in 1984 and centred around the Model 412 airframe. Since 1981, Italy's Agusta has also been an important 412 builder, producing aircraft as the AB 412 family. Agusta previously built the Bell 212 under licence as the AB 212, but production has now switched entirely to the AB 412EP.

In 1983 Bell Helicopter Textron Canada was established in Mirabel, Quebec, and production gradually began to be switched to this new site. Model 212/412 production moved there in 1988/89. The 212 is still being built, largely to order, and some 1200 are currently in service worldwide.

SPECIFICATION	
Bell Model 412SP **Type:** light utility helicopter **Powerplant:** one 1342-kW (1,800-hp) Pratt & Whitney PT6T-3B-1 Turbo Twin Pac turboshaft flat-rated at 1044 kW (1,400 hp) **Performance:** maximum speed 259 km/h (161 mph); initial climb rate 411 m (1,350 ft) per minute; range 695 km (432 miles) with maximum payload	**Weights:** empty 2935 kg (6,470 lb); maximum take-off 5397 kg (11,900lb) **Dimensions:** main rotor diameter 14.02 m (46 ft); fuselage length 12.92 m (42 ft 4 in); height 4.32m (14 ft 4 in); rotor disc area 154.4 m³ (1,662 sq ft) **Payload:** up to 13/14 passengers and 2040 kg (4,500 lb) of cargo in external sling load

The 214B BigLifter is a dedicated civilian model, with an external cargo hook capable of lifting a load of 3629 kg (8,000 lb). Alternatively, specialised fire-fighting equipment may be carried. Internal accommodation remains at 14 passengers.

Bell 222
US commercial twin

N222BX was one of the five Model 222 prototypes. development of the new twin did not go as smoothly as the manufacturer had hoped. With its undercarriage retracted, Bell's first helicopter intended solely for the commercial market was also of its sleekest designs.

Despite its sleek design, Bell's first attempt at producing a helicopter for the highly profitable executive helicopter market met with only limited success. Nevertheless, many 222s remain in service today and have paved the way for Bell's later series of more successful civil designs.

Bell Helicopters toyed with the idea of producing a commercial twin-engined light helicopter in the mid 1960s, but it was some years before its ideas took on a more tangible form. It used the occasion of the annual convention of the Helicopter Association in America in January 1974 to exhibit a mock-up of what was to become the Model 222, and gave the go-ahead for development the following April. Described as the first commercial light twin-engined helicopter to be built in

the United States, the Bell 222 was targeted primarily at the executive transport market, although the type also entered service with several police forces and made a mark in the offshore oil support business. Commercially, this model proved a relative failure, with a total of only 188 built over a 10-year period to 1989.

Time slips
Construction of five prototypes began on 1 September 1974. However, Bell was not at all certain of its design and

During 1993, Bell tested a ducted tail rotor design on a modified 222. This design is quieter than that of a normal helicopter tail rotor, while at the same time enhancing ground safety. Data gained during these test flights will be applied to future Bell designs.

undertook extensive market evaluation, as well as fine-tuning the parameters to meet operators' requirements, both of which delayed the first flight to 13 August 1976. The second prototype followed later that year and all five were operational by March 1977. The flight tests highlighted several shortcomings, requiring major

modifications to be made to the tailplane structure and flight controls, which caused further delays to the programme. As a result, Federal Aviation Administration (FAA) certification (of a pre-production 222) was not obtained until 16 August 1979, with VFR certification of the production 222A following on 20 December. Petroleum

Prior to commencing construction of the helicopter, Bell displayed a full-scale mock-up of the design, then known as Model D306. Market reaction to the helicopter was strong enough for Bell to undertake the construction of five prototypes, although the T-tail configuration was discontinued.

SPECIFICATION	
Bell 222A	**Weights:** : empty 2204 kg (4,850 lb); loaded 3560 kg (7,832 lb)
Type: police patrol helicopter	**Dimensions:** main rotor diameter 12.12 m (40 ft); fuselage length 10.98 m (36 f); height 3.51 m (12 ft); rotor disc area 115.29 m³ (1,240 sq ft)
Powerplant: two 462-kW (620-hp) Lycoming LTS101-750C-1 turboshafts	
Performance: maximum speed 250 km/h (155 mph); service ceiling 6100 m (20,000 ft); range 523 km (325 miles) or 2 hrs 30 minutes of endurance at economical cruising speed	**Payload:** two pilots, two observers or up to six passengers

Above: In 1983 Bell introduced a new variant of the 222. Fulfilling the utility transport role, the Model 222UT enjoys increased fuel capacity and is equipped with fixed twin-skid landing gear.

Right: Announced in 1989, the Bell Model 230 was developed as a successor to the Model 222. Although its airframe is basically the same as that of its predecessor, its power is provided by two Allison turboshafts in place of the Model 222's pair of Lycoming turboshafts. It also features a larger cabin area, seating up to eight passengers .

Helicopters took delivery of the first Bell 222 on 16 January 1980 and another early customer was the Metropolitan Police in London. Certification for single-pilot IFR operations in Category I weather conditions was granted on 15 May that same year.

Practical design

The Bell 222 is a conventional design with a light-alloy fail-safe structure with a limited use of light-alloy honeycomb panels. Access to the avionics and equipment bay is provided via a tilting one-piece nosecone.

The tail unit comprises fixed sweptback vertical upper and lower fins, with a tailplane with endplate fins mounted midway along the rear fuselage. Tail-down loading protection is

provided by a small skid below the ventral fin. Short-span cantilever sponsons are set low on each side of the fuselage, serving as fuel tanks, work platforms and housings for the hydraulically-retractable tricycle landing gear. The self-centring nosewheel has a 360° swivel. All units retract forward.

The rotor system comprises a two-bladed main rotor constructed of stainless steel with bonded glassfibre to retard crack propagation, with a replaceable stainless steel leading edge and Nomex and glassfibre rear. Standard Bell elastomeric bearings hold blades to the titanium rotor hub. The two-bladed tail rotor is also made of stainless steel. Power is provided by two Lycoming

turboshafts mounted in a housing above the cabin, each rated at up to 510 kW (684 shp) for take-off. Fuel is contained in five bladder tanks in the sponsons and the centre fuselage. Standard accommodation is provided for two crew and six passengers in a 2-3-3 layout, with high-density seating for two additional passengers also possible. Access for the crew is via doors on each side of the fuselage ahead of the cabin, while passengers can board through a door each side, immediately forward of the wing. A 1.05-m³ (37-cu ft) baggage hold with a starboard door is provided aft of the cabin.

Model designations

The initial production model was the 222A, which was powered by twin 462-kW (620-shp) Lycoming LTS 101 650C-3 turboshafts. This was replaced from late 1982 by the more powerful 222B. The major differences were the fitting of 510-kW (684-shp) LTS 101 750C-1 turboshafts, a 0.43-m (1-ft 5-in) fuselage stretch, and a 0.69-m (2-ft 3-in) increase in rotor diameter. Strakes were also added to the sponsons. The 222B made its first flight on 1 August 1981 and received FAA certification on 30 June 1982. On 29 July that year, the 222B became the first

transport helicopter to be certificated for single-pilot IFR flight without stability augmentation. Executive versions could be equipped with a Honeywell coupled automatic flight control system, Collins Pro Line avionics, and a luxury interior for five passengers, with automatic temperature control, reading lights, window curtains and ceiling speakers. A stereo system and refreshment cabinet were optional.

From September 1983, deliveries were also made of the 222UT (Utility Transport), which took the largest share of production thereafter. The 222UT incorporated the improvements detailed for the Model 222B, but the most notable feature was the replacement of the tricycle landing gear by a tubular skid gear with lock-on ground-handling wheels. Fuselage-mounted flotation systems were optional. The 222UT first flew on 7 September 1982 and received VFR and single-pilot IFR certification in spring 1983.

In 1990/91, two Model 222s were converted to serve as development models for the Model 230. Various features of the 222 were also used by Bell in the early 1980s to develop the prototype D292 (ACAP) advanced composite-airframe helicopter.

Airwolf – 222 TV star

Probably the most famous Bell 222 was *Airwolf* of TV fame. *Airwolf* was constructed by a covert government agency and flown by Vietnam veteran Stringfellow Hawk played by Jean Michael Vincent and co-pilot Dominic Santini (Ernest Borgnine), owner of the Santini Airways helicopter company. The helicopter was equipped with a number of somewhat incredible systems, including an afterburner which allowed *Airwolf* to reach Mach speeds and a guided rocket system. The latter could effortlessly shoot down fighter aircraft and other helicopters, or could be used with devastating effect against ground targets ranging from trucks to tanks.

Boeing Vertol

The Model 234LR Commercial Chinook was primarily designed for supply flights to oil rigs in the North Sea. Helikopter Service of Norway became the second operator to use the type in this region, utilising three examples from Stavanger.

234 Commercial Chinook

Below: The first Model 234LR, seen here unpainted, made its initial flight on 19 August 1980.

Boeing's big lifter

The Chinook's outstanding record as a military heavylift transport prompted Boeing Vertol to develop a specialised long-range version for the civilian market. Aimed at companies flying to offshore oil rigs, the type has also served in the logging and firefighting roles.

Taking advantage of the substantial upgrade of the military Chinook, which was being modified into the CH-47D, Boeing announced in the summer of 1978 that it had completed the market evaluation of a commercial version. The target was the growing North Sea oil business, in which drilling operations were being pushed further and further from the mainland. The availability of the Commercial Chinook was instrumental in British Airways Helicopters (BAH) obtaining a seven-year contract from Shell to service its

large Brent/Cormorant oil field to the east of the Shetland Islands. In November 1978, BAH duly ordered three Model 234s at £6 million each, and later increased the contract to six. The first Commercial Chinook flew on 19 August 1980 and received Federal Aviation Administration (FAA) and UK Civil Aviation Authority (CAA) certification on 19 and 26 June 1981, respectively.

Although based on the CH-47D, the Model 234 introduced many new features. The most notable were the replacement of metal rotor

blades by wide-chord glass fibre blades, a redesign of the fuselage side fairings to incorporate additional fuel tanks, a lengthened nose to house the weather radar antenna, and a

repositioning further forward of the front landing gear. Duplicated blind-flying instrumentation, weather radar and a dual, four-axis automatic flight control system ensure

---

SPECIFICATION

Boeing 234LR

Type: commercial transport helicopter

Powerplant: two 3039-kW (4,075-hp) (take-off rating) Textron Lycoming AL-5512 turboshafts

Performance: maximum speed 172 mph (278 km/h); maximum cruising speed 269 km/h (167 mph) at 610 m (2,000 ft); range 1149 km (950 miles) with 17 passengers and reserves (average load)

Weights: empty 12020 kg (26,444 lb); maximum take-off 23133 kg (50,893 lb)

Dimensions: rotor diameter 18.29 m (60 ft); fuselage length 15.87 m (52 ft 4 in); height 5.77 m (18 ft 11 in); rotor area 525.34 m² (5,653 sq ft)

Payload: two pilots, maximum of 44 passengers, or up to 9072 kg (20,000 lb) of freight internally or up to 12701 kg (28,000 lb) externally

The Model 234LR programme was launched in November 1978 only after a contract had been signed with BAH. This company's six aircraft were used to carry passengers and cargo to and from North Sea oil platforms operated by the Esso and Shell petroleum companies.

all-weather capability. The fuselage is of all-metal semi-monocoque construction with a basically square section and a loading ramp built into the upswept rear. Landing gear is a non-retractable quadricycle type, with twin wheels on each forward gear, and single wheels on the rear units. Power for the Model 234 is provided by two Avco-Lycoming AL 5512 turboshafts, pod-mounted on the sides of the rear rotor pylon. Each is rated at 3035 kW (4,075 shp) on take-off, and has a maximum 30-minute contingency rating of 3245 kW (4,355 shp).

The rotor system comprises three-bladed rotors in tandem, turning in opposite directions, driven through interconnecting shafts, which enable both rotors to be driven by either engine. The front half of each blade is made of glass fibre, and the rear half filled with Nomex honeycomb. An aluminium screen inserted in the skin provides lightning protection by discharging strikes through the titanium leading edge. Blades also embody electric de-icing blankets. Two blades of each rotor can be folded manually. Power transmission from each engine is accomplished through individual clutches into the combiner transmission, providing a single power output to the interconnecting shaft. An auxiliary transmission lubrication system ensures that flights can be completed even after a total loss of oil in the primary system.

Accommodation is provided for two pilots side-by-side on the flight deck, with dual

controls, and for up to 44 passengers (depending on the variant) in the cabin, three-abreast with a central aisle. Each seat has an overhead bin and underseat stowage for carry-on luggage, with larger items carried in the main baggage compartment. A galley with cabin attendant's seat and toilet between the flight deck and the cabin are standard. Heating and ventilation provides a comfortable environment for pilots and passengers, and a specially-tuned floor construction reduces vibration. Passenger access to the cabin is via a single door on the right-hand side, while the crew has a door on each side of the flight deck. All passenger facilities can be removed and replaced by a heavy-duty floor for cargo-only service. Various arrangements of external cargo hooks are possible, including a single central hook for loads of up to 12.7 tonnes (28,000 lb); tandem hooks for better load stability in high-speed flight; and three tandem hooks for multiple loads.

Into service

The Commercial Chinook entered service with British Airways Helicopters on 1 July

The largest and longest-serving helicopter operator in Alaska, ERA Helicopters, took delivery of a single Model 234ER in 1985. It was operated in support of oil exploration rigs in the Bering Sea.

1981. Deliveries of all six Model 234LRs had been completed by 29 June 1982. The long-range LR version can be distinguished by large continuous fuselage side-fairings of advanced composites, which contain one fuel tank in each with a total capacity of 7950 litres (2,100 US gallons), about twice that of the military Chinook. Internally, the 234LR was fitted out with 44 airliner seats – the same as those used on the Boeing 727 – and walk-on baggage bins on the rear ramp. It could be used in the all-cargo configuration or as a passenger/freight combi (the 234LR Combi was certificated by the FAA in summer 1982). BAH used the Chinook primarily out of Aberdeen in Scotland, flying directly to rigs some 400–480 km (250– 300 miles) out in the North Sea, obviating the need to fly rig personnel via Sumburgh. However, Chinook operations to rigs ceased when one machine was involved in a fatal crash in the North Sea on 2 May 1984. On 23 March 1982, Boeing announced an order for two

234LRs from Helikopter Service of Norway, with an option for one more, which was later taken up. Helikopter Service used its Chinooks in the North Sea region, flying out of Stavanger.

Two 234ER extended-range models were delivered in 1983 to Arco Alaska, also for use in offshore oil rig support operations. The 234ER featured two internal drum tanks in addition to those in the fuselage sides, increasing the range to 1600 km (1,000 miles). Seating was typically provided for 17 passengers, or for 32 with a single internal fuel tank. It received its FAA certification in May 1983.

A 234MLR multi-purpose long-range aircraft was also offered but had no takers. No customers were also found for the 234UT utility helicopter, but the eight 234LRs initially acquired second-hand by Columbia Helicopters in the US have all been converted to this configuration, designed specifically for enhanced lifting capability.

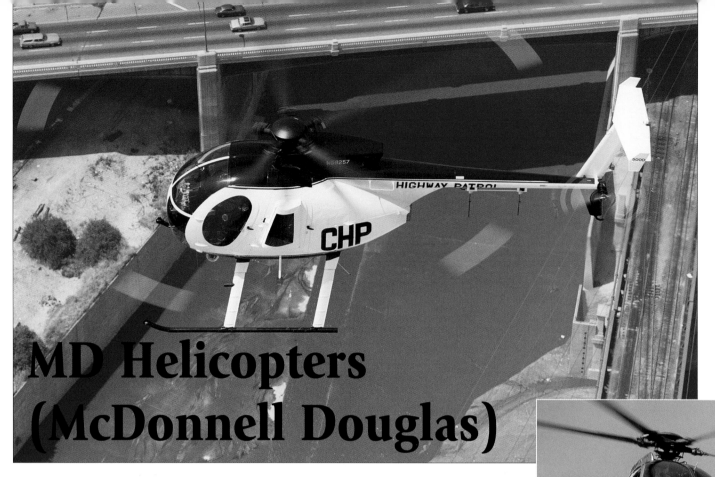

MD Helicopters (McDonnell Douglas)

MD500

The civil versions

The compact and distinctively rounded helicopters of the H 500 family have been on the civil scene for nearly 40 years. In that time, the designs have changed shape, and changed hands, several times.

Credit for what has, at various times, been known as the Hughes/McDonnell Douglas/Boeing/MD Helicopters 'Model 500' lies squarely with Howard Hughes and his Hughes Tool Company, which entered the helicopter business as early as 1949. The massive aerospace corporation that Hughes built up from the 1930s has now been broken up, and sold off to other US firms. The mega-mergers of the 1990s saw the last pieces of the old Hughes empire finally swallowed up but, throughout all the changes, a family of small utility helicopters has survived and prospered as a tribute to its original designers.

In 1956 Hughes flew the prototype of what would become the highly successful Model 269A single-engined, two-seat light helicopter. In 1960 the US Army selected the larger Model 369 as the winner in its LOH (light observation helicopter) competition and acquired over 1,400 aircraft as the OH-6 family. This huge contract provided a springboard from which Hughes developed a civil version. While the official factory designation for this aircraft was the Model 369A, it was sold as the Hughes 500.

By that time, the H 500 was a product of the rechristened

Above: The Hughes 500D is the best-selling variant in the family and was popular with security and police forces, such as the California Highway Patrol.

Right: Members of the Phoenix Police Department's SWAT unit practise assault tactics from a NOTAR-equipped MD520N. The department acquired the first of seven examples in October 1991.

Hughes Helicopter Inc., and it remained so for nearly 20 years. However, in January 1984, against a background of faltering financial performance, Hughes Helicopters was acquired by McDonnell Douglas, from its then-owners, the Summa Corporation. In January 1986 the

company was re-established as McDonnell Douglas Helicopters, the new owner introducing the 'MD' prefix adopted by its commercial jetliners. McDonnell Douglas Helicopters had a life span of 10 years, until December 1996, when it was announced that the Boeing

An impressive top speed and a distinctive egg-shaped cabin made the Model 500 the fashionable choice of wealthy individuals in the 1970s and '80s.

In 1982 Hughes finally ditched the Model 500's distinctive 'bubble' cabin in favour of a new, more streamlined profile. The resulting Model 500E sold well to law enforcement agencies.

Company would take over all of McDonnell Douglas, in a $13.3 billion deal.

The MD500 and MD600 helicopter families became part of Boeing's McDonnell Aircraft and Missile Systems group, alongside such disparate types as the C-17 Globemaster III and the F-15E Strike Eagle. While Boeing was interested in the AH-64 Apache attack helicopter, the smaller, lighter MD500/600 sat uncomfortably within its new product portfolio. Boeing wanted to sell off the civil helicopter line, but anti-trust laws forbade a sale to any of the other US helicopter manufacturers (Bell was the most likely customer). As the future of the MD500/600 line was called into question, sales slowed to a trickle as customers became increasingly wary of buying helicopters that might have no future.

Typical of many US police departments, Los Angeles County Sheriff operates 15 examples of the MD500 family. This example is a NOTAR MD520N.

New owner

Happily, a solution emerged in February 1999 when MD Helicopters Holding Inc. agreed to purchase the Boeing MD500E, MD530F, MD520N, MD600N and Explorer helicopter lines from McDonnell Douglas Helicopter Company – by then an indirect subsidiary of the Boeing Company. MD Helicopters itself is an indirect subsidiary of RDM Holdings, a Belgian defence, aerospace and industrial contractor. MD Helicopters has maintained production at Mesa's Falcon Field Airport, in Arizona. Boeing still retains ownership of the MD520N and MD600N NOTAR (No Tail Rotor) technology, with MD helicopters licensed to use it in the future.

MD Helicopters moved quickly to cut prices and boost sales. In 1999 MD Helicopters delivered 54 aircraft, up from 36 in 1998, and expects to deliver 75 in 2000 and 100 in 2001. Boeing's exclusive deal to supply components to MD helicopters expires in 2001 and the company is now believed to be looking for new industrial partners in order to cut costs.

Based on the military OH-6A, the prototype Model 500 first flew on 13 September 1966 and entered production in November 1968. With five seats, it was powered by a 236-kW (317-hp) Allison 250-C18A turboshaft, driving a four-bladed rotor. It was later joined by a revised utility version, the H 500U. Licence-production was undertaken in Italy, Japan and Korea.

The up-engined Hughes 500C was a 'hot-and-high' version of the basic Model 500, powered by a 298-kW (400-hp) Allison 250-C20 engine. It was also built under licence by Kawasaki and RACA in Argentina.

The Model 500D was the first major revision of the civil design. Announced in February 1975, it introduced a 313-kW (420-shp) Allison 250-C20B engine driving a new five-bladed main rotor. It also featured a distinctive T-tail, with small endplate fins, to improve handling and stability. The Model 500D became the mainstay of the H 500 line and by 1981 over 1,000 had been sold.

The Model 500E took the basic 500D and refined the airframe, adding a longer, streamlined nose. The H 530F Lifter, derived from the H 500E, was optimised for 'hot-and-high' or load-carrying operations.

In 1981 Hughes was awarded a DARPA (Defense Advanced Research Projects Agency) contract to develop NOTAR technology for the US Army. NOTAR does away with the need for vulnerable tail rotors by using the engine exhaust, vented through slots in the tail boom, to provide anti-torque and steering control. By the time that Hughes's commercial NOTAR design was ready for the market, Hughes Helicopters had passed into McDonnell Douglas ownership. The production MD500N design was dubbed the MD520N and was based on the MD500E airframe, but with a completely new all-composite tail and enlarged twin fins. The MD520N is powered by a 317-kW (425-hp) Allison 250-C20R turboshaft and outperforms the conventional MD500E in many areas. A more powerful version, the MD530N, fitted with the engine of the MD530F, was developed and flew on 29 December 1989. However, it did not enter production.

In response to demand for a larger NOTAR helicopter, a stretched version of the MD520N, initially designated the MD630N was developed. This helicopter was later rechristened MD600N and features a 7/8-seat fuselage, lengthened by 76.2 cm (30 in). The MD600N is powered by a 603-kW (808-hp) Allison 250-C47 turboshaft, driving a six-bladed main rotor. Production go-ahead came in March 1995. and the first customer delivery was finally made on 6 June 1997.

SPECIFICATION	
McDonnell Douglas 500C **Type:** light utility helicopter **Powerplant:** one 236-kW (316–hp) Allison 250-C18A turboshaft **Performance:** maximum cruising speed 244 km/h (151 mph) at 305 m (1,000 ft); initial climb rate 518 m (1,700 ft) per minute; range 606 km (375 miles) **Weights:** empty 493 kg (1,085 lb); maximum take-off 1361 kg (2,994 lb)	**Dimensions:** main rotor diameter 8.03 m (26 ft 4 in); length 9.24 m (30 ft 4 in); height 2.48 m (8 ft 2 in); rotor disc area 50.60 m² (545 sq ft) **Payload:** seven passengers or up to 800 kg (1,760 lb) of freight

Above: Offering the safety inherent in twin-engined operations, and with a remarkably low noise signature, the MD 900/902 is especially suited to use over urban areas.

MD Helicopters (Boeing/McDD)
MD 900 Explorer

Above: Aero Asahi of Japan ordered 15 MD 900 helicopters, of which the first was delivered in July 1995.

NOTAR twin

MD Helicopters now produces the MD 900/902 series of eight-seat NOTAR helicopters and hopes to achieve global sales success with this remarkable and uniquely capable helicopter.

The MD 900 Explorer bears a close family resemblance to the earlier MD 500 (previously Hughes 500), yet is in many respects the most revolutionary and exciting helicopter flying today – packed with high-tech features which re-write the book on how light helicopters are designed. The most significant feature of the aircraft

N900MD, the second McDonnell Douglas MD 900, made the type's first flight on 18 December 1992. Ten prototype and trials aircraft were produced, of which seven were reserved for static testing.

is its lack of a conventional anti-torque tail rotor.

The conventional helicopter has traditionally used a single main rotor rotating in the horizontal plane to provide lift, and able to tilt fore-and-aft and from side-to-side for forward or sideways motion. With a large rotor sitting atop the helicopter's fuselage, colossal torque is generated, and the fuselage will want to rotate with the rotor. To stop this, the conventional helicopter uses an anti-torque tail rotor, which produces sideways thrust to counteract this torque and to provide yaw control.

NOTAR

Unfortunately, the tail rotor is an inefficient mechanism, absorbing engine power without contributing to lift or propulsion, imposing a significant maintenance burden, and having to be located well aft, with a long moment arm, to reduce power requirements. The tail rotor is stuck out far behind the pilot, who usually cannot see it, and is vulnerable when the helicopter is operating in confined spaces, while damage to it will often lead to the total loss of the helicopter.

There are alternative ways around the main rotor torque problem. One is to provide contra-rotating rotors, either widely spaced (as on the Chinook), or very closely spaced, inter-meshing 'egg-

Military Explorers and 'drug-busters'

A dedicated military version of the basic Explorer, known as the Combat Explorer (left), was launched in 1995, but has yet to attract orders, despite its impressive armament and FLIR-based sighting systems.

The US Coast Guard began using a pair of leased MD 900s (below left) in March 1999 in a then-secret drug interdiction programme, known as Operation New Frontier. The Coast Guard had originally planned to arm and armour a pair of its HH-65A Dolphin helicopters for the operation, but it soon became apparent that these aircraft lacked the required payload, and MD 900s were leased instead. These helicopters, designated MH-90s by the Coast Guard, were used to intercept high-speed launches (capable of 60 kt/111 km/h/69mph, and known colloquially as 'Go-Fasts') in international waters, operating from WAS Mobile, Alabama and from the cutters *Gallatin* and *Seneca*. Painted in full US Coast Guard white and orange colours, the MH-90s were equipped with undernose radar and high-capacity rescue hoists over the starboard door and were also claimed to be the first armed helicopters used by the USCG. The aircraft were fitted with a pintle-mounted 7.62-mm (0.3-in) machine-gun in the door, as well as a hand-held, bolt-action 12.7-mm (0.5-in) Robar sniper rifle, the latter reportedly being used to disable the engines of target vessels. The helicopters were also fitted with armour – in case the drug runners returned fire.

By September 1999 the programme had resulted in the capture of four boats, 13 smugglers, and three tonnes of cocaine. It was then announced that the aircraft were to be replaced by a pair of MD 902 Enhanced Explorers, with the possibility of the two-aircraft lease being turned into an acquisition programme for eight to 12 aircraft.

Other military customers for the Explorer have included the Mexican navy, though the latter service initially took delivery of two unarmed versions. Two more Explorers, which may be armed, are to be acquired for use on the Mexican navy's frigates. Another pair of MD 900s was acquired by the Belgian gendarmerie, these being fitted with removable crew armour, wirestrike protection, enhanced avionics and Nitesun and Wescam cameras by the US company Hell-Dyne prior to delivery.

SPECIFICATION	
MD 900 Explorer	**Weights:** empty 1543 kg (3,402 lb);
Type: light helicopter	maximum take-off 2835 kg (6,250 lb)
Powerplant: two 478-kW (641-shp)	**Dimensions:** main rotor diameter 10.31
Turbomeca TM319-2 Arrius 2Cs	m (33 ft 10 in); fuselage length 9.85
turboshafts	m (32 ft 4 in); height (3.66 m (12 ft);
Performance: maximum speed 296	rotor disc area 83.52 m² (899 sq ft)
km/h (184 mph); maximum cruising	**Payload:** two pilots or pilot/passenger
speed 259 km/h (161 mph); initial	and six other passengers
climb rate 411 m (1,350 ft) per	
minute; range 584 km (363 miles)	
with maximum payload	

beater style' (as on the Kaman H-43), or even contra-rotating on a common shaft (as on the Kamov Ka-27/29/30/32 family and the Ka-50/52). Each of these solutions brings penalties of weight, cost, and/or complexity, however, and none has been widely adopted.

McDonnell Douglas Helicopters began looking at ways of dispensing with the tail rotor altogether during early studies for a helicopter to meet the US Army's LHX (Light Helicopter Experimental) requirement, driven as much by reducing noise and radar signature as by the 'No Tail Rotor' (NOTAR) configuration's other advantages. Its chosen solution was to use high-pressure air, ejected through a slot in the tailboom. Having already flown an OH-6A NOTAR testbed in December 1981, the company produced and marketed NOTAR versions of

the MD 520 and the stretched MD 600, selling a number to paramilitary and police-type customers. Trials were also conducted using NOTAR-equipped Special Forces AH- and MH-6s, and although these helicopters could back into foliage without concern, the modification was not adopted.

A new aircraft was announced, in February 1988, as the MDX, and the programme to produce an advanced NOTAR lightweight helicopter was formally launched in January 1989. Re-designated as the MD 900, the aircraft was eventually named the Explorer. McDonnell Douglas Helicopters subsequently became MD Helicopters after its parent company was swallowed by Boeing, but has continued work on the MD 900, uninterrupted. The MD 900 is not just another Mesa-designed MD Helicopters

product, however, and a number of important foreign partners are participating in the programme. Hawker de Havilland of Australia designed and built the airframe, while Canadian Marconi tested and integrated the instruments and displays. Other participants included Kawasaki (transmission work), IAI (cowlings and seats), Lucas Aerospace (actuators) and Aim Aviation (the interior).

Certification granted

Bigger and heavier than the MD 520 or MD 600, the Explorer had a taller and more spacious cabin. More compact-looking, the MD 900 featured a quiet five-bladed main rotor, and a modern glass cockpit. The first prototype Explorer made its maiden flight on 18 December 1992, and the type received FAA Certification in December 1994.

Law enforcement agencies, including those in Belgium, the UK and the US, have been quick to realise the Explorer's potential. The aircraft is also ideally suited to medevac operations.

Mil Mi-8/-17 'Hip'

Asahi Helicopters of Japan operated a single 'Hip' on transport/utility roles. The 'Hip' proved to be an export failure in terms of numbers sold.

Mil's multi-role helicopter

Designed from the outset with a civilian role in mind, the Mil Mi-8 and its successor, the Mi-17, have sold in enormous numbers, equipping airlines and freight companies all over the world.

Although the bulk of the more than 12,000 Mi-8/Mi-17 helicopters built were for military use, huge numbers have been delivered to civilian customers, and especially to the Russian airline, Aeroflot. Relatively small numbers of bigger Mi-6s and Mi-26s were also delivered to Aeroflot, along with specialist aircraft like the Mi-10 flying crane and some Kamov Ka-32s, but the backbone of the USSR's massive helicopter fleet consisted of Mi-8s and Mi-17s.

The first prototype Mi-8 (with a single AI-24 engine and a four-bladed wooden main rotor) made its maiden flight during the first half of 1961 and was intended as a replacement for the earlier Mi-4 in Aeroflot and Soviet army/air force service. The V-8 prototype naturally wore Aeroflot markings and was fitted out as a passenger helicopter, with large square windows and streamlined wheel spats. When

it became clear that the Mi-8's full potential would be better exploited by using a twin-engined configuration, the V-8A was similarly equipped and painted. Mil then built V-8AP and V-8AT pre-series aircraft for the civil passenger Mi-8P and utility/military Mi-8T models, respectively. Although the square-windowed Mi-8s generally went to civil operators, and the small, round-windowed versions to military users, there was a degree of crossover, and the Mi-8T, in particular, saw extensive use as a civil utility helicopter. The Mi-8S was a VIP aircraft used by civil and military customers, as was the Mi-8PS, while the Mi-8APS is a VVIP machine, one being used as the Russian presidential helicopter.

Next-generation 'Hip'

When the aircraft was re-engined with TV3-I 17 engines to become the Mi-17, the new version was seen as having both

civil and military applications. The prototype Mi-17 (known to military operators as the Mi-8MT) wore the designation Mi-16 on its nose, and had small, round windows coupled with a full Aeroflot colour scheme and the registration SSSR-22367. Relatively few Mi-17s were built with the larger

square windows associated with the Mi-8P and Mi-8S, but large numbers were delivered to civil customers. There was a dedicated flying crane variant with an operator's gondola replacing the rear clamshell doors, the Mi-17-1VA flying hospital and even a crop-spraying aircraft.

SPECIFICATION
Mil Mi-8T 'Hip-C'

Type: assault transport helicopter

Powerplant: two 1104-kW (1,480-hp) Klimov (Isotov) turboshafts

Performance: maximum speed 250 km/h (155 mph); typical cruising speed 208 km/h (130 mph); service ceiling 4500 m (15,000 ft); radius of action 350 km (217 miles)

Weights: empty 7160 kg (15,752 lb); loaded 12000 kg (26,400 lb)

Dimensions: main rotor diameter 21.29 m (69 ft 10 in); length 25.24 m (82 ft 9 in); height 5.65 m (18 ft 6 in); rotor disc area 365.00 m² (3,831 sq ft)

Accommodation: up to 28 combat troops in a cabin area behind pilots

Armament: combinations of rockets or 250-kg (550-lb) bombs or UV-16-57 rocket pods (16 x 57mm/2.25in projectiles each) astride the fuselage

---

As the most successful European helicopter design, some 12,000 examples of the 'Hip' have been built at Mil plants for 33 military and numerous civilian operators.

The Mi-8 family has seen widespread service all over the world and has not been restricted to service with Aeroflot, or the airlines of the former Soviet bloc or client states. The type has, of course, formed the backbone of the helicopter companies and airlines which sprang up in the new republics formed as the USSR splintered apart. It has also enjoyed a degree of genuine commercial success, having been bought 'on merit' in the face of real competition from Western helicopters. Nor has the type been limited to service in the more primitive parts of the third world. There are Mi-8 and Mi-17 operators in the USA, South Africa and Japan, operating in the utility role, but also as passenger airliners and VIP aircraft, serving luxury island resorts and prestigious city-centre business heliports. This rugged and reliable type remains in low-rate production.

Above: The Mi-17-1VA is a mobile surgical hospital and was produced by the Kazan plant (originally with Hungarian help) to fly to disaster sites.

Top: As an example of its versatility, one 'Hip' was converted to operate on liquid petroleum gas (LPG) and designated Mi-8TG. LPG offers an alternative fuel source when conventional jet fuel is in short supply.

Accommodation
Two pilots sit side by side, though there is provision for a flight engineer if needed. The basic passenger version can typically carry up to 28 people, seated four abreast, while there is also a wardrobe and baggage compartment. The Mi-8 Salon VIP versions have been known to have sofas, tables, armchairs and galley.

Mil Mi-8P

This is a standard passenger transport Mi-8, with square fuselage windows (instead of circular for military versions, though there is some crossover) and Aeroflot markings. The area around the engine jet pipes is painted black as a prevention against the gradual staining of this part of the aircraft by the soot in the hot exhaust gases.

Rotor system
Early Mi-8s had a four-bladed main rotor, but this was superseded by a five-bladed rotor in 1964. In an emergency, the blades and tail gearboxes are exchangeable with those of the Mi-8's predecessor, the Mi-4.

Powerplant
The Mi-8 is powered by two 1268-kW (1,700-shp) Isotov TV2-117As which give a maximum speed of 260 km/h (162 mph) at 1000 m (3,280 ft).

Dimensions
The 'Hip' is 18.31 m (60 ft) in length, with a main rotor of 21.29m (69 ft 10 in) in diameter. The total height of the Mi-8 is 5.6 m (18 ft 4½ in), while the tail rotor is 3.8 m (12 ft 5½ in) in diameter. The main cabin is 5.25 m (17 ft 3 in) in length.

Military duties
During the Cold War, Aeroflot aircraft were regularly seconded to Soviet military activities. Although they were used in the Antarctic for ice patrol and reconnaissance, rescue and the movement of supply and equipment, these Mi-8s were also available as a military reserve, with provision for carrying strap-on weapons. Aeroflot 'Hips' were used in Afghanistan.

Tail rotor
The most notable difference between the Mi-8 and its successor, the Mi-17, is the latter's tail rotor, which was relocated to the port side. In addition, Mi-17s are almost invariably fitted with engine intake guards.

Robinson R22/R44

Lightweight success

From humble beginnings in Frank Robinson's living room in 1973, the Robinson company grew rapidly to produce more aircraft per year than any other general aviation manufacturer in the United States.

Good flight-handling qualities and economical performance have made the R22 popular with helicopter flying schools, particularly in the United States and the UK.

The Robinson Helicopter Company (RHC) has entered its second quarter century, having been founded by Frank Robinson in 1973 to develop, manufacture and market a light two-seat helicopter for the commercial market. In that year, Frank Robinson began work from his living room, but the company is today established in a purpose-built 25000-m² (260,000-sq ft) manufacturing facility at Torrance Airport in California, completed in June 1994. In the early days, Frank Robinson set out to produce a helicopter that was considerably less expensive to purchase, own and operate than any other light helicopter on the market. Since then, production of the R22 has exceeded 2,950 units, making this light helicopter the biggest-selling civil helicopter worldwide. It holds all world performance records in its class, including those of speed, altitude and distance.

Right: The R22 is ideal for private owners, having a total operating cost based on 500 hours per year of only US$68.50 per hour. This economy is a major selling point of the design, with sales approaching the 3,000 mark.

Special-purpose R22s

Unlike many light helicopters, the R22 has been adapted for operations from water. Designated R22 Mariner, the first examples were delivered for operations from tuna fishing-boats off the coasts of Mexico and Venezuela. A total of 12 was delivered in 1996. The Mariner has been superseded by the R22 Mariner II (left), this version having extra reserve power to allow extended flights over water. The type is corrosion-proofed throughout and equipped with utility floats, ground-handling wheels, and gauge/nozzle to check float pressure. The Mariner sits low in the water for added stability in rough seas. The R22 Agricultural (below left) is equipped with an Apollo Helicopter Services DTM-3 spray-system. A low-drag belly tank with a capacity of 151 litres (33.3 Imp gal) is contained within a frame, attached to the landing-gear mounting points using four bolts and wing nuts. The spray boom has a length of 7.31 m (24 ft), and installation of the entire system can be completed in five minutes by one person, requiring no specialised tools.

The R22 taking shape in a small hangar at Torrance Airport was of simple welded steel and light-alloy construction, covered by metal and fibreglass skins, with a two-bladed semi-articulated main rotor, a two-bladed tail rotor on a monocoque tailboom, and welded tube and light-alloy skid landing gear. The single Lycoming piston engine was mounted in the lower section of the rear fuselage.

Accommodation for two people was provided in an enclosed cabin. The prototype made its first flight on 28 August 1975, but it took another three and a half years of extensive testing and technical analysis before the R22 obtained its type certificate from the Federal Aviation Administration (FAA) on 16 March 1979. Deliveries to the first customer began in October of that year.

The initial model was powered by a 112-kW (150-hp) Lycoming O-320-A2C piston engine, replaced by the higher-powered 119-kW (160-hp) O-320-B2C in the R22HP from 1981. The new engine provided a 6-kt (11-km/h; 7-mph) increase in speed and improved in-ground effect (IGE) and out-of-ground effect (OGE) hover performance. Further improvements were incorporated from 1983 in the R22 Alpha, which featured increased gross weight, a modified tail section for greater stability, and optional equipment for use as an instrument flight rules (IFR) trainer. After producing 500 units, Robinson introduced the R22 Beta, which remains the current model, although it has undergone continuous improvements in the intervening years.

New models have included the more powerful R22 Beta II version introduced in 1996, providing nearly 13 per cent more power, with a 134-kW (180-hp) Textron Lycoming O-360-J2A flat-four engine, derated to 97.5 kW (131 hp). Other new features include carburettor heat assist, rpm throttle governor for reduced pilot workload and superior rpm control, high-capacity oil cooler, a more comfortable T-bar cyclic grip, automatic clutch engagement, rotor brake, door windows and an improved hover ceiling.

The R22 IFR Trainer incorporates an enlarged instrument panel to accommodate all instruments and avionics necessary for IFR rating, including artificial horizon, encoding altimeter, turn co-ordinator, horizontal situation indicator (HSI), automatic direction finder (ADF), nav/comm, transponder, marker beacon, digital clock and distance-measuring equipment (DME), the latter being optional.

Robinson has also produced a version for law enforcement known as the R22 Police. Special equipment includes a searchlight with dual peak beam Xenon lights, PA/siren control panel, speaker and siren, 70-amp alternator and single and dual multiple radio controllers.

In the mid-1980s, Frank Robinson began research and development work to expand the product line to include a four-seat helicopter based on the proven design principles of the R22. Designated R44, the new helicopter was designed to the more stringent requirements of FAR part 27 and features higher performance, with a cruise speed of 113 kt (209 km/h; 130 mph), expanded comfort and improved handling characteristics. In addition to incorporating an rpm governor, carburettor heat assist, T-bar cyclic control, automatic clutch engagement, and rotor brake (also later introduced on the R22), the R44 also features advanced warning devices, and crashworthy features including energy-absorbing landing gear and lap/shoulder strap restraints designed for high forward *g* loads. The cabin configuration offers two-plus-two seating with removable dual controls.

The prototype R44 made its first flight on 31 March 1990 and the basic R44 Astro with fixed skids obtained FAA certification on 10 December 1992. Deliveries began in mid-1993, since when Robinson has delivered more than 600 R44s to some 40 countries.

The R44 Newscopter has specialised news-gathering equipment, and was first delivered in spring 1997. Equipped with the FLIR Systems UltraMedia RS stabilised camera system, it also has two Elmo lipstick cameras, four monitors and a complete microwave package for live transmissions. The R44 IFR Trainer accommodates all equipment and avionics necessary for an IFR rating similar to the R22 IFR Trainer.

SPECIFICATION	
Robinson R22 Beta	**Weights:** empty 763 lb (346 kg);
Type: two-seat lightweight helicopter	loaded 589 kg (1,298 lb)
Powerplant: one 119-kW (160-hp)	**Dimensions:** main rotor diameter 7.70
Lycoming O-320-B2C flat four-piston	m (25 ft 2 in); length 6.30 m (20 ft 8
engine de-rated to 96-kW (130 hp) for	in); height 2.60 m (8 ft 9 in); rotor
take-off	disc area 46.2 m² (497 sq ft)
Performance: maximum speed 180	**Payload:** two seats side by side in an
km/h (112 mph); service ceiling 4267	enclosed cabin, dual controls optional
m (14,000 ft); hover ceiling 2133 m	
(7,000 ft); range 595 km (370 miles)	

R44 developments

Following on from the R22 Mariner, Robinson developed a float-equipped version of the R44 named Clipper (right). It, too, is fully corrosion-proofed, and received certification on 12 July 1996. The utility floats enable the Clipper to undertake extended flights over water and to land on remote lakes. It also has mast-mounted lights for night-flying and longer landing-gear struts for water operations. Empty weight is increased by 23 kg (50 lb) and speed reduced by around 16 km/h (10 mph). In 1999 a basic R44

Clipper with no optional extras cost US$293,000. The R44 Police (left) is a dedicated law enforcement model with bubble door windows and optional equipment including PA/siren, UHF/VHF police radio, Spectrolab SX-5E Starburst searchlight, Inframetrics IRTV 445G or Wescam 12DS gyro-stabilised infra-red sensor, and television camera system mounted in the nose turret. The aircraft was certified in July 1997 and the first delivery was to the South Bay Police Agency of Los Angeles, California.

Sikorsky **S-61** Civilian Sea King

Representing an improvement in capacity and comfort compared to previous Western passenger helicopters, the S-61 never fulfilled its early promise, but achieved some success in the improved S-61N form.

The Sikorsky S-61 was by no means the first helicopter airliner, though it was one of the first to be powered by turbine engines. With its excellent performance, spacious cabin and its ability to carry up to 28 passengers, it may also have been the most practical civil helicopter of its era. The civil S-61L was derived from the military (anti-submarine) S-61, which had first flown as the XHSS-2 on 17 March 1959, and which subsequently entered US Navy service as the HSS-2. The HSS-2 was re-designated as the SH-3A after the 1962 reorganisation of designations, and is best known as the Sea King. Work on the civil version of the S-61 began even before flight trials of the XHSS-2 were complete.

S-62 origins
The XHSS-2 itself was extremely similar in appearance to the S-62, a commercial helicopter which used many features of the S-55, married to the dynamic system of the S-58, and featuring a new amphibious hull

and a single T58 turboshaft engine. Despite its 'later' numerical designation, the S-62 actually pre-dated the S-61, and the prototype first flew in May 1958. The first S-62 had been delivered to launch customer Los Angeles Airways (LAA) in September 1960, in whose hands the potential of a stretched, more powerful twin-turboshaft helicopter became clear. This was good news for Sikorsky, which was already working 'full-tilt' on the S-61L.

With a stretched fuselage, 11 airliner-style windows per side and a lightweight fixed landing gear, the civil S-61L also had a modified rotor head and a longer-span braced tailplane. The first prototype made its maiden flight on 6 December 1960, with a colour scheme and interior designed by the prestigious Raymond Loewy Associates. The standard interior accommodated 25 passengers and a single flight attendant, with an optional hot-meal galley able to replace the single seat opposite the main door (which naturally incorporated an airstair)

Above: Los Angeles Airways inaugurated the world's first multi-engined, turbine-powered transport helicopter service, using its newly acquired S-61L, on 1 March 1962.

Above: The S-61L was the first truly practical transport helicopter in airline service, offering turbine performance combined with multi-engine safety and a 28-passenger load.

and with an optional toilet replacing the two rearmost seats. The rear bulkhead could be moved forwards to increase the size and volume of the cargo compartment.

Sikorsky offered a three-engined version of the civil S-61, with a third CT-58 turboshaft above the fuselage behind the main rotor, though this variant remained unbuilt, and civil S-61s remained twin-engined. The launch customer for the type was LAA, which ordered five aircraft. Chicago Helicopter

Airways ordered six aircraft, later reduced to four. LAA's aircraft were delivered with a purpose-designed pair of pre-loadable baggage pods which fitted into the lower fuselage just behind the cockpit. These could be slid out directly onto a trolley for unloading in the terminal, and replaced by a pair of pods loaded with the outgoing passengers luggage. Chicago's aircraft had five similar pods, and both operators' aircraft had carry-on baggage and freight compartments.

The S-61L returned a seat/mile cost of between eight and nine cents – this figure was half that of contemporary piston-engined helicopters – making the aircraft much more practical on routes where helicopters had previously been considered financially impossible. LAA, for example, restricted itself to serving terminals within a 80-km (50-mile) radius of the Post Office in downtown LA. Despite the 1969 introduction of an S-61L Mk II with more powerful engines and better sound-proofing and vibration dampers, the non-amphibious civil variant attracted few orders, and Sikorsky production totalled only 13 aircraft. But this did not mean that the civil S-61 was a failure, although the original version's 3311-kg (7,300-lb) payload (including the crew and all fuel) was really too limited for the number of seats packed into it, except over short distance transfers. There was also the fact that most customers ordered the more versatile S-61N, which added sponsons containing Sea King-type flotation gear, and an 'amphibious' sealed hull.

Water operations

The S-61N was, as delivered, not intended to operate routinely from water, but was well provided for in the event of a ditching. Even airline customers appreciated this, and were prepared to pay for it. Specialised sub-variants of the S-61N for SAR and offshore oil rig support were more properly amphibious, though even these aircraft did not routinely take off and land on the water. The prototype S-61N first flew on 7 August 1962, and quickly proved popular. On 2 November 1961 the original S-61L had been the first twin-turbine civil helicopter to receive FAA certification, and the S-61L and S-61N together were certificated for full IFR operation – the first civil helicopters to be so certificated. The same powerplant, soundproofing and vibration damper improvements which resulted in the S-61L Mk II were also applied to the S-61N to produce the S-61N Mk II.

The S-61N Mk II also introduced slightly larger sponsons and nose-mounted weather radar as standard. By 1970, the Sikorsky S-61L and S-61N were in service with LAA,

New York Airways received three S-61Ns from Sikorsky's parent company, United Aircraft Corporation, in April 1964. The aircraft were initially used to carry passengers to the New York World's Fair, operating from the rooftop of the Port of New York Authority building at the Fair. The S-61s were subsequently used to carry passengers from Pan Am's building in Manhattan to JFK Airport.

New York Airways, San Francisco and Oakland Helicopter Airlines, and with Australia's Ansett-ANA, Britain's BEA, Elivie in Italy, and Greenland Air. The early hopes that the S-61L and S-61N might offer a viable alternative to fixed-wing aircraft of a similar size did not materialise; the helicopters tended to be used only to serve terminals inaccessible to fixed-wing aircraft, often in city centres, or on islands or in mountain areas without a 'proper runway'. BEA, for example, used the aircraft to operate a service between Land's End (and later Penzance)

and the Scilly Isles – a service previously dependent upon biplane de Havilland Rapides.

Of the S-61's foreign licensees, only Italy's Agusta has been licensed to produce civil versions of the aircraft. Agusta designed the unique AS-61N-1 Silver, which was effectively an S-61N, 'shortened' back to standard Sea King length. The type retained seven fuselage windows, big S-61N-type sponsons and an S-61N-type tail unit. Most of Agusta's customers for the variant have been military, however, with Malaysia taking two as AS-61NSs.

British European Airways Helicopters' S-61N G-ASNM is seen demonstrating the type's suitability for overwater operations before it entered service on the Land's End-Scilly Isles route.

SPECIFICATION	
Sikorsky S-61N	**Weights:** empty 5674 kg (12,340 lb);
Type: all-weather helicopter transport and rescue aircraft	loaded 9299 kg (19,000 lb)
Powerplant: two 1119-kW (1,500-hp) General Electric CT58-140-1/2 turboshafts	**Dimensions:** main rotor diameter 18.90 m (46 ft); length 22.20 m (72 ft 10 in); height 5.32 m (17 ft 6 in); rotor disc area 280.47 m² (3,020 sq ft)
Performance: maximum speed 241 km/h (150 mph) at sea level; service ceiling 3810 m (12,500 ft); range 797 km (518 miles) with 30-minute reserves	**Payload:** up to 26 passengers

Oil rig supporter

The market for helicopter airliners was very limited, with the lower seat-mile costs of conventional fixed-wing aircraft limiting the use of helicopters to routes to and from destinations which had no runway – usually in city centres. The S-61 had to find alternative roles in the civilian field.

BEA Helicopters used the S-61N on both passenger services (including serving the Scilly Isles from Penzance) and on North Sea oilfield support. The entire business was sold to entrepreneur Robert Maxwell in 1986.

The S-61 was originally designed for airliner operations, but was soon pressed into use for other 'less cosmopolitan' roles and tasks. The aircraft's new roles have tended to concentrate around two main areas – flying crane-type operations and austere utility transport duties.

Sikorsky itself developed a stripped-down version of the S-61N as the Payloader, combining a stripped version of the S-61N airframe with the simple, 'sponson-less' fixed undercarriage of the S-61L. Low weight maximised payload (which rose to 4990 kg/11,000-lb), and the Payloader was used principally as a flying crane, moving underslung loads for logging companies, pipeline and powerline companies, and even for construction and building contractors.

But the Payloader was still carrying around a lot of unnecessary and largely unused weight – in the form of a huge, empty cabin. The logical solution was to further reduce airframe weight by removing a section of

airframe, taking the aircraft back to the length of the military Sea King. Probably the first 'shortened S-61' was N4503E, an S-61L aircraft of Carson Helicopters of Perkasie, Pennsylvania.

Canadian helicopter repair, maintenance and support company Helipro has set up a programme to convert S-61Ls and S-61Ns to a similar 'Shortened' configuration as the S-61L Shortsky or S-61N Shortsky. All conversions are now known by the name S-61 Short. The Helipro conversion consists of the removal of a 1.27-m (50-in) section between Station 110 (immediately behind the flight deck) and Station 160 (just in front of the intake leading edge). All rotor, tailrotor and engine control cables are

Carson Helicopters is one of the largest civil operators of the S-61, operating S-61Ns (illustrated) and converted HH-3s and SH-3s. The fleet is divided between Perkasie in Pennsylvania and Jacksonville, Oregon.

removed, shortened and then re-installed, and extensive changes are made to the aircraft's electrical and hydraulic systems.

Apart from the 'shortening' of the airframe, the S-61 Short had local strengthening at Stations 243 and 290, with heavy-duty hardpoints, and an emergency hook release, and was fitted with new bubble windows on the flight deck (to allow the pilots a better view downwards). The aircraft was also fitted with a new VFR avionics package in a single avionics tray, for low weight and reduced maintenance. The conversion programme takes between

4,000 and 5,000 man-hours and an elapsed time of between 10 and 12 weeks. In 1996, the price was quoted at US $650,000. The company has since converted two S-61Ls for the Canadian Helicopters Corporation, and S-61Ns for BIH (one aircraft, leased from Helipro), the Hayes Heli-Log Group (two), Huisson Aviation (two) and VIH Logging (two).

Offshore work

The S-61N has found its niche in the offshore oil rig support role, thanks to the flight safety advantages offered by its watertight hull and thanks to its ability to transport large

Military S-61s

Military use of the S-61 centres around three main variants: the S-61A short-body transport, S-61D/SH-3 ASW/maritime utility aircraft and S-61R/HH-3 long-body rescue/transport. Only a few S-61As are in service, notably with Denmark (left) and Malaysia. The S-61D was for many years the US Navy's primary ASW helicopter, and also serves with other navies, including that of Brazil (above).

numbers of passengers in comfort, or mixed loads of passengers and freight. With the oil boom in the North Sea, the S-61 became a support workhorse, operating with Bristow, British Airways Helicopters, Norway's Helikopter Service and KLM Nordzee Helikopters. Elsewhere, offshore oil support S-61Ns were used by Okanagan Helicopters in Hudson Bay and in the Atlantic, by Bristow and Brunei Shell in Malaysia, and by Helicopter Utilities off Australia's Northern Territories. The intensity of such operations is staggering, and in the North Sea Bristow alone

soon accumulated some impressive statistics, carrying 5 million passengers in half a million flights before 1992. Other operators could tell similarly impressive stories.

Helipro, responsible for the S-61 Short for logging and flying crane operations, produced a similar conversion for offshore support work, similarly shortened, but fitted with a winch in the aft door and with water-tight underfloor baggage bins which did not compromise the type's amphibious capabilities.

The final role for the civil S-61 has been that of Search and

Rescue. Civilian S-61Ns have replaced some military (RN and RAF) British-built Westland Sea Kings and Wessexes since the partial 'privatisation' of SAR services. Bristow operates a number of specially modified S-61N Mk IIs on behalf of HM Coastguard.

These aircraft are fitted with a company-developed SAR package, with a fully-coupled Flight Path Control and Auto-Hover system, a nose-mounted Bendix RDR 1400C colour weather, mapping and search radar and an undernose FLIR turret, as well as a variable-speed rescue hoist with 90 m (295 ft) of cable. Irish Helicopters operate similarly modified S-61Ns (with FLIR and LN450 auto-hover) from Shannon to fulfil an Irish government SAR contract.

Bristow Helicopters has also used its S-61Ns to fulfil military contracts for the UK armed forces, most notably in the Falkland Islands. For the Falkland operations the S-61Ns are fitted out to carry 18 troops and internal freight or baggage. The aircraft are fitted with a nose-mounted radar, and also carry VOR, ILS and NDB (non-directional beacon). They are fitted with military VHF and UHF

radio equipment and have a Helicopter Health and Usage Monitoring System (HUMS). In the Falklands the Bristow S-61Ns are almost universally known as 'Erics', after the well-known cockney darts player, Eric Bristow.

Military service

The S-61 has also been used by a number of military customers, most notably in S-61B and S-61D (SH-3 Sea King), and S-61R (CH-3C, E, and MH-3E) forms. Some export customers use S-61- or Agusta-Sikorsky AS-61-based designations rather than the US military H-3 series designations, including Argentina (with S-61D-4s and AS-61s), Brazil (with S-61D-3s and AS-61Ds), Denmark (with S-61A-1s), Iran (with AS-61A-4s), Iraq (with AS-61A-4s), Italy (with HH-3-based AS-61Rs and ASH-3 Sea Kings), Libya (with AS-61A-4s), Malaysia (with S-61A-4s and AS-61NSs), Peru (with AS-61Ds), Saudi Arabia (with AS-61A-4s), and Venezuela (with AS-61A-4s). Japan, characteristically, uses its own unique designation system based on the aircraft's original HSS-2 designation, while Canada calls its S-61s CH-124s. Spain continues to use the SH-3 designation.

The S-61 became the workhorse of the North Sea, transporting oil workers to the rigs. Bristow (below) and KLM Helicopters (right) operated weather radar-equipped aircraft on these duties.

Sikorsky S-76 Spirit

Spirit of Sikorsky

In the early 1970s Sikorsky Aircraft turned its attention to the civil sector. After lengthy and studied evaluation of the needs of potential customers, Sikorsky chose a twin-turbine design for 12 passengers as the best way to gain a bigger share of the market. Given the designation S-76 to mark the American bicentennial, the new design was announced to the world on 19 January 1975.

From the outset, the S-76 was equipped for all-weather operation and the design clearly benefited from the research and development work undertaken on the dynamic system of the S-70 military helicopter, which became known as the Black Hawk. The main rotor is a scaled-down version of that of the S-70, with its four blades built around a hollow titanium spar covered in glassfibre over a Nomex honeycomb core. The leading-edge strips are made of titanium and nickel, while the blades have swept Kevlar tips. The fully-articulated rotor head has elastomeric bearings which need no lubrication, and is fitted with dampers and vibration absorbers. The four-bladed tail rotor is of composite construction.

The carefully streamlined fuselage makes extensive use

Sikorsky was able to combine the practicality of a large cabin capable of accommodating four-abreast bench seating with an exceptionally streamlined body.

of composites, comprising glass fibre, light alloy and Kevlar. The S-76's retractable tricycle landing gear has a single wheel on each leg and is hydraulically operated. The nosewheel retracts rearward and the main units inwards into the rear fuselage, all fully enclosed by doors when retracted. Non-retractable landing gear with low-pressure tyres is available on the utility version. The turboshaft engines (initially the Allison 250-C30) are

Above: S-76s have worn a variety of colourful liveries. This example served with Petroleum Helicopter Incorporated.

The Royal Jordanian air force bought 18 S-76s, of which four were for medevac duties in paramilitary service and 12 for the SAR/general transport role, with two others for VIP use. Jordan transferred two of its S-76s to Iraq and four are reported to have gone to Guatemala. It has disposed of its remaining S-76s.

mounted above the cabin behind the drive shaft. The standard fuel system is comprised of a single 1064-litre (281-US gallon) fuel tank in the fuselage, although auxiliary tanks totalling another 401 litres (106 US gallons) for extended-range operations are available as an option. Accommodation varies considerably depending on customer specification. In typical passenger configuration, the S-76 carries a maximum of 12 passengers, in addition to the pilot and co-pilot, seated on three rows of four seats. However, many are operated by corporate owners in luxurious executive configurations for as few as four people, featuring full carpeting, extra soundproofing, telephone and co-ordinated furniture. Cabin heating and ventilation are standard.

The S-76 can also be converted into an air ambulance with up to three stretchers and two medical attendants, and is additionally being used in the search and rescue (SAR) role, with searchlight, rescue hoist and emergency flotation gear. Access to the cabin is via two large hinged doors on each side of the fuselage, although sliding doors can be fitted. Baggage compartments in the rear fuselage can be reached by external doors from each side.

Model progression

The original S-76A version, sometimes referred to as the S-76A Spirit, was replaced from 1 March 1982 by the S-76A Mk.II, which remained in production until 1993. This incorporated some 40 improvements, highlighted by the more efficient 485-kW (650-shp) Allison 250-C30S turboshaft with a 5 per cent increase in guaranteed power output, a new cabin ventilation system without performance degradation, and various refinements to the major dynamic components. Additional fuselage access panels were fitted to simplify maintenance. Kits incorporating these changes were made available to update the earlier model to the new standard.

A subsequent retrofit with Turbomeca 523-kW (700-shp) Arriel 1S turboshafts produced the S-76A+ and, with the improved and more powerful Arriel 1S1, the S-76A++.

The S-76A Utility is a more basic version with sliding doors on each side, dual controls and a stressed cabin floor for cargo operations. Options included fixed landing gear and low-pressure tyres for rough terrain, crash-resistant fuel tanks, and an auxiliary fuel tank for installation in the baggage hold. A few were produced for military purposes with armoured crew seats, removable cabin seats, cargo hook, rescue hoist, engine air particle separators and provisions for stretchers.

The S-76B, production of which was discontinued at the end of 1997, is basically an S-76A Mk.II, but with two 716-kW (960-shp) Pratt & Whitney Canada PT6B-36 turboshafts. The S-76B began flight testing on 22 June 1984 and obtained certification in early 1987. The extra power resulted in a 50 per cent increase in useful load under hot-and-high conditions.

Next came the S-76C, which was similar to the S-76B, but fitted with the 539-kW (723-shp) Turbomeca Arriel 1S1. It entered service in April 1991, but has now been replaced by the S-76C+, which first flew on 30 June 1994 and obtained FAA and CAA certification in June 1996. This model is distinguished by the uprated Arriel 2S1 turboshafts, each rated at 638 kW (856 shp) for take-off, which is improved,

and this model offers one-engine inoperative (OEI) performance. It also has full authority digital engine control (FADEC) and makes use of single-crystal blade technology. The S-76C+ is now the only model in production – at the beginning of 1998, a total of 467 S-76s had been delivered.

Being a civil design, the helicopter never really caught on with the military. The Philippine Air Force took delivery of 12 AUH-76s configured for COIN, logistics support and medevac duties, but the dedicated armed military H-76 has found no customers since its first flight in February 1985. Six of the S-76N naval derivative have, however, been delivered to the Royal Thai Navy, equipped for maritime patrol, ship-to-shore personnel transport and search and rescue.

The S-76N features a protective airframe coating, health and usage monitoring system (HUMS), strengthened landing gear, deck lock and tie-down system capable of weathering Sea State 7, manually-folding rotor blades, self-sealing fuel system and hover-in-flight refuelling (HIFR) capability.

Interesting one-offs were the S-76 SHADOW demonstrator for the US Army Rotorcraft Technology Integration (ARTI) programme, which first flew on 24 June 1985, and an H-76 fitted with the Boeing Sikorsky Fantail anti-torque system, the latter being first flown on 6 June 1990.

Military variants and experimental models

Sikorsky was keen to expand the military capabilities of the S-76 and a multi-mission variant known as the H-76 was developed. Configured for the anti-tank role (illustrated above), the H-76 was equipped with TOW anti-tank missiles and a mast-mounted sight but, although live firing exercises were conducted by the US Army, no orders were placed for the attack variant. The excellent handling qualities of the S-76 allowed it to be utilised as an experimental test-bed for a number of military programmes. One of the most unusual was known as SHADOW. Mounted ahead of the fuselage in a pod was a single-seat cockpit, which was used to test future battlefield helicopter pilot workloads.

SPECIFICATION

Sikorsky S-76 Spirit
Type: medium capacity helicopter
Powerplant: two Allison 250-C30 turboshaft engines each rated at 484.7 kW (649 shp)
Performance: maximum speed 289 km/h (180 mph); normal cruising speed 269 km/h (167 mph); service ceiling 1555 m (5,100 ft); range 1100 km (683 miles)

Weights: empty 2241 kg (4,940 lb); loaded 4400 kg (9,700 lb); maximum take-off 5171 kg (11,400 lb)
Dimensions: main rotor diameter 13.41 m (44 ft); length 16 m (52 ft 6 in); height 4.41 m (14 ft 5 in)
Payload: 12 or 13 passengers in the main cabin

Unlike its naval counterpart, the British Army's Westland Lynx did not attract export orders, but it was developed into the Army Air Corps' main battlefield helicopter. It continues to serve in that capacity, but is being replaced by the Apache Longbow.

Assault Helicopters

Aérospatiale/Eurocopter Puma/Super Puma/Cougar

The French Aviation Légère de l'Armée de Terre (Army Light Aviation) operates more than 130 SA 330 Pumas. This example belongs to det. ALAT 188 based in Djibouti, one of three permanent overseas detachments.

SA 330 Puma

In the 1970s and 1980s the SA 330 Puma became the standard medium transport helicopter for many world air forces. Only the arrival of the Sikorsky Black Hawk nudged it off its perch. Few changes were ever made to the basic design, a sure sign that it was a good one and, despite its cost and complexity, the Puma even found acceptance in the civil market.

By the late 1960s the efficacy of the battlefield transport helicopter was not in doubt. Proven in Vietnam, no modern army could afford to be without such an aircraft. The European nations had an unsuitable collection of helicopters in service, largely based on obsolete American designs; Britain and France, in particular, had the most pressing need to replace their ageing helicopter fleets. This led to the 1967 Anglo-French helicopter agreement, and a production/ purchase deal encompassing the Westland Lynx, Aérospatiale Gazelle and Aérospatiale Puma. While this agreement was ultimately weighted heavily in favour of the French, it did lead to three excellent helicopter designs, the largest of which was the SA 330 Puma.

The Puma story actually began several years earlier with a French army requirement to replace its S-55s and H-34s, all licence-built by Sud Aviation.

By 1962 the French were looking for a new utility transport helicopter, capable of carrying up to 20 troops and fulfilling a range of other tasks. Sud Aviation toyed with the idea of developing one of its existing (Sikorsky) designs but instead started work on a wholly indigenous design, the SA 330 – which was initially dubbed the Alouette IV. This project was launched in 1963 and the prototype first flew, rechristened as the Puma, on 14 April 1965.

Design profile

The Puma was built around two Turbomeca Bastan VII turbines, driving a four-bladed main rotor. The high-sided main cabin, with a sliding door to port, sat on what was then a novel retractable tricycle undercarriage, with wide sponsons on either side of the rear fuselage. The helicopter could accommodate 18 passengers and two crew.

Sud Aviation went on to build a series of eight prototypes and soon re-engined the Puma with the Turbomeca Turmo IIIC.4 turboshaft (as used on the Super Frelon). As the development programme progressed, UK interest in the new helicopter grew and the last prototype was transferred to Britain for evaluation. It was this that ultimately led to the selection of the Puma by the Royal Air Force as a Whirlwind and Belvedere replacement, and to the Anglo-French helicopter

For many years, a flight of RAF Pumas was based in Belize to provide the British garrison there with mobility, search and rescue and rapid response capability.

Right: Both British and French Pumas have been involved in UN peacekeeping deployments in the 1990s. Often operating in potentially hostile environments, the aircraft could be fitted with infra-red decoy flares, as demonstrated by this example.

Above: Of the first three SA 330 prototypes seen here, the nearest two are carrying test instrumentation probes attached to the nose of the aircraft, away from the downwash of the rotors.

Above: Tested during the Gulf War, where it was carried by French Army Pumas (such as this example), the HORIZON heliborne radar system is now deployed operationally on Cougars.

agreement. French Army Aviation (ALAT) adopted the SA 330B Puma as its basic aircraft. A similar version, designated Puma HC.Mk 1 (SA 330E), was acquired by the RAF. The RAF's Pumas were built under licence by Westland, at Yeovil, where all 48 HC.Mk 1s were assembled. Westland continued to have rights to the Puma design until 1988, but never sold any aircraft to any other customers. The export version of the basic aircraft, the SA 330F, was controlled by Sud Aviation and sold widely to military operators around the world.

Company merger

In January 1970 Sud Aviation was merged with Nord Aviation and SEREB to form Aérospatiale. Aérospatiale continued to refine the Puma, developing the SA 330G powered by uprated Turmo IVC turboshafts, and aimed at the commercial market. The Puma did find favour with civil operators, mainly in the offshore oil support role. For this mission an emergency flotation system was developed, which could be fitted to the nose and undercarriage sponsons. The same equipment was fitted to SAR aircraft, such as those acquired by Portugal. The

SA 330H was a military version, similar to the SA 330G, and many SA 330F operators had their aircraft upgraded to this standard.

Aérospatiale next introduced some new technology on the Puma with the addition of weight-saving composite main rotor blades. Two models were built with the new blades, the SA 330J (based on the SA 300G) and the SA 330L (based on the SA 330H). Again, several existing operators had the new dynamic system retrofitted to their aircraft. Finally, Aérospatiale used Puma airframes for test and trials duties of its own. The sole SA 330R featured a stretched fuselage and was used for development work on the SA 332 Super Puma. The SA 330Z was fitted with a fenestron tail rotor and served as a testbed for the SA 360 Dauphin project.

Aérospatiale allocated production licences for the Puma to IPTN in Indonesia and IAR Brasov in Romania. Both firms went on to build basic aircraft, chiefly for their own armed forces and government agencies – though Romania has quietly exported Pumas to several customers abroad. IPTN built approximately 20 SA 330Js from French-supplied kits and

locally-built components, before moving on to build the Super Puma. IAR, on the other hand, has built close to 200 Pumas and developed its own indigenous versions. The basic Romanian Puma was designated SA 330L (IAR 330L) and, from the transport version, IAR developed a Puma gunship with 20-mm (0.79-in) cannon in cheek-mounted pods, and side-mounted launch rails for anti-tank missiles and rockets.

Romanian developments

Another version of the IAR 330L was developed for coastguard use and fitted with flotation gear and comprehensive navaids. IAR is currently working on the

SOCAT Puma upgrade with Israel's Elbit. SOCAT adds a nose-mounted FLIR, a 20-mm (0.79-in) turret-mounted cannon and advanced anti-tank missiles to the basic IAR 330L and has been ordered by the Romanian MoD. One important customer for Romanian Pumas was South Africa, which used the SA 330s to develop its own improved, indigenous version – the Atlas Oryx. South Africa took delivery of about 70 aircraft before arms sanctions against the apartheid regime took hold. The South African Air Force reinforced its Puma fleet with IAR 330Ls, re-engining its aircraft with the Turboméca Makila 1A1 engine, for improved performance.

SPECIFICATION	
Aérospatiale (Westland) SA330L Puma	**Dimensions:** main rotor diameter 15 m
Type: medium transport helicopter	(49 ft 3 in); length 18.15 m (59 ft 6 in);
Powerplant: two 1175-kW (1,575-hp)	height 5.14 m (16 ft 10 in); rotor disc
Turbomeca Turmo IVC turboshafts	area 176.7 m² (1,901 sq ft)
Performance: maximum speed 294	**Accommodation:** up to 20 fully
km/h (182 mph); service ceiling 6000	equipped troops or 3200 kg (7,000 lb)
m (19,700 ft); range 572 km (355	of cargo
miles) at cruising speed	**Armament:** optional provision for
Weights: empty 3615 kg (7,953 lb);	various combinations of weapons
maximum take-off 7400 kg (16,280 lb)	including cannons, machine guns,
	rockets and missiles

Agusta-Bell AB 412 Grifone

Assault and multi-role helicopter

Collaborating closely with Bell, Agusta launched production of the Model 412 in civil guise during 1981 as the **Agusta-Bell 412** and began deliveries to customers in January 1983. The Model 412 is essentially a Model 212 (AB 212) with a four-bladed main rotor. Agusta proceeded to develop a dedicated military variant, largely to meet the requirements of the Italian military and quasi-military services. This was first flown in August 1982, with the designation **AB 412 Grifone** (**Griffon**).

Military variants

The type was designed to cope with a wide variety of roles that could include direct fire support and area suppression with one or two side-mounted cannon (or various combinations of light and heavy machine guns); scouting and reconnaissance with rocket pods (each carrying seven, 12 or 19 81-mm (3.2-in) Medusa or SNORA unguided rockets) and cable cutters; air defence with AAMs or other weapons; assault transport carrying up to 14 combat-equipped troops; and battlefield support including the casevac role with the facility for carrying six litters plus two attendants. Subsequently, a maritime model was evolved for SAR, surveillance, mission monitoring etc., for which it was provided with a 360° search radar with its antenna in a radome above the roof of the cockpit, FLIR and TV sensors, four-axis autopilot, and a special navigation system.

Special features of the Grifone include strengthened landing gear to absorb higher landing impacts; energy-absorbing

Sweden's Helicopterflottilj is a relatively new operator of the AB 412 Grifone, acquiring the first of its eight (now five) examples in 1993. The local designation for the aircraft is HKP 11 and the aircraft have the dual role of transport, and military and civilian medevac in the remote and unreachable parts in the north of Sweden.

SPECIFICATION	
Agusta-Bell AB 412 Grifone **Type:** 16-seat medium utility helicopter **Powerplant:** one 1342-kW (1,800-shp) Pratt & Whitney Canada PT6T-3B Turbo Twin Pac coupled turboshaft **Performance:** maximum speed 259 km/h (161 mph) at sea level; cruising speed 232 km/h (144 mph) at 1500 m (4,920 ft); initial climb rate 438 m (1,437 ft) per minute; service ceiling 5180 m (17,000 ft); range 805 km (500 miles)	**Weights:** empty 2841 kg (6,263 lb); maximum take-off 5400 kg (11,905 lb) **Dimensions:** main rotor diameter 14.02 m (46 ft); length overall 17.07 m (56 ft); height 4.32 m (14 ft 2 in); main rotor disc area 154.40 m² (1,661.90 sq ft) **Aramament:** options include one or two 25-mm (1-in) Oerlikon Contraves KBA-B cannon, four or eight BGM-71 TOW anti-tank missiles, or two multiple rocket launchers

armour-protected seats; armour for selected airframe areas; cabin floor fittings to provide for a wide variety of attachments for seats, stretchers, internal hoist or other special equipment; crash-attenuating seats; plus provision for IR emission-reduction devices on the engine exhausts.

In Italy, the AB 412 is now used by no fewer than six military and government agencies, including the national forest service and national fire service. A major user is the Carabinieri, which received 32, while the SNPC (national civilian protection service) took at least four. Under Italian navy control, the coastguard has 24 vessels likely to enter service.

Military service

At least 23 out of an original 25 AB 412s remain in service with

Italy's Cavalleria Dell'Aria (air cavalry), under the designation **EM-4**, indicating the fourth type of **Elicottero Multiruolo**, or multi-role helicopter.

Agusta has also sold five Grifones to the Uganda People's Defence Force, which uses them as gunships in an armed anti-guerrilla role and retained four in service late in 2003; and 12 to the Air Force of Zimbabwe, including two equipped for VIP/ambulance missions, of which total around seven remained operational late in 2003.

Other operators have included the Finnish coast guard (two aircraft), the Dubai air wing (six), Lesotho (two) and the Venezuelan army (two). The AB 412 is also operated in the UK by the Defence Helicopter Training School, as the **Griffon HT.Mk 1**.

British use of the Huey includes the Bell 412 Griffin HT.Mk 1s at RAF Shawbury. The HT.Mk 1s of No. 60(R) Sqn/Defence Helicopter Flying School are used for the training of RAF personnel on multi-engined operations. Two Griffins are usually detached to the Search and Rescue Training Unit (SARTU) at Valley, and are equipped with a winch installation and flotation bags.

Atlas Oryx/IAR 330L Puma

The licence-built IAR 330 is the mainstay of the Romanian air force's rotary-wing fleet. Note that this aircraft is fitted with the larger sponsons.

Foreign Puma developments

South Africa was a major customer for the French-built Aérospatiale Puma and began to add improvements and upgrades to the aircraft early in its career. Atlas soon built considerable experience and expertise with the type, and in order to circumvent UN sanctions, manufactured frequently required items such as tyres, transparencies, acrylic floor panels, gearboxes, engine hot sections, and rotor blades. It also manufactured newly-designed components optimised for SAAF use, including fuel tanks and armoured seats.

XTP-1 Beta

The first major upgrade programme resulted in the **XTP-1 Beta**, which featured extended engine intake filters, denoting installation of the Super Puma's Makila turboshafts, and a tail unit similar to that fitted to the AS 532 Cougar. These modifications

were later disclosed to be intended for retrofit across the Puma fleet, whereas the other modifications, which gave the aircraft its XTP- (**Experimental Test Platform**) designation, were not. These modifications included a long air data probe projecting from the port side of the cockpit, and stub wings mounted on the cabin sides, which apparently required the cabin doors to be 'sealed shut'. The wings each carried two articulated weapons pylons and a 20-mm (0.79-in) GA1 cannon was installed in a ventral turret and was aimed by helmet-mounted sight.

Originally the XTP-1 was expected to form the basis of a gunship conversion of the Puma, but in fact it was a systems and weapons testbed, marking a further step towards the indigenous Rooivalk. The aircraft was later used as the basis of a low-cost alternative to the Rooivalk, and several stub-winged, cannon-armed Pumas

entered operational evaluation during mid-1990. These had wingtip launch rails for the IR-homing Darter or Viper AAM, and a laser designator for the Swift anti-tank missile. Atlas offered offered various gunship configurations, but none seems to have entered regular service.

Oryx

The XTP-1's tail and engine modifications, together with a new Super Puma-style nose radome, formed the basis of the **Oryx**, originally known as **Gemsbok**, upgrade. The Oryx cockpit is also configured for single pilot operations. Pumas converted to this standard were delivered from 1988, entering

full service in 1994. Some confusion exists concerning their exact status and some sources suggest that Atlas, later Denel, built most, if not all, of the aircraft from new.

Romanian production

Under licence agreements with Aérospatiale, IAR in Romania established a production line for the SA 330L Puma in 1977. Exports have reportedly included some for the SAAF, but the majority of IAR production was for the Romanian air force, and included an armed variant developed locally. This carries two 20-mm (0.79-in) cannon cheek pods on the lower front fuselage sides and with steel tube mountings on each side of the main cabin (behind the entry doors) capable of carrying four rocket pods and AT-3 'Sagger' anti-armour missiles.

The **IAR 330L Puma** is powered by Turbomecanica (Romania) Turmo IVC turboshafts of 1175 kW (1,575 shp) each, but IAR has also produced the **Puma 2000**, featuring more powerful engines and a range of advanced equipment as standard or optional fit. The standard Puma 2000 has hands on collective and stick (HOCAS) controls, helmet-mounted sights, EFIS and MIL STD 1553 technology. The cockpit is NVG compatible.

SPECIFICATION	
Atlas Oryx **Type:** twin-engined medium-assault helicopter **Powerplant:** two Turbomeca Makila 1A1 each rated at 1400 kW (1,877 shp) for take-off and 1184 kW (1,588 shp) for continuous running	**Dimensions:** main rotor diameter 15 m (49 ft 2 ½ in); length overall rotors turning 18.15 m (59 ft 6½ in) and fuselage 14.06 m (46 ft 1½ in); height overall 5.14 m (16 ft 10½ in) and to top of rotor head 4.38 m (14 ft 4½ in); main rotor disc area 176.71 m² (1,902.2 sq ft)

Bell Boeing
V-22 Osprey

Tilting troop carrier

Development of the remarkable Osprey is continuing despite heated debates by politicians over the future of the project.

The second Osprey prototype takes on fuel during an evaluation exercise. When the V-22 finally makes it into service, its radical tiltrotor system will revolutionise assault transport operations.

In late 2000, squadron HMM-204 at Marine Corps Air Station New River, North Carolina, now a helicopter training squadron, will be redesignated VHMM-204 and will become the first to fly the Bell Boeing V-22 Osprey.

The Osprey looks in some ways like a helicopter, but the resemblance is misleading. Called a 'tiltrotor', the V-22 with its digital fly-by-wire flight controls can take off vertically like a helicopter, but, once aloft, shift into horizontal flight like a fixed-wing aircraft. This capability offers higher speed and range than the Marines' current CH-46E Sea Knight helicopter, many of which are now 40 years old, have flown up to 9,500 hours of a projected 10,000-hour life expectancy, and need to be replaced. Because it carries up to 24 troops, the V-22 can become the spearhead of

an attack from offshore launched by ships that remain safely outside an enemy's coastal defences. If technical problems can be solved, large numbers of Marines can 'hit the beach' not on a sandy, well-defended shoreline but far inland, attacking the enemy by surprise.

In its helicopter mode, the V-22 can hover, fly sideways, to the rear and forward. It can carry a variety of slung loads weighing up to 6803 kg (15,000 lb). When the rotors have tilted forward to act as turboprops, the Osprey can achieve a top speed of 315 kt (584 km/h; 363 mph). As a troop transport – even when operating from seaborne platforms in difficult conditions near an enemy's coast – the V-22 has a combat radius of 550 nm (1017 km/633 miles) and can be refuelled in flight.

The pilot of the V-22 will be, in many respects, a new breed. When Bell's closely-related civil Model 609 tiltrotor reaches the civil market, the distinction between a 'fixed wing' and 'rotary wing' pilot's license will disappear inside a new category. Apart from its tiltrotor concept, the V-22 has an advanced flight deck with instruments that dispense with dials entirely. Further, the V-22 will incorporate a new helmet which will integrate both infra-red and image intensification to improve night vision; a magnetic

head tracker slaved to the IR system plus any future turreted weapons systems, and display symbology like that found on a head-up display (HUD).

Boeing builds the Osprey's fuselage components at its plant in Philadelphia (Ridley Township, Pa.). This factory makes extensive use of robotics and fabricates the fuselage structure almost entirely from graphite-epoxy composite materials. The finished fuselage is then transported by air to the Bell factory in Fort Worth where it is 'mated' with wings and tail.

SPECIFICATION	
Bell Boeing V22 Osprey	**Weights:** empty 15032 kg (33,140 lb); maximum take-off 27422 kg (60,500 lb)
Type: twin-engined tilt-rotor multi-mission aircraft	
Powerplant: two 4392-kW (5,890-shp) Allison T406-AD-400 turboshafts	**Dimensions:** rotor diameter (each) 11.61 m (38 ft 1 in); fuselage length 17.47 m (57 ft 4 in); height 6.73 m (22 ft 1 in); rotor disc area (each) 105.82 m² (1,139 sq ft)
Performance: maximum speed 565 km/h (351 mph); maximum cruising speed 509 km/h (316 mph); climb rate 707 m (2,320 ft) per minute; service ceiling 7925 m (26,000 ft) range 1759 km (1,093 miles)	
	Armament: three crew and 24 fully combat-equipped troops

The Osprey flies like a normal fixed-wing aircraft, with greater speed and endurance than most helicopters.

When nearing the landing zone, the Osprey begins the transition from wingborne flight by the translation of its radical tiltrotor system.

To pick up or drop its cargo, the V-22's rotors are raised like a helicopter, enabling the aircraft to descend vertically.

A new Bell factory is being constructed in Amarillo, Texas and will take over the company's V-22 responsibilities in the near future. The total buy of Ospreys by all US services is subject to deliberations in the US Congress. The current plan is for the Bell Boeing team to deliver 425 MV-22Bs to the US Marine Corps, 50 CV-22Bs to US Air Force special operations forces, and 48 HV-22Bs to the US Navy. The production run is slated to stretch through 2035, and other countries may well become Osprey users.

Two V-22s have been lost in mishaps, adding to the controversy surrounding the aircraft. The first occurred on 12 June 1991 in Wilmington, Delaware when the No. 5 Osprey (BuNo. 163915) went down, without loss of life. The no. 4 Osprey (BuNo. 163914) crashed in the Potomac River on approach to Quantico, Va. on 20 July 1992, killing seven personnel.

V-22 Osprey

The idea of the tiltrotor had been debated for many years, but it was not until the advent of the V-22 that the concept became operationally viable. Its advantages are numerous; it can do anything a helicopter can, but go twice as far and twice as fast. The aircraft here is the second prototype. Its initial flight tests covered flight control systems, development tests, icing and flying qualities.

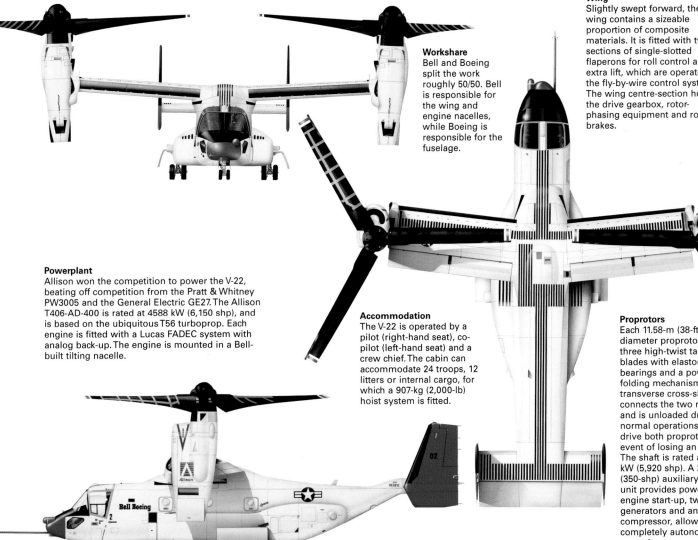

Workshare
Bell and Boeing split the work roughly 50/50. Bell is responsible for the wing and engine nacelles, while Boeing is responsible for the fuselage.

Wing
Slightly swept forward, the wing contains a sizeable proportion of composite materials. It is fitted with two sections of single-slotted flaperons for roll control and extra lift, which are operated by the fly-by-wire control system. The wing centre-section houses the drive gearbox, rotor-phasing equipment and rotor brakes.

Powerplant
Allison won the competition to power the V-22, beating off competition from the Pratt & Whitney PW3005 and the General Electric GE27. The Allison T406-AD-400 is rated at 4588 kW (6,150 shp), and is based on the ubiquitous T56 turboprop. Each engine is fitted with a Lucas FADEC system with analog back-up. The engine is mounted in a Bell-built tilting nacelle.

Accommodation
The V-22 is operated by a pilot (right-hand seat), co-pilot (left-hand seat) and a crew chief. The cabin can accommodate 24 troops, 12 litters or internal cargo, for which a 907-kg (2,000-lb) hoist system is fitted.

Proprotors
Each 11.58-m (38-ft) diameter proprotor has three high-twist tapered blades with elastomeric bearings and a power-folding mechanism. A transverse cross-shaft connects the two rotors and is unloaded during normal operations, but can drive both proprotors in the event of losing an engine. The shaft is rated at 4416 kW (5,920 shp). A 261-kW (350-shp) auxiliary power unit provides power for engine start-up, two generators and an air compressor, allowing completely autonomous operations.

Bell
UH-1 Huey
Introduction

Since the Vietnam War the UH-1 Huey has been the world's best-known helicopter, for many people the definitive symbol of the conflict. It will serve into the next century, carrying troops and supplies.

During the Vietnam War the UH-1 became famous as an excellent troop carrier, casualty evacuation craft and support helicopter.

During the Korean War, the US Army was given its first major opportunity to evaluate the helicopter under operational conditions, first with the Bell H-13 Sioux and then the Sikorsky H-19. After studies conducted during the war, the US Army issued a requirement for a helicopter with a primary casevac mission, but suitable also for utility use and as an instrument trainer. In 1955 the design submitted by Bell was announced as the winner of the competition, three prototypes of the Model 204 being ordered under the designation XH-40. The first example acquired by the US Army, aircraft 55-4459, was flown initially on 22 October 1956 with its 615-kW (825-shp) Lycoming XT53-L-1 turboshaft engine derated to 522 kW (700 shp). The XH-40s were followed by six YH-40s

which were used for trials duties and had a number of small modifications made, the most important being a 30.5-cm (1-ft) fuselage stretch. When ordered, the helicopter was given the designation HU-1 and officially named Iroquois in keeping with the Army practice of naming its helicopters using Native American tribal names or words. However, from its designation, the HU-1 quickly received the nickname 'Huey' and this name was always more popular, even when the designation of the helicopter was changed to UH-1 in 1962.

The initial production HU-1A had the T53-L-1 engine and a crew of two, plus the capacity to carry six passengers or two stretchers. It was followed by the HU-1B with revised main rotor blades and an enlarged cabin seating seven passengers

or three stretchers. Early production models soon incorporated the 716-kW (960-shp) Lycoming T53-L-5, while late production machines were powered by the 820-kW (1,100-shp) T53-L-11. In 1962 the HU-1A and HU-1B were redesignated UH-1A and UH-1B respectively, and in 1965 the UH-1B was superseded by the UH-1C.

Other military versions have included the UH-1E used by the United States Marine Corps. This version incorporated a rescue hoist, rotor brake and special avionics and a TAT-101 chin-turret housing two 7.62-mm (0.3-in) M60 machine-guns. The USMC also operated the TH-1E with dual controls for training. The USAF used the UH-1F for ICBM support and the TH-1F for training purposes. The US Navy had 27 HH-1Ks for use in the Search and Rescue role, 90 TH-1Ls for training and eight

UH-1Ls for utility work. The model 204B was extensively license built for both civil and military use by Agusta in Italy as the Agusta-Bell AB 204 and by Fuji in Japan as the Fuji-Bell 204B-2 with increased engine power and a tractor tail rotor.

Initial Model 204 production for the US armed forces totalled some 2500 airframes.

Updated 'Huey'

Early in 1960, Bell proposed an improved Bell Model 205 to the US Army. A contract followed in June 1960 which called for seven YUH-1Ds for evaluation. These retained the Lycoming T53-L-11 turboshafts of their predecessors but differed from the Model 204s by having a larger diameter main rotor and a lengthened fuselage for two pilots and 12–14 troops or six stretchers and a medical attendant, or 1814 kg (4,000 lb) of freight. Additionally the Model

The USAF's UH-1Ns are operated by Air Mobility Command, Air Education and Training Command and Air Force Space Command. This example wears the high-visibility markings of a test aircraft.

205 had increased fuel capacity and provision was made for auxiliary fuel. The first prototype flew in August 1961 and the type was subsequently ordered into production for the US Army under the designation UH-1D, with the first example entering service in August 1963. Some 2008 of these aircraft were built, followed by the generally similar UH-1H, which differed by introducing an uprated 1044-kW (1,400-shp) T53-L-13 turboshaft. Production of this variant continued until 1986.

A number of other variants of the 205 were built including three EH-1H ECM conversions and some 220 UH-1V medevac/rescue types. The USAF also received 30 HH-1H rescue aircraft. Ultimately the US Army received 3,573 examples of the UH-1H and the aircraft is expected to remain in service into the next century.

Global UH-1

Following negotiations in 1968 between Bell and Pratt & Whitney, Canada, it was mutually agreed to initiate a jointly funded programme covering the development of a twin-turbine version of the UH-1. The resulting design was designated the Model 212 and the aircraft soon entered service with the USAF, USMC and Canadian Armed Forces. The type also sold successfully world-wide equipping various armed forces, including those of Germany, the Philippines and Tunisia, while the civil variant, known as the Model 212, has been purchased by over 40 nations.

Evolved from the privately built Huey Plus is the Model 214A which is named Isfahan by its Iranian operators. This helicopter has a more powerful engine and is used as a troop carrier by the Iranians. Iran, Iraq, Brunei, Oman, Thailand and Peru also operate the Model 214ST which has an increased capacity and higher safety margins and further improved 'hot and high' performance.

Huey at war

The UH-1 made its combat debut in Vietnam when it was introduced to support the H-21 Shawnee. The H-21s had been equipped with a single 7.62-mm (0.3-in) machine-gun to suppress groundfire. However, when the Utility Tactical Transport Helicopter Company introduced the Huey in 1963, and fitted its helicopters with two 7.62-mm (0.3-in) machine-guns and 16 70-mm (2.75-in) rockets, the armoured helicopter definitely became part of military life. The initial UH-1As were not terribly effective, however, and their perceived mobility was no match for the guerrilla tactics of the Vietcong.

By November 1963, US forces were receiving UH-1Bs, and these were armed with four M60 machine-guns and 16 70-mm (2.75-in) Folding Fin Aircraft Rockets. Troops would also customise their aircraft and a door mounted M60 was often also added. The sight of these armed helicopters swooping over the Vietnamese rain forests became a familiar sight on 1960s and 1970s television. As the war dragged on, Hueys appeared in greater numbers and with further modifications including a searchlight for night operations and an XM-5 40-mm (1.57-in) grenade launcher in the nose. However, it was in the casualty evacuation role that the Huey truly excelled. Few battles took place out of the range of rotary-winged support and, as result, the proportion of American casualties who survived their wounds in Vietnam was higher than in previous conflicts because the Hueys were able to evacuate soldiers to hospitals from combat sites so quickly.

Hueys have also been involved in a number of conflicts since Vietnam, both with American and other countries' forces. Israel used UH-1s to transport troops during the Six Day War. Iran used its Bell 214A Isfahans as transports, while Iraq operated gunship-configured 214STs during the Iran-Iraq War. Since the 1970s, the US DEA (Drug Enforcement Agency) has used UH-1s to help in its drug war in South America. USAF Hueys made a combat appearance during the 1990/91 Gulf War, with UH-1H and V versions successfully operating in the transport and casevac roles.

Above: The Heeresflieger is one of the many operators of the UH-1. The Heeresflieger's UH-1Ds were assembled in Germany by Dornier and are used in the troop transport and search and rescue roles.

Left: The versatile 'Huey' is able to operate in all environments – this CH-118 can be seen taking part in a Search and Rescue practice mission with the Canadian Forces. ▶

Huey development

The first of many: 55-4459 was the very first Bell 204 helicopter, known to the US Army as the XH-40. Years later, the type would become better known as the Vietnam-era UH-1 'Huey'.

In the 1950s, the US Army coined the term 'airmobility' when searching for its aircraft of the future. Bell responded with a helicopter design that looked exceedingly promising in early tests.

Today, the Huey helicopter is one of the most familiar of all aircraft, as well known to the public as the Supermarine Spitfire, the Douglas DC-3 or the Boeing 747. However, this was not always the case.

Korean lessons

The US Army had little to feel proud about in the early 1950s in the field of rotary-wing aviation. The army had been so late in introducing effective helicopters during the 1950–53 Korean conflict that one officer described this performance as 'delinquent'. This was in embarrassing contrast to the US Marine Corps, which had recognised the value of helicopters from the beginning, and now the US Army sought to correct matters.

A handful of pioneers, especially Generals James M. Gavin and Hamilton Howze, insisted that the army needed to become 'airmobile'. It simply made no sense, they said, to transport ground infantry troops to the battlefield by truck. In the Pentagon, officials turned to Bell Aircraft of Fort Worth, Texas, and ordered the company's Model 204 helicopter under the designation XH-40. 'This will become our truck of the air,' one officer told company president, Lawrence D. Bell.

This early publicity photo of the XH-40 Iroquois shows it hovering above M60A1 (left) and M47 main battle tanks at Fort Hood, Texas. Years later, the 'Huey' would become an 'aerial tank' over Vietnam.

New helicopter

Powered by a 522-kW (700-shp) Lycoming XT53-L-1 turboshaft engine with a two-bladed, 13.40-m (44-ft) diameter rotor, the prototype Bell XH-40 completed its maiden flight on 22 October 1956 in the hands of Bell engineering pilot, Floyd Carlson.

The tadpole-shaped XH-40 performed well, which was fortuitous – the US Army had already ordered a pre-production batch. By the end of that year, flush with enthusiasm over a number of initiatives in aviation, the army created its own system for designating military aircraft and ditched the USAF-style XH-40 nomenclature in favour of XHU-1. Soon afterwards, early production HU-1A and HU-1B models were given the popular name Iroquois,

Hauling an M551 Jeep during trials by the Army Aviation Board, this Olive Drab example '56-6726' was one of six YH-40 models, later to be referred to as the HU-1A in production.

Although it could carry a nuclear warhead, the MGM-29A Sergeant missile was soon a footnote in history. However, like the C-130A Hercules in the background, this HU-1A Iroquois was on the brink of immortality as an aeronautical design.

honouring an American Indian tribe indigenous to the northwest. The HU-1A designation prompted the legendary nickname 'Huey', although another change in designation in 1962 made the type the UH-1.

Early development

Nine developmental helicopters were followed by nine pre-production machines; in the mid-to late 1950s, there was plenty of funding. Soviet leader Nikita Khrushchev was brandishing his nuclear weapons, and world trouble spots were festering in

Asia and Africa, especially in the Congo. By the time Bell received what the company's Bob Leder called a 'no kidding, serious' production contract for 173 helicopters in May 1959, a member of the Senate, John F. Kennedy, was predicting that American troops might have to fight on real battlefields in the coming decade.

The first HU-1B made its initial flight on 27 April 1960 and demonstrated a capability to carry two pilots and seven troops at 203 km/h (126 mph) over 393 km (244 miles). In the new decade, longer and more

powerful UH-1D and UH-1H models would greatly improve this performance, but the Huey was already being received warmly by troops. It was also welcome to harried US Army maintainers, who finally had a helicopter that was sensible to repair and keep flying.

The Army Aviation Board, also known to some as the Howze board after one of the army's most visionary generals, tested the new Bell helicopter in a variety of climates, conditions, and missions. The Cold War could turn hot at any time, so the army tried out the Huey as a battlefield taxi for its Honest John, Little John and Sergeant battlefield nuclear rocket projectiles. Later, when the US Air Force picked up on the potential of the Huey, it ordered the UH-1F model to supply intercontinental ballistic missile sites.

In 1961, Kennedy inspected a Huey during a visit to Fort Bragg, NC. By then, the US Army – encouraged by the new president's fascination with unconventional warfare – was establishing a unique battle formation. The 1st Cavalry Division, identified by a badge containing a silhouette of a stallion's head, would adopt a doctrine of vertical air mobility and would be redesignated as an Air Cavalry Division. Bell

could now look to production orders going well above the 1,000 mark. A company memo noted that the new helicopter 'is now almost certain to be regarded everywhere as a success'. At this late juncture, no one yet knew how much of a success it would, in fact, be.

The army refined 'airmobility' tactics, showed the foresight to breed a new generation of warrant-officer pilots, and began the 1960s by supplying UH-1B Hueys to the 'First Cav' and to its training facility at Fort Rucker, Alabama.

The potential of the new helicopter in air evacuation duties was obvious and, in March 1962, soldiers of the 57th Medical Detachment (Helicopter Ambulance) at Fort Bliss, Texas, were alerted to become the first Huey operators sent overseas. At first, they thought they were going to Europe. As recounted by a UH-1B crew chief, they were finally given the word by their commanding officer.

'I know where we're going,' the crew chief said to his commander. 'It's in the headlines. A real hot spot. They're sending us to the Congo.'

'That's wrong,' the officer replied. 'Our helicopters are going to a place I never heard of until last week.' He paused and added, 'Vietnam.'

Above: Reflecting consecutive changes in type designation, 60-3547 was an XH-40 on the drawing board, an HU-1B when it first flew, and a UH-1B, alias 'Huey', after 1962.

Left: Wearing high-visibility US Army colours (white fuselage, red trim), this trio of Bell HU-1Bs is pictured while on an early service acceptance flight.

Boeing CH-47 Chinook

Heavylift twin-rotor

In service for over 40 years, the Chinook has become the West's primary medium-lift helicopter. Its capacious cabin and and weight-lifting capability have made it a highly versatile battlefield helicopter.

The origins of the CH-47 Chinook lie in the Vertol Model 114 of 1958 (the Vertol company was originally named after Frank Piasecki, pioneer of the tandem-rotor configuration, and has been part of Boeing since 1960). The straightforward idea behind the Chinook was to devise a more capable development of the maker's earlier Model 107 twin-engined assault transport helicopter, better known today as the US Marine Corps' CH-46E Sea Knight, or 'Bullfrog'. The US Army did consider the Model 107 in 1959 under the military designation YCH-1, but found it too small. Curiously, when the Chinook came along, it was given a follow-up designation of YHC-1B, subsequently changed to CH-47A.

From 1965, the US Army relied heavily on the CH-47A, CH-47B and CH-47C for lifting duties. It is claimed that no fewer than 10,000 downed aircraft were retrieved from Vietnamese rice paddies and mountain sides, and brought home for salvage or repair slung beneath the belly of a Chinook. Considering that A, B and C models were all hampered by having only one sling point to which to attach a load – replaced by three sling points in

the post-Vietnam CH-47D – this was quite an achievement. The Chinooks became a familiar sight throughout the country, virtually all painted flat olive drab and devoid of any colour or noteworthy markings. By 1971, the Vietnamese air force was also equipped with the CH-47.

The Chinook has the most available and usable cargo space of any US Army helicopter. Its fuel supply is carried externally in pods running the length of the fuselage, which results in a constant cross-section cabin, similar to that of many fixed-wing transports. The cabin measures 9.14 m x 2.51 m x 1.98 m (30 ft x 8 ft 3 in x 6 ft 6 in), provides a volume of 40.78 m³ (1,440 cu ft), and is long enough to accept two M551 Jeeps – the standard tactical vehicle in use at the time of the helicopter's design. Only a single example will fit – just – of today's standard US Army tactical vehicle, the M998 'Humvee'.

For most routine cargoes, the Chinook's cargo space is more than ample and the type is usually called the US Army's heavylift helicopter, although it technically falls into the medium-lift category. Around the Chinook's cargo space, the helicopter's surrounding fuselage is remarkably compact.

*Above: The first **CH-47C** lifts off on its maiden voyage. The aircraft was actually a converted CH-47B (66-19103), re-engined with the uprated T55-L-11s that constituted the main change from the earlier model.*

*Top: The **YCH-1B** development programme was to have involved five flying prototypes, but the first was badly damaged in a ground-running accident. The nearest of this pair is extensively tufted on the undersides, around the nose and on the front rotor pylon to allow the accurate monitoring of airflow patterns.*

Twin-rotor design

The Chinook's tandem rotor design allows the entire length of the fuselage to be put to good use, since none of it is required as a boom for a tail rotor. Loading and unloading can be accomplished through a full-length rear ramp, which can be lowered to the ground or raised

to match the level of truck beds. One soldier using a built-in winch can pull cargo in or out of the aircraft. Extremely long cargo can extend beyond the opened rear ramp, if necessary.

The Chinook's high rotor blades allow soldiers to enter or exit the helicopter quickly and safely, even with the rotors

Chinook gunships

The ACH-47A, initially known simply as the 'Armed CH-47A', was the battlefield gunship version of the Chinook. Boeing modified four helicopters in 1965 for operational evaluation in Vietnam. In the ACH-47A, engineers deleted all cargo-handling equipment, soundproofing, and all but five troop seats, then added 907 kg (2,000 lb) of armour plating and weapons pylons on each side of the aircraft outboard of the front wheels, plus a nose gun installation. Nicknamed 'Guns A Go-Go', the ACH-47A carried two 20-mm (0.79-in) fixed forward-firing, pylon-mounted

cannon, up to five 12.7-mm (0.5-in) machine-guns (two on each side of the aircraft plus one firing down from the ramp), and two pylon-mounted XM128 19-round pods of 70-mm (2.75-in) rockets, plus a single chin-mounted M5 40-mm (1.57-in) automatic grenade-launcher. In February 1964, the US Army established a requirement for the use of a heavily-armed helicopter in combat operations, and ordered four modified CH-47As in June 1965. The prototype ACH-47A made its initial flight on 6 November 1965 and an official roll-out ceremony was held four days later. The First Air Cavalry Division took three of the four ACH-47A gunships to Vietnam in June 1966. The Vietnam detachment of 'Guns A Go-Go' was the 228th Aviation Battalion of the First Cavalry Division, which flew numerous sorties, providing direct support to American and Australian ground combat troops. Eventually, the development of the smaller, more nimble AH-1 Cobra made a Chinook gunship unnecessary, and the concept was not developed further.

The third production CH-47A demonstrates the ability of the Chinook to deliver paratroops. A standard load was 33 fully-armed troops, although this figure later rose to 44. During the Falklands War, the sole in-theatre RAF Chinook once carried 81 troops.

turning. The standard troop load is 44 fully-equipped troops on standard sidewall seating, but the Chinook can carry up to 59 infantrymen by placing additional seats in the centre aisle. For medical evacuation missions, the cabin can take 24 litters and two medical attendants.

Although its four-point undercarriage is nothing more than a logical solution for an aircraft of this size and shape, it has proven aptly suited to harsh environments. The quadricycle landing gear provides good stability during loading and unloading operations, preventing roll-overs when landing at unprepared sites.

Every Chinook's hull is sealed at the factory so that the helicopter can land and take off from water in conditions up to Sea State 3; this amphibious capability enables it to operate from a larger number of locations.

Chinook at war

The 1st Air Cavalry Division brought a new form of warfare

to the world in 1965, creating the largest helicopter base ever hacked out of the jungle (at Anh-Khe) and launching infantry attacks in which air cavalrymen leapfrogged the enemy. The UH-1 Huey was the principal player in this new kind of fighting, but the supporting role played by the Chinook was invaluable.

The Pentagon stepped up CH-47 production and the Army experimented with methods, tactics and crew composition. In Vietnam, a Chinook's crew complement consisted of pilot, co-pilot, flight engineer/crew chief (who also doubled as a gunner) and gunner. In the combat zone, soldiers removed the rear cabin windows, and sometimes other windows,

to create rifle ports for onboard infantrymen. Chinooks in Vietnam carried a pintle-mounted 7.62-mm (0.3-in) M60D machine-gun in the port escape hatch opening and a second M60D on a mounting in the forward starboard crew door.

The widespread use of the CH-47C in Vietnam and elsewhere ended complaints that the type was under-powered. The CH-47C was both more powerful and more capable. It was able to carry four internal fuel tanks in the cargo compartment, making possible a ferry range of over 1610 km (1,000 miles) when flying at 3048 m (10,000 ft).

In a real-world environment, it is rarely possible to self-deploy a Chinook force, and US Army

personnel were frustrated during 1990's Operation Desert Shield when it took nearly 30 days to deliver Chinooks to the war zone, taking into account 'cocooning', sea lift, unloading and rebuilding needs. Still, the CH-47D proved invaluable. In Operation Desert Storm in 1991 – in company with British Chinook HC.Mk 1s, among many other types – CH-47Ds participated in the famous 'left hook' ground manoeuvre that isolated much of the Iraqi army.

Inflight refuelling to extend the range of the Chinook has always been a possibility but has been pursued only with a few specialised aircraft. The MH-47D and MH-47E special operations variants later appeared with refuelling booms ▶

Below: The MH-47E is optimised for covert low-level penetration, usually undertaken at night. As well as Special Forces insertion, it has an important 'fat cow' forward refuelling point role.

Above: The interim MH-47D was the first Chinook to carry a refuelling probe as standard. The type equips the 3/160th SOAR at Fort Campbell, Georgia, although this machine is a Boeing demonstration aircraft.

Right: South Korea acquired 18 standard CH-47Ds for the army, and a further number (believed to be six) for the air force's 235th Squadron (illustrated). Dubbed HH-47D, the air force aircraft are used for SAR work and have large tanks and radar.

and include air-refuelling as part of their routine tactics.

Foreign Chinooks

Despite competition from other, possibly superior, types, the Chinook has enjoyed notable sales success, with 14 international users operating the type. The first overseas customer was Australia, which took delivery of 12 CH-47C models. The Italian firm Agusta acquired rights to manufacture the CH-47C in 1968 and sold its first batch of 20 to Iran. Agusta-built CH-47Cs also equip the Italian army. Further examples went to Egypt, Greece, Libya and Morocco.

Kawasaki became a builder of Chinooks for the Japanese ground and air arms, and still manufactures a few today, the only overseas builder to produce an aircraft comparable to the US Army's CH-47D.

Taking advantage of the substantial upgrade of the military Chinook when it was being modified into the CH-47D, Boeing announced in the

summer of 1978 that it had completed the market evaluation of a commercial version. The target was the growing North Sea oil business, in which drilling operations were being pushed further from the mainland.

The availability of the Commercial Chinook was instrumental in British Airways Helicopters (BAH) obtaining a seven-year contract from Shell to service its large Brent/Cormorant oil field off the Shetland Islands. In November 1978, BAH ordered an eventual six Model 234s and the type entered service on 1 July 1981. However, a catastrophic crash in the mid-1980s led BAH to retire the type, and it is now used for other duties.

Italy's Elicotteri Meridionali (EM), part of the Agusta group, acquired rights to manufacture the CH-47C Chinook in 1968 in collaboration with SIAI-Marchetti. The biggest customers for the Agusta CH-47C were the Italian army (above) which took 35 (plus two Boeing-built aircraft) and Iran, which acquired 38 assembled from Boeing kits, and 30 wholly-built by Agusta.

Chinook derivatives

Although the CH-47 was a success in its own right, plans were soon under way to build bigger and more advanced variants that would be capable of carrying loads up to main battle-tank weight.

Model 360

Privately developed to verify advanced technologies which would be useful to Boeing for further rotorcraft projects, the Model 360 features advanced aerodynamics and is the world's largest all-composite helicopter, being comprised of a Kevlar skin with a nomex honeycomb core. It is also extremely fast, achieving top speeds of 214 kt (397 km/h; 246 mph). Tests conducted in the Model 360 helped to pave the way for technologies applied to the Comanche, CH-47D, MH-47E and the V-22 Osprey.

Model 347

The Boeing Model 347 was a Chinook development with a longer fuselage, four-bladed rotors and a higher rear pylon with extensively modified systems. Much more than just a stretched Chinook, the Model 347 was a technology demonstrator which ultimately tested fly-by-wire systems and winged flight. The large wing, which was added later, swivelled, being held almost vertically when the aircraft was in the hover.

XCH-62

The XCH-62, or US Army HLH (Heavy Lift Helicopter), was an outgrowth of Boeing's years of experience with the Chinook design and was a bigger and wholly new aircraft in every respect. The machine resulted from a tri-service arrangement aimed at avoiding the duplication which had occurred just a few years earlier when the US Army invested in the Chinook and the Marines in the Sikorsky CH-53A Sea Stallion. The XCH-62 was a tandem-rotor helicopter powered by three Allison XT701-AD-700 gas turbine engines rated at 6027 kW (8,079 hp) each. Due to its size and imposing bulk, the XCH-62 was often compared in literature of the 1970s to the outsized Boeing 747 and Lockheed C-5 Galaxy. Its design gross weight was 53525 kg (118,000 lb) and its primary mission payload was 20412 kg (45,000 lb), which apparently could be nearly doubled to 31751 kg (70,000 lb) for short-distance operations. A heavier version at 67133 kg (148,000 lb)

was also contemplated. The XCH-62, seen here at the Ridley Township works, had reached this hardware stage at the time of its cancellation in 1976.

'Chinook Crane' family

In 1967, Boeing began studies for a huge crane-equipped, cargo-hauling helicopter as an intended follow-on to the CH-47 helicopter. With a standard Chinook model for size comparison, these models show the Model 237 (centre), intended primarily for crane operations, and Model 227 (left) which could carry loads internally. The 'Chinook Crane' family never emerged as a fully-fledged aircraft, but the design work led to the eventual XCH-62 and Model 301 design efforts.

Model 297 Chinook Crane

The Model 297 Chinook Crane would have employed many of the features then being developed for the CH-47C, but incorporating a tall landing gear unit with a 'kneeling' capability, an external hoist system, a rearward-facing loadmaster's station beneath the cockpit (much in the manner of the Sikorsky CH-54A Tarhe), and a lengthened fuselage compared to the standard Chinook. It was to have a twin-winch system with two lift points. The 'kneeling' feature was meant to enable the Model 297 to be lowered onto podded loads from a straddle position. By 'kneeling', the height of the Chinook Crane would be reduced to 5.94 m (19 ft 6 in), sufficient to clear the 6.09-m (20-ft) hangar deck of US Navy LPH-2-class helicopter-carriers. The Model 297 would have had rotor blades able to be folded manually for deck storage. Although the smallest of the three designs in this family to reach a fairly advanced stage, it was so big that the bottom of its fuselage stood 2.84 m (9 ft 4 in) off the ground, and its rear rotor head was some 8.22 m (27 ft) in height.

▶

Cockpit
The Chinook's cockpit is spacious and modern, with side-by-side seating for the captain (to starboard) and co-pilot (to port) and with a folding jump seat in the cockpit entrance. Like all RAF and Army Air Corps tactical helicopters, the Chinook HC.Mk 1 is fitted with Decca TANS, a useful precision navigation computer. Only a handful of RAF Chinooks have NVG-compatible cockpits. One of these was *Bravo November* which, in the Falklands War, escaped the destruction of the *Atlantic Conveyor* and performed invaluable heavylift duties across the war zone.

Rescue winch
A hydraulically-powered rescue winch can be fitted above the main door on the starboard side of the fuselage. The strong rotor downwash produced by the Chinook gives a rather high minimum hover height, and the lack of an internal 'wet fit' means that saltwater 'wet' winching is not regularly practised.

Main landing gear
The Chinook is fitted with non-retractable quadricycle-type landing gear with twin-wheel forward units. All units have oleo-pneumatic shock absorbers, and the forward units are fitted with single-disc hydraulic brakes. There is provision for detachable wheel skis. Mainwheel tyres are inflated to 6.07 bar (88 lb/sq in).

Chinook HC.Mk 1

The Royal Air Force has been operating the Boeing Helicopters Chinook for almost 20 years, during which time the helicopter has become the premier workhorse of the Support Helicopter Force. The Chinook's serviceability, lift and multi-mission capabilities continue to match or exceed planned requirements. As new global strategic and tactical missions and operational priorities change, with the emphasis turning to more mobile and flexible force structures, the RAF Chinook's versatility and mission flexibility continue to expand. This HC.Mk 1 wears the colours of No. 7 Sqn, based at RAF Odiham, Hants – like all RAF HC.Mk 1s, it has since been upgraded to HC.Mk 2 standard.

RAF Chinooks at war

Since the Chinook entered service with the RAF, it has been involved in a number of conflicts. In 1982 four Chinooks were shipped to the Falklands during the conflict to provide heavy-lift support. However, three were destroyed when the *Atlantic Conveyor*, the ship on which they were travelling, was hit by an Exocet missile. Meanwhile, Chinooks were heavily engaged in supporting British troops in Germany, ready to block a potential Soviet advance. RAF Chinooks operated in two roles during Desert Storm: regular army support and Special Forces duties. For the latter, several aircraft received hastily applied 'experimental night camouflage', SATCOMs (satellite communications) and door guns. Chinooks were then used in the Kurdish humanitarian effort, distributing food and supplies. Over Bosnia, six RAF HC.Mk 2s supported the UK's 24 Airmobile Brigade and were given a series of upgrades including armour-plating and defensive avionics. Two Chinooks of No. 7 Sqn were painted white and undertook UN humanitarian missions in the Krajina region. In June 1999 eight Chinooks formed the main transport element of NATO's opening insertion into Kosovo. The aircraft airlifted elements of the UK's 5 Airborne Division into key positions, including the vital Kacanik gorge, which secured the main route from Macedonia to the capital, Pristina.

Refuelling points

Gravity refuelling points are located along the top of the fuselage fairings, and are augmented by a single pressure refuelling point on the starboard side. This allows for the simultaneous refuelling of all tanks, or the selective refuelling of any combination of tanks.

Powerplant

The first batch of RAF Chinook HC.Mk 1s was delivered with metal rotor blades and Textron Lycoming T55-L-11E turboshafts. The Chinooks were later retrofitted with uprated T55-L-712s, developed for the CH-47D (HC.Mk 2) programme, providing 2797 kW (3,750 shp), along with a Cobra engine fire prevention system. The original metal rotor blades were replaced by larger, 64-cm (25-in) chord glass-fibre rotor blades with titanium leading edges which were 12.7 cm (5 in) wider than the original metal blades, and provided reduced maintenance and an increased operational life of over 3,000 hours.

Hooks

The Chinook has three hooks under the fuselage for transporting cargo. The forward hook has a maximum capacity of 9000 kg (19,841 lb). The centre hook, which is the main lifting hook, can carry up to 11300 kg (24,912 lb), including loads such as the FH-70 Howitzer. Like the front hook, the rear hook has a capacity of 9000 kg (19,841 lb) and can be used for lifting individual loads or in conjunction with the front hook to take tandem slung loads such as ISO containers or even another Chinook. The triple hook system gives tremendous flexibility and adaptability.

The CH-47JA has radar, AAQ-16 FLIR and long-range tanks to increase greatly the operational capability of the type in JGSDF service. In addition to the Kyoiku Sien Hiko-tai at Akeno, CH-47JAs serve with the JGSDF's Dai 1 Konsei-Dan and Dai 1 Herikoputa-dan. The Seibu Homen Herikoputa-tai (Western Army Helicopter Squadron) has, in 1999, begun to receive this advanced variant to replace the KV-107-II.

CH-47 Chinook
Briefing

CH-47D Chinook

Cutaway key
1 Pitot tubes
2 Forward lighting
3 Nose compartment access hatch
4 Vibration absorber
5 IFF aerial
6 Windscreen panels
7 Windscreen wipers
8 Instrument panel shroud
9 Rudder pedals
10 Yaw sensing ports
11 Downward vision window
12 Pilot's footboards
13 Collective pitch control
14 Cyclic pitch control column
15 Co-pilot's seat
16 Centre instrument console
17 Pilot's seat
18 Glideslope indicator
19 Forward transmission housing fairing
20 Cockpit overhead window
21 Doorway from main cabin
22 Cockpit emergency exit doors
23 Sliding side window panel
24 Cockpit bulkhead
25 Vibration absorber
26 Cockpit door release handle
27 Radio and electronics racks
28 Sloping bulkhead
29 Stick boost actuators
30 Stability augmentation system actuators
31 Forward transmission mounting structure
32 Windscreen washer bottle

33 Rotor control hydraulic jack
34 Forward transmission gearbox
35 Rotor head fairing
36 Forward rotor head mechanism
37 Pitch change control levers
38 Blade drag dampers
39 Glassfibre rotor blades
40 Titanium leading-edge capping with de-icing provision
41 Rescue hoist/winch

42 Forward transmission aft fairing
43 Hydraulic system modules
44 Control levers
45 Front fuselage frame and stringer construction

46 Emergency exit window, main entry door on starboard side
47 Forward end of cargo floor
48 Fuel tank fuselage side fairing
49 Battery
50 Electrical system equipment bay

51 Aerial cable
52 Stre tcher rack (up to 24 stretchers)
53 Cabin window panel
54 Cabin heater duct outlet
55 Troop seats stowed against cabin wall
56 Cabin roof transmission and control run tunnel
57 Formation-keeping lights
58 Rotor blade cross section

59 Static dischargers
60 Blade balance and tracking weights pocket
61 Leading-edge anti-erosion strip
62 Fixed tab
63 Fuselage skin plating
64 Maintenance walkway
65 Transmission tunnel access doors
66 Troop seating, up to 44 troops
67 Cargo hook access hatch
68 VOR aerial
69 Cabin lining panels
70 Control runs

71 Main transmission shaft
72 Shaft couplings
73 Centre fuselage construction
74 Centre aisle seating (optional)
75 Main cargo floor, 40.78-m³ (1,440-cu ft) cargo volume
76 Ramp-down 'dam' for waterborne operations
77 Ramp hydraulic jack
78 Engine bevel drive gearbox

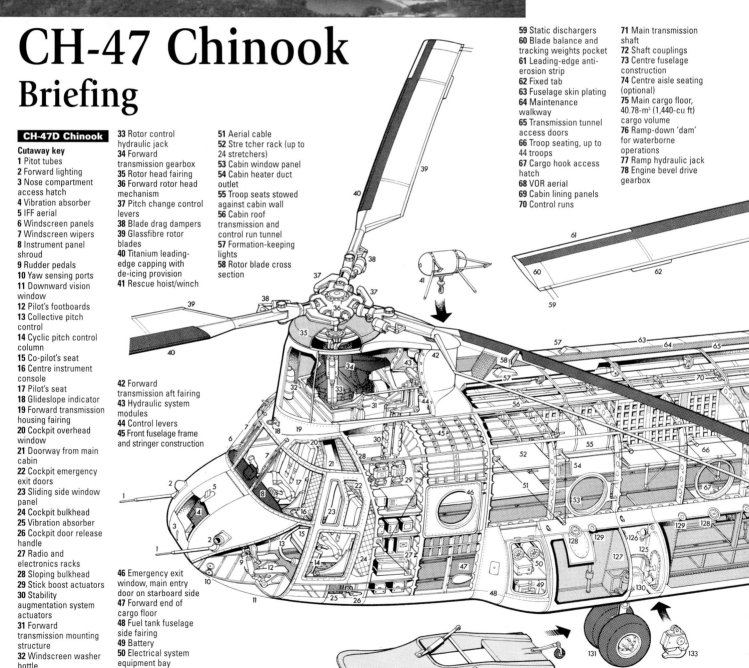

A Dutch CH-47D repositions a tactical vehicle during manoeuvres. Equipped with EFIS cockpit, nose radar and T55-L-714 engines, the Dutch Chinooks are among the most advanced in service. The first seven were converted from ex-Canadian CH-147s.

SPECIFICATION

CH-47D Chinook

Dimensions

Length overall, rotors turning: 30.14 m (98 ft 10¾ in)
Fuselage: 15.54 m (51 ft)
Height to top of rear rotor head: 5.77 m (18 ft 11 in)
Wheel track: 3.20 m (10 ft 6 in)
Wheel base: 6.86 m (22 ft 6 in)
Rotor diameter: 18.29 m (60 ft)
Rotor disc area: 525.34 m² (5,654.86 sq ft)

Powerplant

Two Textron Lycoming T55-L-712 turboshafts each rated at 2796 kW (3,750 shp) for take-off and 2237 kW (3,000 shp) for continuous running, or two Textron Lycoming T55-L-712 SSB turboshafts each rated at 3264 kW (4,378 shp) for take-off and 2339 kW (3,137 shp) for continuous running, in both cases driving a transmission rated at 5593 kW (7,500 shp) on two engines and 3430 kW (4,600 shp) on one engine

Weights

Empty: 10151 kg (22,379 lb)
Normal take-off: 20866 kg (46,000 lb)
Maximum take-off: 22679 kg (50,000 lb)

Fuel and load

Internal fuel: 3899 litres (1,030 US gal)
External fuel: None
Maximum payload: 10341 kg (22,798 lb)

Range

Ferry range: 1,093 nm (2026 km/1,259 miles)
Operational radius with maximum internal and maximum external payloads respectively: Between 100 and 30 nm (185 and 56 km/115 and 35 miles)

Performance

Maximum level speed at sea level: 161 kt (298 km/h; 185 mph)
Maximum cruising speed at optimum altitude: 138 kt (256 km/h; 159 mph)
Maximum rate of climb at sea level: 669 m (2,195 ft) per minute
Service ceiling: 6735 m (22,100 ft)
Hovering ceiling: 3215 m (10,550 ft)

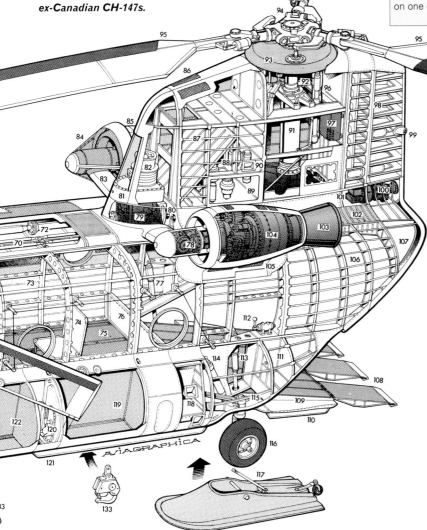

79 Transmission combining gearbox
80 Rotor brake
81 Transmission oil tank
82 Oil cooler
83 Engine drive shaft fairing
84 Engine screen
85 Starboard engine nacelle
86 Cooling air grilles
87 Tail rotor pylon construction
88 Hydraulic equipment
89 Access door
90 Maintenance step
91 Tail rotor drive shaft
92 Tail rotor bearing mounting
93 Rotor head fairing
94 Tail rotor head mechanism
95 Main rotor blades, glassfibre construction
96 Rotor control hydraulic jack
97 Vibration absorber
98 Pylon aft fairing construction
99 Rear lighting
100 Solar T62T-2B auxiliary power unit

101 APU-driven generators
102 Maintenance walkways
103 Engine exhaust duct
104 Avco Lycoming T55-L-712 turboshaft engine
105 Detachable engine cowlings
106 Aft fuselage frame and stringer construction
107 Rear cargo doorway
108 Ramp extensions
109 Cargo ramp, lowered
110 Ramp ventral strake
111 Fuselage side fairing aft extension
112 Ramp control lever
113 Ramp hydraulic jack
114 Rear landing gear shock absorber
115 Landing gear leg strut
116 Single rear wheels
117 Rear wheel optional ski fitting

118 Maintenance steps
119 Rear fuel tank
120 Fuel tank interconnections
121 Ventral strake
122 Main fuel tank; total system capacity 3899 litres (1,030 US gal)
123 Floor beam construction
124 Fuel tank attachment joint
125 Fuel system piping
126 Fire extinguishers
127 Forward fuel tank
128 Fuel filler caps
129 Fuel capacity transmitters
130 Front landing-gear mounting
131 Twin forward wheels
132 Forward wheels optional ski-fitting
133 Triple cargo hook system; forward and rear hooks 9072-kg (20,000-lb) capacity
134 Main cargo hook, 12701-kg (28,000-lb) capacity

CH-47 Chinook
Operators

United States of America

The US Army is the largest operator of the Chinook today. It initially received 349 CH-47As, followed by 108 improved CH-47Bs from May 1967. From early 1968 270 Boeing-built CH-47Cs were acquired and 11 Agusta-built CH-47Cs in 1985. This version served as a medium-lift helicopter, while four were converted to ACH-47As for the gunship role in Vietnam. From 1982 the US Army received the first of 472 upgraded CH-47Ds, remanufactured from earlier As, Bs and Cs. After successfully operating a number of MH-47D special operations aircraft, 26 improved MH-47Es were produced. Both types were remanufactured from older variants. The current plan for US Army Chinooks again includes remanufacture – to the improved CH-47F standard.

Australia

Australia became the first overseas operator of the Chinook, when 12 CH-47Cs (above) arrived aboard HMAS *Melbourne* on 9 April 1974 to fulfil a medium-lift helicopter requirement. Delivered to No. 12 Squadron RAAF, they served until July 1989 when they were retired, the army taking responsibility for battlefield helicopters. A lack of US army airlift capability resulted in a deal in which seven of the CH-47Cs were transferred to the US Army, thus paying for the remaining four (one having crashed in 1985) to be returned to Boeing for upgrade as CH-47Ds. They re-entered service in mid-1995 with the army's C Sqn, 5 Aviation Regiment, based at Townsville. Two new CH-47Ds were added to the fleet in early 2000.

The Boeing CH-47 Chinook is the standard Western medium/heavy-lift helicopter. It has served with the armed forces of 18 nations and remains in service with all but two of these.

South Korea, Taiwan and Thailand

The South Korean air force and the army both use the Chinook. Six air force Chinooks (equipped with winches), designated HH-47Ds, are operated by the 235th Squadron for SAR work. The army uses 18 CH-47Ds in a transport squadron based at Taegu. The Taiwanese army uses three Boeing-Vertol Bv234MLRs, based at Kuejien-Tainan, and delivered in 1985. Thailand (below) received four CH-47As in 1972, which were replaced by five new CH-47Ds in 1989 and augmented in 1991 by three upgraded CH-47Cs.

Previous operators – Vietnam and Canada

In late 1972, under the Enhance Plus programme, South Vietnam (above right) received 20 CH-47As. They served with the 237th Helicopter Squadron, until the fall of Saigon, when they were operated by the Communists for a while. In the early 1990s they were offered on the world market. Canada (above) operated nine CH-47Cs as CH-147s between late 1974 and mid-1991, serving with Nos 447 and 450 Squadrons. Seven were later acquired by the Dutch air force.

Japan

Japan is one of two countries to licence-produce the Chinook. Kawasaki Heavy Industries builds CH-47Js (equivalent to the CH-47D) and CH-47JAs (equivalent to the CH-47SD/Model 414-100) for both the Japanese Air Self-Defence Force (JASDF), for logistical support of radar sites, SAR and other transport duties, and the Japanese Ground Self-Defence Force (JGSDF), which uses them in the heavy-lift transport role. The JASDF fleet is divided among SAR flights based at Misawa, Iruma, Kasunga and Naha. The first two Japanese-built Chinooks were delivered on 26 December 1986, one going to each service, but they were preceded by two Boeing-built examples (above, wearing the standard JGSDF scheme). Procurement of the type continues, and by mid-1999 the JGSDF had received 45 and the JASDF 16. Two more CH-47JAs for the JGSDF and two Js for the JASDF were planned in 2000.

European CH-47s – UK, Holland, Greece, Spain and Italy

Five European nations use the Chinook. The first to order the type was the UK's RAF (top right), which ordered 15 CH-47Bs in 1967. This order was cancelled, reinstated in 1971 and again cancelled, before 33 Chinook HC.Mk 1s were ordered in 1978. The first arrived in October 1981, with No. 18 (based at RAF Odiham) being the first squadron to gain them after No. 240 OCU. They were followed by No. 7 Sqn and No. 1310 Flt in the Falklands (which later became No. 78 Squadron). Another eight were ordered in 1983. Upgraded to Chinook HC.Mk 1B status with glass-fibre rotor blades, 32 of the fleet were further modernised to HC.Mk 2 standard (similar to the CH-47D). No. 27 Squadron (ex-No. 240 OCU) was the first unit to operate the Mk 2. In

September 1995 a further three HC.Mk 2s were ordered, with six HC.Mk 2As and eight special operations HC.Mk 3s. The RAF fleet has proved to be invaluable to the Joint Helicopter Force, which now controls all of the UK's battlefield helicopters.

The latest European operator of the Chinook is the Netherlands (right), which uses seven ex-Canadian CH-147s upgraded to CH-47D standard and six new-build Ds. All are operated by No. 298 Squadron based at Soesterberg, as part of the Tactical Helicopter Group.

The Greek army's 3 Loko/2 TEAS (3rd company/2nd Hellenic army aviation battalion), based at Megara, operates 17 CH-47D/DGs. Initially, five Meridionali-built CH-47Cs were delivered in the early 1980s, five more coming from the air force in 1988. All were upgraded to CH-47DG standard, and seven more CH-47Ds were acquired.

Spanish army unit BHELTRA (transport helicopter battalion) V's fleet of 16 Chinooks (above left) consists of Bv-414s, CH-47Cs and CH-47Ds. The Bv-414s (five) and CH-47Cs (two) are in the process of being upgraded to D standard. They are based at Colmenar Viejo.

A total of 35 Agusta-built and two Boeing-built CH-47Cs have served with the Italian army (left) in the heavy-lift role since 1972. Currently based at Viterbo, the helicopter is known as the ETM-1 in the Italian army designation system.

Argentina

Argentina acquired two CH-47Cs for the Comando de Aviación del Ejército Argentino, one of which was lost in the Falklands War, and three for the Fuerza Aérea Argentina. Two now serve with the FAA, having been upgraded with nose radar – they fly with Grupo 7 on Antarctic duties.

Egypt, Libya and Iran

Ten of 15 Agusta-built CH-47Cs delivered are still in use with the Egyptian air force, these aircraft being reinforced by an order for four CH-47Ds placed in 1997. The Chinooks are based at Kom Awshim. Libya (below left) received 20 from the Italian production line, commencing in 1976. Six were used by the air force and the remainder by the army. Serviceability of the type in Libyan use is thought to be low, because of the arms embargo. Iran (above left) was the largest operator of the type after the US Army, taking 95 from Italy (38 built from kits supplied by Boeing). Despite years of isolation and conflict, a fair number of Chinooks still operate with the air force and army.

Morocco

Morocco bought a fleet of nine Agusta-built CH-47Cs, the first being delivered in 1979. Seven are still in use with a heavy helicopter squadron based at 1 Air Base, Rabat-Sale. The fleet was heavily used in the fighting against the Polisario guerrillas in the south of the country.

Desert Storm and beyond
United Nations operations

During the 1990s, RAF and US Army Chinooks were called upon to flex their muscles in support of UN and NATO operations in Iraq and former Yugoslavia.

Chinooks from both the US Army and Royal Air Force played a large part in Desert Storm operations. US machines were instrumental in pre-positioning troops and equipment prior to the launch of the ground war in General Schwarzkopf's famous 'Hail Mary' manoeuvre. When the assault opened in the early hours of 24 February 1991, CH-47s from the 101st Airborne Division (Air Assault) partnered UH-60 Black Hawks in lifting a force of 2,000 troops to point 'Cobra' (Salman airfield), some 80 km (50 miles) inside Iraq – the largest helicopter assault operation ever undertaken.

'Cobra' was established as an airhead for further advances behind the main enemy defences. US Army helicopters supported the troops as they rapidly moved to cut off the Iraqi forces in Kuwait. CH-47Ds moved artillery, ammunition and supplies forward as the ground forces gathered momentum. As well as those from the 101st, CH-47s came from a variety of other units, notably the 159th Aviation regiment.

The RAF deployed eight Chinooks to operate in the standard army support role, in which they moved men and supplies forward, and returned with prisoners of war. Over 3,000 PoWs were carried, and around 1 million kg (2.5 million lb) of materiel.

More interesting was the work of the seven Chinooks used by No. 7 Squadron Special Forces Flight, which were employed to insert SAS and other special forces units into Iraq. Hastily modified with intake filters, GPS, Satcoms and weapons, and with black disruptive patterns applied over the 'desert pink' camouflage, the SFF aircraft operated deep

Above: The sand encountered during Desert Storm operations was harsh on dynamic systems, yet the Chinook weathered well during the campaign. Creating its own sandstorm, this pair of US Army CH-47Ds picks up supply pallets.

Top: Seven RAF Chinooks of No. 7 Squadron Special Forces Flight supported SAS and other special forces during Desert Storm. This aircraft shows the hastily applied 'night' camouflage.

A US Army CH-47D slings in supplies during Operation Provide Comfort, the UN effort to provide humanitarian support to the Kurdish population which had fled to the mountains of northern Iraq in the aftermath of the Gulf War.

Included in the RAF 'Bosnia fit' for its Chinook HC.Mk 2s were the ALE-40 chaff/flare dispensers for defence against ground-launched missiles. Flare launch is demonstrated here by an aircraft from No. 1310 Flight at Divulje Barracks, Split.

Chinooks were deployed from both the RAF and US Army to instigate a massive resupply effort, known to the US as Provide Comfort, and to the British as Haven. Operations were based at Silopi in Turkey, and lasted until June, by which time UN 'safe havens' had been established for the Kurds.

Yugoslavia

Chinooks from the RAF and US Army were also deployed to Bosnia, from 1995, to assist UN-led peacekeeping operations. RAF aircraft first went to Ploce, in Croatia, although they later established a regular detachment at Divulje Barracks, Split, later designated No. 1310 Flight (Operation Palatine). Both British and American Chinooks proved of inestimable value in Bosnia, being able to resupply remote observation posts, and being available for humanitarian relief operations when required.

In March 1997 two of the Divulje-based Chinooks undertook a mission to insert troops into the British Embassy in Tirana, Albania, to secure the site and allow the evacuation of British nationals.

Two years later, the Chinooks were back in action, this time leading the occupation of Kosovo by NATO peacekeepers following the end of the Allied Force air campaign. Helicopter operations had previously begun in Albania to assist in the refugee crisis. RAF Chinooks had also operated from Albania over the border into Kosovo to insert Special Forces. As the air campaign drew to a close, attention switched to Macedonia, where the main occupation force was being assembled.

Chinooks had already inserted a Pathfinder platoon, which took and held Pristina airport (before surrendering to a large Russian contingent), when the main force moved on 12 June 1999 to begin Operation Joint Guardian. Six Chinooks inserted paratroopers into the strategically important Kacanik gorge. When ground forces arrived, the Chinooks, and Paras, moved on to occupy Pristina itself. As well as the RAF, other forces using Chinooks in subsequent Kosovo operations were Italy (three), Netherlands (three) and the US Army (six).

into Iraq, reputedly flying an insertion mission into downtown Baghdad on the first night of the war.

For much of the campaign the Chinooks were used to insert, supply and extract reconnaissance and demolition patrols. Many of these missions were into the western desert of Iraq, where mobile 'Scud' launchers operated. SAS patrols worked closely with their American counterparts, leading one observer to dub western

Iraq the 'Special Forces Theme Park'. On the last day of the war, 27 February, an SFF Chinook fast-roped an SBS team on to the roof of the British Embassy in Kuwait. The Ambassador was subsequently returned to his embassy by SFF Chinook.

In the aftermath of the war, the UN faced a humanitarian crisis in northern Iraq, to where many Kurds had fled to escape persecution. Hiding in the mountains, they were without food. In early April 1991

Right: Chinooks from several nations were deployed in the wake of the Kosovo campaign to aid the peacekeeping forces. As well as US and UK aircraft, Chinooks came from Italy and the Netherlands (illustrated), while Greek Chinooks helped refugee relief operations in Albania.

Below: Leading the NATO forces which occupied Kosovo were the 1st Battalion, Parachute Regiment, British Army. Here four RAF Chinooks depart a cemetery in Pristina after delivering Paras into the town, shortly after Serb forces had left.

Eurocopter AS 532 and EC 725 Cougar

Medium helicopter

Logically, if unimaginatively, known as the **Super Puma** when first proposed in 1974, the **Aérospatiale AS 332** was devised as a successor to the SA 330 Puma. Retaining the Puma's overall appearance, but profiting from the introduction of more advanced features made possible by developments in glassfibre rotor technology, the Super Puma is most readily identifiable by its prominent ventral fin and nose radome. Aimed primarily at the civil market, the helicopter nevertheless incorporates features of value to military operators, including a gearbox operable for one hour without lubricant and rotors which remain safe for 40 hours after hits by 12.7-mm (0.5-in) small-arms fire.

Super Puma

First flown on 13 September 1978 with Makila engines, multi-purpose air inlets, a lightweight Starflex rotor head, uprated transmission, thermally de-iced main rotor blades, and wider-track main landing-gear units with single wheels, the Super Puma entered service in 1981 as the military **AS 332B** and civilian AS 332C. Both these initial variants retained the Puma's cabin, with accommodation for 12–15 fully-equipped troops. During the following year delivery began of the 'stretched' civil AS 332L and military **AS 332M**, with their fuselages lengthened by 0.76 m (2 ft 6 in).

In January 1990, the military variants were renamed **Cougar** (later **Cougar Mk I**), renumbered **AS 532** and accorded new variant suffixes: the **AS 532AC** and **AS 532UC** were the armed and unarmed short-fuselage helicopters, the **AS 532AL** and **AS 532UL** were the armed and unarmed long-fuselage helicopters, the **AS 532MC** was the unarmed

At least four AS 532A2 Cougar MK II helicopters have been ordered by l'Armée de l'Air for use in the CSAR and special ops roles. The CSAR aircraft are named Cougar RESCO (Recherche et Sauvetage en Combat) in service and up to 14 are required.

naval SAR and surveillance helicopter, and the **AS 532SC** was the armed naval ASW/AShW helicopter. Both maritime models had previously been known by the designation **AS 332F**. Later examples of the Cougar Mk I have 1400-kW (1,877-shp) Makila 1A1 engines.

Cougar Mk II

On 6 February 1987 the development prototype of the **Cougar Mk II**, known in its civil form as the **AS 332L2 Super Puma Mk II**, made its first flight with the powerplant of two 1569-kW (2,104-shp) Makila 1A2 engines, Spheriflex main and tail rotor heads with elastomeric bearings, longer main rotor blades, larger lateral sponsons carrying additional fuel, life rafts, etc., and a further 'stretch' of the fuselage to provide accommodation for 28

SPECIFICATION

Eurocopter France AS 532UC Cougar Mk I
Type: two/three-crew general-purpose tactical medium helicopter
Powerplant: two Turbomeca Makila 1A1 turboshaft engines each rated at 1400 kW (1,877 shp)
Performance: maximum cruising speed 262 km/h (163 mph) at sea level; initial climb rate 420 m (1,378 ft) per minute; service ceiling 4100 m (13,450 ft); hovering ceiling 2700 m (8,860 ft) in ground effect and 1600 m (5,250 ft) out of ground effect; range 618 km (384 miles) with standard fuel
Weights: empty 4330 kg (9,546 lb); maximum take-off 9350 kg (20,615 lb)
Dimensions: main rotor diameter 15.6 m (51 ft 2¼ in); length 18.7 m (61 ft 4¼ in) with the rotors turning; height 4.92 m (16 ft 1¾ in); main rotor disc area 191.13 m² (2,057.42 sq ft)
Payload: up to 21 troops or 4500 kg (9,921 lb) of freight carried as an internal or external load

passengers. The Mk II version of the Super Puma and Cougar entered service in 1992 and was to have been used as the platform for French army aviation's HORIZON (Hélicoptère d'Observation Radar et d'Investigation sur ZONe) battlefield surveillance radar in the late 1990s. However, the combination of the Orchidée radar system and the Cougar Mk II proved prohibitively expensive and the combination was abandoned in 1990, only to be resurrected for the 1991 Gulf War. The experience gained from 24 missions with an SA 330-mounted Orphée radar led to the HORIZON concept being resurrected. Eurocopter

Right: Along with UH-1s, AB 212s and Chinooks, Spanish Army Aviation operates AS 532 Super Pumas/Cougars in the crucial battlefield mobility role.

Below: The Icelandic Coast Guard operates a single AS 332L2 Super Puma from Reykjavik airport for search and rescue (SAR), air ambulance and fisheries patrol work.

received a development contract in October 1992 for two aircraft, combining the capabilities of Orchidée with the endurance of the AS 532UL. The first of four such **AS 532UL Cougar Horizon** helicopters was delivered in April 1994. The French army has also replaced some of its original AS 330s with AS 532s, the first 22 aircraft being delivered to the Force d'Action Rapide by the

end of 1991. In addition, in November 2002, the French air force ordered ten of the re-engined **EC 725 Cougar** for special ops/CSAR work. Due for certification in 2003, the EC 725 also features advanced avioncs.

Weapons

While armament options for the army Cougar are restricted to gun and rocket pods, the naval AS 532SC has provision for a

pair of AM.39 Exocet AShMs or homing torpedoes. Operation from ship platforms is also possible, using hauldown gear to permit flying in rough seas. Large sponsons with inflatable floats are standard naval equipment. IPTN (Eurocopter) in Indonesia produces the AS 332C and AS 332L as the **NAS-332**. Other foreign designations include Brazil (**CH-34**) and Spain (**HD.21** for SAR).

Mil Mi-8/9/14/17 'Hip'/'Haze'

Above: About 150 Mil Mi-8/17 'Hips' remain in the Indian air force's inventory, equipping some 15 units. This Mi-8, of No. 115 Helicopter Unit from Jodhpur, is seen overflying the Umaid Bhawan Palace.

Mi-8 into service

The most numerous and important helicopter possessed by the Soviet forces in the latter part of the Cold War, the Mi-8 'Hip' remains in widespread service with air arms in Russia and around the world in a wide variety of roles.

Above: The first prototype Mi-8 (V-8) made its maiden flight during 1961 and was demonstrated to members of the Soviet government in September 1962.

The Mi-8 came from the design bureau of the brilliant Soviet helicopter pioneer Mikhail Leontyevich Mil, who died in 1970. A string of mass-produced and record-breaking helicopters remains the testament to his engineering and design skills. The Mi-8, a turbine-powered development of the Mi-4 'Hound' (itself a shock to the West), was first seen in public at Tushino in 1961 and was powered by a single 2013-kW (2,700-shp) Soloviev turbine mounted above the cabin roof. Although the fuselage was new, with the pilots' seats at the front instead of over the cabin, the helicopter employed the rotor hub, rotor blades, transmission and boom of the Mi-4. The second prototype, which flew in September 1962, was powered by two 1044-kW (1,400-shp) Isotov TV2 turboshafts, and the production version was given a five-bladed main rotor in place of the four-bladed rotor inherited from the 'Hound'.

'Hip' structure

The Mi-8's fuselage is a conventional all-metal semi-monocoque structure of the pod and boom type. The tricycle landing gear is non-retractable, with a steerable twin-wheel nose unit which is locked in flight, and a single wheel on each main unit. Two pilots sit side-by-side in the cockpit, which also has provision for a flight engineer's seat. The standard passenger version has 28 four-abreast tip-up seats with a centre aisle, a wardrobe and luggage compartment, or 32 seats and bulkheads that are removable for the carriage of cargo. The Mi-8T has cargo tie-down rings on the floor, a winch of 200-kg (441-lb) capacity, an external cargo sling system with a capacity of 3000 kg (6,614 lb), and 24 tip-up seats along the side walls of the cabin. Clamshell freight doors and hook-on ramps facilitate vehicle-loading, while a passenger airstair is standard on the commercial version. The Mi-8 Salon (a VIP version for 11 passengers) was demonstrated at the Paris air show in 1971.

NATO allocated the reporting names 'Hip-A' and 'Hip-B' to the Mi-8 prototypes, and at the spectacular 1967 Domodedovo

The Egyptian air force equipped many of its 'Hips' with distinctive squared-off sand filters, manufactured by APME (Aircraft Porous Media Equipment) in Britain. They dramatically increase serviceability and prolong engine life.

air display the 'Hip' appeared in military colours. Military production was under way, and no time was lost in taking advantage of the Americans' hard-won experience in Vietnam. The 'Hip' became the standard Soviet utility/assault helicopter (able to carry 24 armed troops) and was well to the fore in the Soviet development of the airmobile concept.

Armament

Outriggers with two pylons were added on each side of the cabin to carry four UV-32-57 packs, each containing 32 55-mm (2.17-in) S-5 air-to-surface rockets. This version was designated Mi-8T 'Hip-C', but by 1979 a more potent variant, the 'Hip-E', had become the world's most heavily-armed helicopter with six UV-32-57 packs housing 192 rockets, four AT-2 'Swatter' anti-tank guided missiles on rails above the rocket packs, and a nose-mounted 12.7-mm (0.5-in) machine-gun. Even when fully fuelled and armed, the 'Hip-E' can still lift 12–14 troops, though operations at maximum gross weight allow little power for manoeuvring at low speed and in the hover.

Other military versions in use include the 'Hip-D' and 'Hip-G', which have been developed for command and control duties. The 'Hip-D' is similar to the 'Hip-C', but features canisters on the outer stores racks and added antennas for the battlefield communications-relay role, while the 'Hip-G' has rearwards-inclined antennas projecting from the rear of the cabin and from the undersurface of the tailboom, though intended for the same task as the 'Hip-C'. The 'Hip-F' is an export version of the 'Hip-E' and is equipped with six AT-3 'Saggers' in place of the four 'Swatters'. This version first entered service with the East German 'Adolf von Lotzow' Combat Helicopter Regiment. The 'Hip-J' is an ECM version identifiable by additional small boxes on the sides of the fuselage, fore and aft of the main landing-gear legs. The 'Hip-K' is a communications-jamming ECM version with a large antenna array on each side of the cabin.

Over 1,600 Mi-8s served with the USSR's Frontal Aviation, 900 with Transport Aviation and a further 100 with Naval Aviation, many of which remain in service

today with Russia and former Soviet states. Mi-8s were also exported to 39 other countries and have tasted combat in several theatres of action. During the first evening of the Yom Kippur War in 1973 a force of about 100 'Hips', carrying crack 18-man Egyptian commando teams, crossed the Suez Canal to attack Israeli oilfields and to hinder the movement of reinforcements. The commandos were supported by 'Hips' armed with rockets and bombs, while others were modified to carry two fixed heavy machine-guns and up to six light machine-guns to provide suppressive fire around LZs. Napalm bombs were also reported to have been rolled out through the clamshell doors on to Israeli positions along the Canal. Egyptian Mi-8s were additionally used for resupply and medevac duties. The Syrians employed about a dozen 'Hips' to deliver commandos 2440 m (8,000 ft up Mount Hermon to capture an Israeli observation post.

In the bitter Ogaden war, the Soviet commander of the Ethiopian forces used Mi-8s to airlift troops and light armoured vehicles over a mountain and place them behind forward Somali positions. And earlier, in 1974, two Soviet 'Hips' operated from the deck of the ASW helicopter cruiser *Leningrad* as they helped to sweep mines from the southern end of the Suez Canal. The Soviet Union also widely operated the Mi-8 for both troop transport and as gunships in the protracted

Afghanistan conflict. More recently, Russia has utilised the 'Hip' in two hard-fought campaigns in Chechnya.

Like the Huey 'slicks' and 'hogs' of the Vietnam War, troop-carrying 'Hips' are usually escorted by the more heavily-armed Mi-24 'Hind' gunships. It has been claimed in the USA that both these helicopters were used to wage chemical and biological warfare against the Afghan guerrillas, with loads generally fired in 55-mm (2.17-in) rocket rounds.

Humanitarian role

Mi-8s have also been put to humanitarian use. During 1985, for instance, Soviet and Polish 'Hips' took part in famine-relief operations in drought-stricken Ethiopia. The Polish Relief Helicopter Squadron arrived at Assab aboard the MV *Wislica* with 100 tons of food and equipment. Three days later, the Mi-8Ts were assembled and began airlifting supplies for distribution to the starving people in the desert.

In Finland, the Mi-8 helicopters of the Finnish air force (Suomen Ilmavoimat) andof the Frontier Guard (Rajavartiolaitos) have added a useful and reliable dimension to the country's communications network, particularly through the long, arctic conditions winters when overland routes are frequently blocked by snow or floods. Other military air arms use the Mi-8 as dedicated search and rescue aircraft fitted with radar and specialised rescue equipment.

SPECIFICATION	
Mi-14PL 'Haze A' **Type:** land-based anti-submarine helicopter **Powerplant:** one 1434-kW (1,925-hp) Klimov (Isotov) TV3-117MT turboshaft **Performance:** maximum speed 230 km/h (143 mph); maximum cruising speed 259 km/h (161 mph); climb rate 468 m (1,535 ft) per minute; range 1135 km (704 miles)	**Weights:** empty 8902 kg (19,584 lb); loaded 13000kg (28,600 lb); maximum take-off 14000 kg (30,800 lb) **Dimensions:** main rotor diameter 21.29 m (69 ft 10 in); length 18.37 m (60 ft 3 in); height 9.63 m (31 ft 7 in); rotor disc area 362 m² (3,895 sq ft) **Armament:** torpedoes and depth charges, as well as sonobuoys/smoke/flare floats

NH Industries NH 90
Medium assault helicopter

In 1985 five European nations signed a memorandum of understanding covering a 'NATO helicopter for the '90s', or **NH 90**. The UK dropped out of the programme in 1987, leaving France, Germany, Italy and the Netherlands in the project by means of NH Industries, established in France during August 1992 to control a collaborative programme involving Eurocopter France (41.6 per cent with NFT [Norway] as a risk-sharing partner from 1994), Agusta (28.2 per cent), Eurocopter Deutschland (23.7 per cent) and Fokker (6.5 per cent).

Stated requirements were 220 helicopters for France, 214 for Italy, 272 for Germany and 20 for the Netherlands, and it was anticipated that a first flight in 1995 would pave the way for deliveries from 1999. The two initial versions are the NH 90 NFH (NATO Frigate Helicopter) and the **NH 90 TTH** (**Tactical Transport Helicopter**) for assault transport, rescue, electronic warfare and VIP transport duties. The TTH variant is being developed under Eurocopter Deutschland leadership, with a cabin for 20 troops or one 2000-kg (4,409-lb) vehicle. It can carry area-suppression and self-defence weapons. A FLIR is standard to

provide a night and adverse-weather nap-of-the-Earth flight capability, and both models are controlled via a quadruplex fly-by-wire control system.

Export success

Two engine types are available to increase the NH 90's export potential. By the autumn of 2003, NH Industries had received initial orders for 60 TTH helicopters from Italy for its army, plus 10 for its navy; 50 for the German army and 30 for the Luftwaffe (of which as many as 23 may be used for CSAR). In addition, the Portuguese military has committed to 10 TTH

NH 90 has suffered a somewhat protracted development period, but in the autumn of 2003 was approaching operational service. A prototype machine is shown here.

aircraft; Sweden to 13 specially-equipped dual-role assault/SAR **TTT/SAR** aircraft for delivery during the period 2005–2009; and Finland to 20 TTH helicopters for assault and search and rescue for delivery in the period 2004–2008.

On 29 August 2003, Greece ordered 16 TTHs and four TTH special forces helicopters for its army, with another 12 TTH and two special ops aircraft on option. If the options are taken up, deliveries should be completed in 2010.

Some of the nations to have committed to TTH will also fly their aircraft on SAR duties. Germany and Greece intend to use some aircraft for CSAR and special ops work, respectively.

SPECIFICATION	
NH Industries NH 90 TTH	**Weights:** empty 5400 kg (11,905 lb); maximum take-off 10000 kg (22,046 lb)
Type: two-crew medium tactical transport helicopter	
Powerplant: two RTM 322-01/9 turboshaft engines each rated at 1566 kW (2,100 shp) or two General Electric/Alfa Romeo T700-T6E turboshaft engines each rated at 1521 kW (2,040 shp)	**Dimensions:** main rotor diameter 16.30 m (53 ft 5½ in); length 19.56 m (64 ft 2 in) with the rotors turning; height 5.44 m (17 ft 10 in) with the rotors turning; main rotor disc area 208.67 m² (2,246.18 sq ft)
Performance: (estimated) maximum speed 300 km/h (186 mph); endurance 4 hours 30 minutes	**Payload:** up to 20 equipped troops or 4600 kg (10,141 lb) of freight

The major operator of the Sea Stallion and the Super Stallion is the US Marine Corps, which prizes the helicopter for its load-carrying ability. The CH-53D was the second transport version to enter service.

Sikorsky H-53

Designed to a US Marine Corps requirement for a heavy-lift assault helicopter, the Sikorsky S-65 and later S-80 helicopters have been used for such diverse roles as presidential transport and anti-mine warfare.

The Sikorsky S-65 was selected by the US Marine Corps in 1962 to be its new heavy assault transport to replace the H-34s then in service. Designated the CH-53A Sea Stallion in military service, the maiden flight of the prototype YCH-53A took place on 14 October 1964. Powered by a pair of General Electric T64 turboshafts, the design featured a full-size rear loading ramp and soon demonstrated its outstanding load-carrying ability by establishing a new unofficial payload weight record for a production helicopter built outside the Soviet Union of 12927 kg (28,500 lb). For a large helicopter, the Sea Stallion was also manoeuvrable; a Marine Corps CH-53A performed a series of rolls and loops in 1968.

After the production of 139 CH-53As, an improved Sea Stallion for the Marines, the

The second production Super Stallion flight-tested the features of the MH-53E Sea Dragon, including the large fuel sponsons and nose-mounted mirrors.

CH-53D, which had first flown on 3 March 1969, was put into production. Both types represented the heavy-lift assets of the US Marines during the difficult years of the Vietnam War, doing sterling service moving equipment and personnel around the country. The Sea Stallion was also capable of recovering downed aircraft – by 1970, H-53s of the USMC and USAF had recovered 1,029 aircraft downed during the war.

Super Jolly to Pave Low

USAF interest in the helicopter began with its involvement in the Apollo programme, when a long-range recovery and rescue helicopter was required to recover the Apollo command module from the sea. Seven ▶

In Israeli service, the CH-53 is known as the Yas'ur. It has seen long and hard service from 1970 as heavy-lift support for the army. 42 examples are being upgraded by IAI.

Flown by courageous crews in the Vietnam war, HH-53s of the USAF plucked many airmen to safety after they had been shot down. Missions over North Vietnam required inflight refuelling by HC-130Ps.

HH-53Bs were acquired – replacing a similar number of CH-53As loaned from the Marines – before 40 of the improved HH-53C entered service. The HH-53s were best known for their work in Vietnam, where they were nicknamed the 'Super Jolly' (after the smaller HH-3 'Jolly Green Giant' which shared its roles and looked similar). Twenty CH-53Cs were bought for transport duties.

Eleven 'Super Jollys' were later modified for the all-weather rescue mission as HH-53H Pave Low IIIs. And, in 1986, 31 HH-53B/Cs and CH-53Cs and eight surviving HH-53Hs were upgraded to the MH-53J Pave Low III standard. Based at Hurlburt Field, FL, Osan AB, RoK and RAF Mildenhall, the MH-53J is, today, Air Force Special Operations Command's primary long-range recovery and special warfare helicopter.

Export customers

The Sikorsky Model S-65 was exported to a number of countries. The major user abroad is the German army, which acquired 112 of what were basically CH-53Ds, as the CH-53G. Sikorsky built two and supplied major components for others to VFW-Fokker. VFW-Fokker assembled the other 110, increasing the percentage of German-built components during the programme. Some German army CH-53Gs are being upgraded to CH-53GS standard, with improved self-protection equipment.

Austria used two S-65Oes for a short while from 1970 as mountain rescue helicopters, before selling them to Israel. The IAF/DF is thought to have had about 45 S-65s, locally called the *Yas'ur* (Petrel). Forty-two are currently in the process of being upgraded to the Yas'ur 2000 standard.

Mine-hunters

Experiments with RH-3A Sea Kings had validated the idea of using helicopters as mine-hunting platforms, towing a sled to explode mines harmlessly. The CH-53 had more surplus power than the Sea King and thus made an ideal mine-hunting helicopter. Fifteen CH-53As were modified as RH-53As and served with HM-12, until the 30 RH-53Ds built as such for the US Navy entered service. Pre-revolutionary Iran acquired six RH-53Ds. In 1979, when Iranian students seized American hostages after the Islamic revolution, RH-53Ds were chosen for the abortive Eagle Claw rescue attempt, partly because the Iranians also had the type (acquired in 1977).

Super Stallion

The replacement for the United States Marine Corps Sea Stallion fleet was a three-engined development, the CH-53E Super Stallion. First flown on 1 March 1973, delivery commenced in June 1981, with over 150 aircraft currently in service with the Marines and the Navy. An anti-mine warfare version, the MH-53E Sea Dragon, is also in service with the US Navy. The MH-53E Sea Dragon has been exported to Japan as the Sikorsky S-80M, 10 being in service by early 1998.

Four of the eight RH-53Ds involved in the disastrous Eagle Claw rescue attempt sit on the flight deck of the USS Nimitz in April 1979. Only one of the helicopters ever made it back to the aircraft-carrier.

The second YCH-53A (Bureau No. 151614) made the type's first flight on 14 October 1964 from Stratford, Connecticut. Only two YCH-53As were used in flight tests before production aircraft were delivered.

H-53 development

A Marines CH-53A carries a CH-46 helicopter fuselage during testing at Patuxent River. This heavylift capability allowed the Sea Stallion to recover over 1,000 downed aircraft in Vietnam.

Developed from a US Marines specification for a heavylift assault helicopter that could operate from ships, the H-53 family of helicopters has given sterling service in conflicts ranging from Vietnam to the Gulf War.

Development of the versatile H-53 family began in October 1960 when the United States Marine Corps declared a wish to replace its Sikorsky HR2S-1s with a new ship-based heavy assault helicopter. The HR2S-1 (later redesignated CH-37C) had validated the long-standing Marines conviction that helicopters were the ideal vehicles in which to bring troops and equipment ashore during amphibious raids. However, the HR2S-1 was growing old and proving difficult to maintain and so it was decided that a replacement was needed.

Initially, the USMC joined the Army, Air Force and Navy in sponsoring the development of the medium-sized Tri-Service VTOL transport. However, the resulting Vought-Hiller-Ryan XC-142A programme became over-ambitious and ran late, and so the Marines decided to make their own request for a new heavylift helicopter. In a requirement issued by the

Bureau of Naval Weapons on 7 March 1962, the Marines called for a ship-based helicopter capable of lifting an 3630-kg (8,000-lb) payload over a radius of 100 nm (185 km/115 miles) at a speed of 150 kt (278 km/h; 172 mph). Its missions would be ship-to-shore transport, downed aircraft recovery, personnel transport and aero-medical evacuation.

Three companies responded, Boeing Vertol with a redesign of its HC-1A, Kaman Aircraft with a development of the British-designed Fairey Rotodyne and Sikorsky indicating its intent to develop a twin-turbine S-65. Having lost a previous competition to supply the Marines with a medium-lift helicopter, Sikorsky went all-out to win the contract. It was selected as the winner in July 1962 when the S-65 was chosen as a result of technical, production capability and cost considerations. However, due to insufficient funds in the USMC budget, the anticipated contract

for four prototypes could not be realised until Sikorsky lowered its R&D bid, and the revised number of two prototypes was ordered. This revised proposal gained acceptance and, on 24 September 1962, the DoD announced that Sikorsky's helicopter had been accepted – the two YCH-53A prototypes, a static test airframe and a mock-up were built in a $9,965,635 contract.

Sikorsky's design was powered by two General Electric T64 shaft turbines and incorporated many proven

features of other Sikorsky designs. There was the main transmission of the S-64 (CH-54) crane helicopter and the 22-m (72-ft) diameter, six-bladed main rotor and anti-torque rotor of the S-56 (CH-37) heavylift helicopter. The winning design itself was of similar configuration to, but larger than, its S-61 (SH-3A) stablemate. First flown on 14 October 1964 and smoothly completing trials while encountering few problems, the initial production variant, the CH-53A, entered service with the Marine Corps in September ▶

Above: The simple idea of adding an extra engine to the H-53 airframe resulted in a far more powerful aircraft. This test YMH-53E (without the typical large sponsons of the MH-53E) is able to drag its anti-mine sled through the roughest seas.

The HH-53C was a development of the interim HH-53B rescue helicopter. Its design meant that the internal and external fuel capacity had to be reduced but, due its telescopic refuelling probe, its combat radius was not affected. HH-53Cs of the 55th ARRS also flew in support of every Apollo space mission, ready to retrieve the manned capsules in the event of an abort after launch.

1965. The 141 'A' model Sea Stallions were followed on the production lines by three other heavylift transport variants (20 CH-53Cs for the USAF; 126 CH-53Ds for the USMC; and two CH-53Gs for West Germany) with more powerful T64 engines and other improvements. In addition, 20 CH-53Gs were assembled in West Germany and 90 more were built under licence.

Whether in combat or while undergoing trials, the heavylift transport variants of the twin-engined S-65 series proved highly satisfactory. This can be seen in the fact that, in Vietnam between 13 January 1967 and 18 May 1971, Marine Heavy Helicopter Squadron 463 (HMH-463) was credited with recovering a total of 1,096 fixed-wing aircraft and helicopters; the dollar amount saved far exceeded the total acquisition cost of all CH-53As and CH-53Ds. HMH-463 gained further recognition as being part of Operations Eagle Pull and Frequent Wind which saw its helicopters being used to pull American citizens and their allies out of Phnom Penh and Saigon. During the course of the war, the Marines lost 19 CH-53A/Ds to a variety of causes.

Back in America, Sea Stallions were making the headlines by establishing unofficial payload and gross weight records for a helicopter built outside the USSR. A CH-53A also became the first helicopter to be fitted with an automatic terrain clearance system.

H-53 variants

All of these successes did not go unnoticed and the interest of the Air Force and Navy plus several foreign customers led

Sikorsky to design specialised rescue and mine-countermeasure variants of its twin-engined helicopter. Development of the HH-53B, prompted by the need to provide a more powerful, better armoured and defended combat rescue aircraft, was initiated in September 1966. Sikorsky quickly developed the Super Jolly rescue helicopter and the first HH-53B flew on 15 March 1967. Sikorsky went on to build 44 HH-53Cs for the USAF, two S-65C-2s for Austria and 33 S-65C-3s for Israel.

In Vietnam, Super Jollies proved to be a highly effective combat rescue aircraft and in their first three years of combat they saved the lives of some 371 aircrew. HH-53s also gained fame for their participation in the Son Tay prison raid and the rescue of the *Mayaguez* crew from captivity in Cambodia. During the conflict, the USAF lost some 14 CH-53/HH-53s in combat, including one shot down by a MiG-21. After the war, the Super Jollies had their capabilities expanded when they were brought up to HH-53H Pave Low III and then Pave Low III Enhanced standard. This was partly due to the poor performance by the Navy RH-53Ds during the attempted rescue of American hostages in Iran in April 1980. In Pave Low III Enhanced form, the HH-53 is the most capable special operations helicopter in service with the Air Force Special Operations Command and, in 1986, its designation was changed to MH-53J to reflect its expanded special operations role.

Minesweepers

Experiments with minesweeping helicopters led to the conclusion that only the CH-53 was powerful enough to drag the heavy minesweeping gear. However, due to the need for CH-53As to support the Marines in Vietnam, the first

experiments with minesweeping Sea Stallions did not occur until winter 1970. Fifteen helicopters were given the appropriate equipment and were redesignated RH-53As prior to their assignment to Helicopter Mine Counter-measures Squadron Twelve (HM-12). They gained notoriety during Operation Endsweep, the removal of mines from North Vietnamese waters between February and July 1972. These first RH-53As were later supplemented by 30 specially-built RH-53Ds in Navy service. They have been used since in several mine-clearance operations from Nimbus Star in 1964 to Earnest Will in the 1980s. Iran also received six essentially similar mine countermeasures helicopters before the fall of the Shah. The Iranian RH-53Ds were the last S-65s built as the success achieved with military customers did not repeat itself in the civilian world.

Three-engined S-80

By autumn 1970, the USMC's experience with the CH-53A had convinced it that a helicopter was needed that could lift 1.8 times the load that could be lifted by the Sea Stallion. The first step towards acquiring such an aircraft was the approval on 24 October 1967 of a specific requirement calling for a helicopter with an 18-ton capability, but which was small enough to operate from LPH amphibious assault ships. In addition to the Marines' needs, the Navy also wanted a new vertical re-supply helicopter, and the Army a heavylift helicopter.

Sikorsky responded to this by placing a third engine inside the CH-53 upper fuselage fairing. The new helicopter proved exceedingly popular with the US Marine Corps (not the US Army), while the Navy adopted the three-engined minesweeping derivative, the MH-53E, in April 1988.

Above: The ability to perform mid-air refuellings, invariably with a C-130 variant, enables the H-53 family, and in particular the MH-53J, to undertake missions over great distances. MH-53Js undertook long-range missions in Operation Just Cause in Panama and in Operation Desert Storm, where they inserted British and American special operations troopers behind Iraqi lines.

Above: Marines still use landing craft, but in today's conflicts the helicopter is equally important. The CH-53 in various forms has soldiered on since the Vietnam War and has generally been a great success, being involved in many aspects of American military operations. Its successor, when it eventually makes it into service, will be the V-22 Osprey tilt-rotor aircraft.

Left: A pair of Marine CH-53Es which are transporting Marine Piranha LAVs (light attack vehicles) takes on fuel from a KC-130. The movement of such heavy cargo loads became an easy task for the CH-53E. Super Stallions currently provide the principal heavylift capability for the USMC and are a vital element of amphibious operations where they partner the smaller personnel-carrying CH-46s. ▶

Main rotor

The six blades of the main rotor are made almost entirely of extruded or thin sheet aluminium alloy, but later CH-53 versions have blades with an extruded titanium spar and honeycomb-filled glassfibre skin. The massive main rotor hub is mainly constructed from steel and titanium forgings. Each blade can be folded when the aircraft is parked. The large disc on top of the rotor is a lightweight fairing to streamline the hub and reduce drag at cruising speed. On each side of the giant central rotor pylon are fairings which cover the diagonal drive shafts carrying the drive from the engines to the main rotor gearbox. Each drive shaft links the front of the engine to an input pinion of the speed-reducing gearbox.

Tail rotor, tailplane, lights and gearbox

The tail rotor has four blades of aluminium alloy mounted in a titanium hub. The fixed tailplane (called a stabiliser) extends only on the right side of the fin-like tail-rotor pylon. A powerful 'strobe' (anti-collision) light above the tail gives a series of flashes visible from a great distance. At the rear is a less powerful, steady white navigation light. A blister on the tail covers the right-angle gearbox which takes drive to the horizontal tail-rotor shaft. There is another angle-box inside the extreme tail end of the fuselage.

S-65C-3 (CH-53D)

The Israeli Defence Force/Air Force acquired 33 S-65C-3s (basically CH-53Ds) via the United States Marines Corps' procurement programme. Two further machines of S-65C-2 configuration were acquired from Austria during 1981. After the Gulf War another 10 ex-USMC CH-53As were also delivered. This aircraft wears the standard IDF/AF camouflage colours for operations in the desert theatre. As usual with IDF/AF aircraft, operating units and squadron insignia are almost impossible to verify. Today Israel operates two squadrons, 114 Tayeset Ha'Super Frelon (The Super Frelons) and 118 Tayeset Ha'Yassuriet Ha'Rishona (The 1st Yas'ur Squadron), of S-65C-3s both based at Tel Nof. IAI is currently involved in an upgrade programme, known as Yas'ur 2000, which will keep the aircraft effective well into the next century.

Cockpit area

Main entry to the cockpit is provided by a door on the front right of the aircraft. There are no side doors to the cockpit, but the large side windows can be jettisoned for emergency escape. The CH-53 is one of the few helicopters with an instrument landing system to enable landings to be made in bad visibility to ILS-equipped air bases. The curved handle-like aerial directly under the centre of the windscreen serves the glideslope receiver which gives vertical guidance. Mounted above each side of the cockpit is a pitot/static tube to measure airspeed. Below the cockpit is the inflight-refuelling tube which telescopes back under the cockpit floor when not in use.

Sponsons

On each side of the aircraft is a large and capacious sponson. It contains fuel tanks and, at the rear, the retracted twin-wheel main landing gears. Navigation lights (bluish green on the right, red on the left) are mounted on both sponsons. Special cantilever pylon mounts extend diagonally upwards from the tips of the sponsons to carry the auxiliary tanks. The Israeli CH-53s, like the majority of versions, can carry jettisonable auxiliary fuel tanks, each of 1703-litre (450-US-gal) capacity. Each fuel tank is stabilised by down-sloping or swept-back tail fins. These drop tanks obscure the view of the left and right navigation lights, so these lights are duplicated on projections extended from the tips of the tank pylons.

Service history

The USMC has been the major operator of the CH-53D and many remain in service today, despite the appearance of the CH-53E. Sea Stallions have been involved in many actions following the Vietnam War, notably in Grenada, Panama, Lebanon and in the Gulf. In the air assault role in these conflicts, the D model was configured for the carriage of 55 fully-equipped troops or 3630 kg (8,000 lb) of cargo internally. However, because of the availability of the CH-46, the Sea Stallion usually transported supplies and materials in most of these conflicts rather than personnel.

▶

H-53
Briefing

Bulky loads are carried underneath a central cargo hook. This CH-53 is delivering a field gun to troops. Such capability allows rapid mobility around the battlefield for heavy equipment, or early deployment so that artillery is in place soon after the first troops land.

CH-53E

Cutaway key
1 Telescopic-in-flight refuelling boom
2 Refuelling boom fairing
3 Instrument compartment access door
4 Glideslope aerial
5 Fresh air intakes
6 Yaw control rudder pedals
7 Landing lamp
8 Downward vision windows
9 Nose undercarriage leg strut
10 Twin nosewheels
11 Radio and electronics bay, port and starboard
12 Cockpit floor level
13 Collective pitch control lever
14 Cyclic pitch control column
15 Co-pilot's armoured seat
16 Instrument panel shroud
17 Windscreen wipers
18 Windscreen panels
19 Rescue hoist/winch
20 Pitot tube
21 UHF aerial
22 Overhead control panel
23 Pilot's armoured seat
24 Cockpit eyebrow window
25 Flight leader's folding jump seat
26 Cockpit bulkhead
27 Jettisonable side window panel
28 Starboard side crew entry door
29 Fuselage and stringer construction
30 Emergency exit window
31 Engine air intake particle separator
32 Bevel drive gearbox
33 Engine oil cooler
34 Auxiliary power unit (APU)
35 Cabin heater unit
36 Starboard engine intake particle separator
37 Engine cowlings armoured on lower surface

38 Auxiliary gearbox
39 Hydraulic reservoirs
40 Gearbox drive shaft
41 Port engine transmission shaft
42 Folding troop seats maximum 37 troops
43 Cargo loading floor
44 Roller conveyor

45 Cargo hook support links
46 General Electric T64-GE-416 turboshaft engine
47 Gearbox mounting fuselage main frame
48 Engine exhaust duct
49 Centre engine intake
50 Main transmission gearbox

51 Blade pitch control rotating swashplate
52 Rotor head mechanism
53 Blade pitch control links
54 Blade folding hinge points
55 Rotor head fairing
56 Seven-bladed main rotor 24.08-m (79-ft) diameter

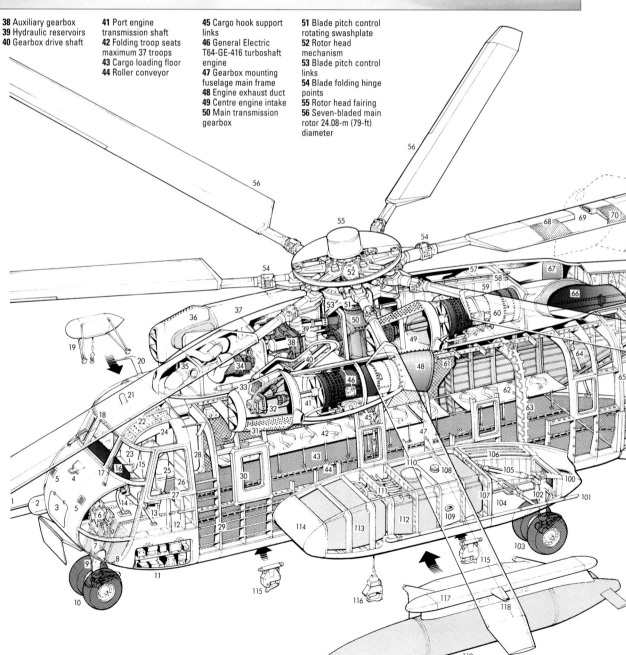

78

SPECIFICATION

CH-53E Super Stallion

Dimensions

Length overall, rotors turning: 30.19 m (99 ft ½ in)
Fuselage length: 22.35 m (73 ft 4 in)
Length with rotor and tail folded: 18.44 m (60 ft 6 in)
Height overall: 8.97 m (29 ft 5 in)
Main rotor diameter: 24.08 m (79 ft)
Tail rotor diameter: 6.10 m (20 ft)
Main rotor disc area: 455.38 m² (4,901.7 sq ft)
Tail rotor disc area: 29.19 m² (314.2 sq ft)

Powerplant

Three General Electric T64-GE-416 engines rated at 3266 kW (4,380 shp) for ten minutes, 3091 kW (4,145 shp) for 30 minutes and 2756 kW (3,696 shp) for continuous running

Weights

Empty: 15072 kg (33,228 lb)
Maximum take-off with an internal payload: 31640 kg (69,750 lb)
Maximum take-off with an external payload: 33340 kg (73,500 lb)

Fuel and load

Internal fuel: 3849 litres (1,017 US gal)
External fuel: up to two 2461-litre (650 US gal) drop tanks
Maximum payload internally over 185-km (115-mile) radius: 16330 kg (36,000 lb)
Maximum payload externally over 92.5-km (57.5-mile) radius: 14515 kg (32,000 lb)

Performance

Maximum level speed 'clean' at sea level: 315 km/h (196 mph)
Cruising speed at sea level: 278 km/h (173 mph)
Maximum rate of climb at sea level with a 11340-kg (25,000-lb) payload: 762 m (2,500 ft) per minute
Service ceiling: 5640 m (18,500 ft)
Hovering ceiling: 3520 m (11,500 ft)

Range

Ferry range without aerial refuelling: 2075 km (1,290 miles)
Radius with a 9072-kg (20,000-lb) external payload: 925 km (575 miles)
Radius with a 14515-kg (32,000-lb) external payload: 92.5 km (57.5 miles)

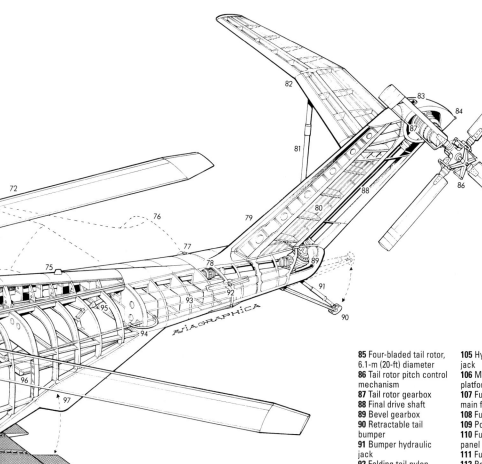

H-53 in Vietnam

It was the shortcomings of other helicopters in Vietnam that provided the impetus for the construction of the H-53. First entering service in 1967, the CH-53A, and soon after the HH-53B, proved popular for transporting supplies and rescuing downed aircrew all over the region. Two years later, in September 1969, the HH-53C made its combat debut. Outwardly similar but possessing many upgraded capabilities the Super Jolly was equipped with an external cargo hook which enabled it to carry loads of up to 9072 kg (20,000 lb), while for the rescue mission it was fitted with a hoist complete with a 76-m (250-ft) cable to penetrate the tallest jungle canopy. For defence up to three 7.62-mm (0.3-in) Miniguns were carried, and these could suppress enemy forces intent on reaching the downed crews before the rescue helicopter.

57 Centre engine oil cooler
58 Maintenance handrail
59 Engine compartment firewall
60 Centre General Electric T64-GE-416 turboshaft engine
61 Cabin wall soundproofing trim panel
62 Rear troop seats
63 Fuselage/main undercarriage main frame
64 Cargo ramp hydraulic jack
65 Production break double frame
66 Centre engine exhaust duct
67 Oil cooler exhaust
68 Rotor blade cross-section
69 D-section titanium spar
70 Honeycomb trailing edge panel
71 Glass-fibre blade skin
72 Leading edge anti-erosion strip
73 Dorsal spine fairing
74 Tail rotor transmission shaft
75 TACAN aerial
76 Tail pylon folded position
77 Pylon hinge point
78 Transmission shaft coupling
79 Glass-fibre fin leading edge
80 Tailfin construction canted 20° to port
81 Stabiliser bracing strut
82 Gull-wing horizontal stabiliser
83 Anti-collision light
84 Tail navigation light
85 Four-bladed tail rotor, 6.1-m (20-ft) diameter
86 Tail rotor pitch control mechanism
87 Tail rotor gearbox
88 Final drive shaft
89 Bevel gearbox
90 Retractable tail bumper
91 Bumper hydraulic jack
92 Folding tail pylon latches
93 Tail boom construction
94 VOR/localiser aerial
95 Upper cargo door hydraulic jack
96 Upper cargo door, open position
97 Doorway side strakes
98 Cargo loading ramp down position
99 Ramp hydraulic jack
100 Formation keeping light
101 Fuel jettison pipe
102 Main undercarriage leg strut
103 Twin mainwheels
104 Mainwheel bay
105 Hydraulic retraction jack
106 Maintenance platform walkway
107 Fuselage sponson main frame
108 Fuel filler cap
109 Port navigation light
110 Fuel tank access panel
111 Fuel system piping
112 Port main fuel tank; total internal capacity 3850 litres (1,017 US gal)
113 Secondary fuel tank
114 Sponson nose fairing
115 Two-point suspension cargo hooks
116 Single-point cargo hook; maximum external slung load 14606 kg (32,200 lb)
117 Auxiliary fuel tank pylon
118 Pylon navigation light
119 Auxiliary fuel tank capacity 650 US gal (2461 litres)

OPERATION EAGLE CLAW

When US civilians were taken hostage by Iranian militants, it was decided that a military response was needed. Special Forces troops prepared for a daring mission which would strike at the heart of Tehran. However, the mission was ultimately over-ambitious, and the poor serviceability of the helicopters involved resulted in a tragic failure.

4–9 November 1979
The US Embassy in Tehran is seized by militant Islamic students. A total of 66 American hostages is taken, some being moved to the Iranian Foreign Affairs building. Thirteen hostages are subsequently released. President Carter authorises the creation of a joint task force to investigate the possibility of rescuing the hostages. Delta Force is selected to carry out the rescue.

10–20 April 1980
After negotiations fall through, a spokesman for the Iranian students declares that if America or any of its Middle East client states invade or intervene, the hostages will be executed. Climatic conditions in the region make an early operation desirable. Carter authorises the operation on 14 April and on the 20th Delta Force troopers leave Pope AFB for Frankfurt aboard two C-141 Starlifters. In Frankfurt, they are joined by a 13-man squad whose task will be to rescue the hostages in the Foreign Affairs building.

The desert-camouflaged RH-53s wait aboard Nimitz *before the rescue attempt. These helicopters were chosen for their good range and payload, plus their shipboard capability.*

21 April 1980, am
Delta Force arrives at Wadi Kena, Egypt. This remote, Soviet-built airfield will act as the headquarters for the mission. Mission commander General Vaught has satellite communications equipment and a Boeing E-3 Sentry on station over the Gulf. Delta Force troopers have their final run through and briefings.

24 April 1980, 14.00 to 16.30
Delta arrives at Masirah, Oman. At 16.30, the attackers board the MC-130s. The troops are wearing black unmarked uniforms and carry a range of weaponry.

24 April 1980, 18.00 to 19.30
The first MC-130 takes off at 18.00 and the other MC-130s and three tanker-configured EC-130s follow in the next hour. At 19.30, eight RH-53Ds take off from USS *Nimitz* for the journey to Desert One. RH-53 no. 6 receives warning of imminent main rotor failure and lands. Crew transfer to aircraft no. 8 and the helicopter is abandoned. Some time later RH-53 no. 5's cooling systems fail and it returns to the *Nimitz*.

The wreckage of an RH-53D confirms the failure of the mission. Contrary to orders, the crews of the surviving helicopters left them intact. Thus, when the Iranians finally arrived, they found a haul of intelligence material including codes and details of US agents in Iran.

24 April 1980 22.00 to 23.00
The first MC-130 lands at Desert One, the refuelling rendezvous 256 nm (474 km/294 miles) south east of Tehran. A road watch team is deployed and 15 minutes later an Iranian civilian bus is seen driving along the road, adjacent to Desert One; it is stopped and the passengers held as prisoners. A fuel truck is then encountered on the same road, but the driver ignores orders to stop and the vehicle is destroyed with an anti-tank missile. However, the driver escapes in a following car. At 22.45 the first MC-130 departs, and at 23.00 the remaining two MC-130s with the Delta Force troopers and the three EC-130s arrive.

25 April 1980, 00.30 to 02.00
The RH-53Ds arrive, one hour late. One further RH-53 is found to be unserviceable, beyond repair using available resources. Five helicopters are not judged sufficient to carry out the mission, so it is aborted. The RH-53s are not to be abandoned, however.

25 April 1980, 02.40 to 02.56
One of the RH-53s collides with an EC-130 tanker as it moves into position for a fuel top-up before returning to the *Nimitz*. A major fire follows the explosion, eight men die and several others are badly injured. A number of the RH-53s are damaged and the rest are now abandoned. Delta Force leaves Desert One aboard the MC-130s.

25 April – What should have happened
At 05.00, the RH-53s were due to arrive at Desert Two, where they were meant to unload Delta and then move into cover. The Delta troopers would have been taken into Tehran by truck, driven by agents from the area, to assault the Embassy and rescue the hostages. Support was to be on offer from AC-130s orbiting Tehran and strike aircraft from the *Nimitz*. Delta would then call the RH-53s to pick up the hostages from the football stadium, or the Embassy itself if its anti-helicopter obstructions were destroyed. A company of Rangers would then seize Desert Three, a disused aerodrome at Manzariyeh. Delta and the hostages would arrive here aboard the RH-53s; they would transfer to C-141s and a C-9 Nightingale and fly to Masirah.

MC-130E Special Operations Hercules were chosen to fly men and stores from Masirah to Desert One. MC-130Es have an inflight refuelling capability, uprated engines and an avionics suite far superior to normal C-130s to allow them to penetrate hostile airspace and infiltrate Special Operations troopers.

IRAQ

Tehran

Manzariyeh (Desert Three)

Desert Two

Desert One

IRAN

PAKISTAN

Chah Bahar

USS *Nimitz*

OMAN

CH/RH-53
Operations

Offering a heavylift capability for amphibious operations, the CH-53 was quickly developed into a host of variants to fulfil roles for both the USAF and West German forces.

After winning the HH(X) competition, Sikorsky struggled to complete the YCH-53A prototypes in the face of a shortage of design personnel, and late delivery of sub-contracted components and government-furnished equipment. Weight increases extended the proposed delivery date of the initial 16 production CH-53As. Production CH-53As, as first delivered to HMH-463 at MCAS Santa Ana, California in September 1965, were initially identical to the YCH-53As, and like these prototypes were powered by 1864-kW (2,500-shp) T64-GE-6s. Before accelerated training could commence and deployment to Southeast Asia was authorised, four developments were made to improve the usefulness of the CH-53A in combat: (1) an engine air particle separator (EAPS) filtering system was installed in front of the air intake of the engines; (2) defensive armament was provided (a pintle-mounted M60 machine-gun being added to fire from

hatches on both sides of the forward fuselage); (3) 204 kg (450 lb) of amour was added to protect the crew and vital components; and (4) the CH-53A was tested in the 'flying crane' role, as combat operations in Vietnam had revealed that the Marines' most urgent need was for a helicopter capable of retrieving aircraft without the need for removing parts and equipment to reduce weight. Trials revealed the need to increase power if the CH-53A was to be able to retrieve the CH-46A, the standard Marine medium helicopter. Accordingly, plans were made for the installation of T64-GE-1 engines that would be allowed to operate for short periods at a maximum rating of 2296-kW (3,080-shp) instead of the standard 2125-kW (2,850 shp) and for their replacement beginning in early 1968 by specially modified 2561-kW (3,435-shp) T64-GE-12s or T64-GE-16s, the retrofitting of these more powerful engines being made without airframe changes.

Easing away after refuelling from a USMC KC-130, a CH-53E demonstrates the precise flying qualities of the type. Some Soviet helicopters have outstripped the -53 in terms of power and lifting capability, but the Stallion remains a true giant of the helicopter world.

Production CH-53As had a crew of three (pilot, co-pilot and crew chief) and were designed to carry internally either 38 assault troops, 42 litter patients and four attendants, or 3630 kg (8,000 lb) of cargo. The cabin measured 9.14 m (30 ft) in length, 1.98 m (6 ft 6 in) in height, and 2.29 m (7 ft 6 in) in

Marine assault! The principal raison d'être for the Sikorsky H-53 was to provide rapid transport between ship and shore for the USMC. Although it is a very capable troop transport, the helicopter was tailored for the carriage of the heavy equipment that accompanies the Marines during amphibious assaults.

width and incorporated roller conveyors and a tie-down system. Bulkier loads weighing up to 9070 kg (20,000 lb) were carried externally. Although primarily intended for use in the transport role, the CH-53As' usefulness increased when, from the 34th production machine, they were fitted with hardpoints for towed minesweeping equipment.

Minesweeping

Fifteen CH-53As modified as RH-53As were acquired by the US Navy. All were fitted with hardpoints for towed minesweeping equipment. The Navy decided that further modification would be required, and the 15 Sea Stallions were ▶

Left: Self-protection is an increasingly important part of helicopter operations. Over the battlefield, shoulder-launched heat-seeking missiles like the SA-7 'Grail' are particularly dangerous, and are best countered by the release of flares from dispensers on the rear fuselage sides. They provide a dense heat source much greater than that of the helicopter itself, thereby drawing away the missile.

Below: The USAF was quick to exploit the potential of inflight refuelling with the H-53 in an effort to increase the helicopter's range. Shown below is an HH-53 preparing to engage one of the trailing refuelling drogues from an HC-130P tanker.

re-engined with 2926-kW (3,925-shp) T64-GE-413 shaft turbines. They were operated by the Navy pending availability of the specialised RH-53D variant. Rear-view mirrors were fitted in tubular mounts on each side of the nose to enable the pilot and co-pilot to visually track the towed minesweeping equipment, and a rectangular frame was attached to the rear ramp to prevent the towing cable from hitting the airframe or tail rotor. Following their replacement in Navy service by RH-53Ds, the RH-53As were returned to the Marine Corps and were once again designated CH-53As.

USAF interest

Having closely observed the progress made by the USMC with the CH-53, the USAF perceived a similar need for a heavy lift helicopter. Twenty CH-53Cs were built for the USAF, which requested a change of powerplant to the 2926-kW (3,925-shp) T-64-GE-7, and these variants differed externally from Marine CH-53As in being fitted to carry 1703-litre (450-US gal) external tanks. The CH-53C was distinguished from the HH-53C by its lack of inflight-refuelling probe. CH-53Cs first replaced CH-53As on loan from the Marines for covert operations in Laos with the 21st SOS, and were later operated by TAC and United States Air Forces Europe to airlift equipment for the Tactical Air Control System, and by MAC for pilot training. The type was gradually withdrawn from service to undergo a

modernisation programme which brought the remaining seven examples up to MH-53J standard.

More improvements

First flown on 27 January 1969, the CH-53D was to all intents and purposes nothing more than an improved version of the CH-53A, with strengthened transmission to enable early T64 variants to be replaced first by 2755-kW (3,695-shp) T64-GE-412s, then by 2926-kW (3,925-shp) T64-GE-413s and later by 2926-kW (3,925-shp) T64-GE-413s. The transmission was rated at 5637-kW (7,560-hp) single-engined operation, but the additional power enabled CH-53Ds to operate without significant limitations even under hot-and-high conditions. Other improvements incorporated during production included use of the Sikorsky Blade Inspection Method to eliminate the need for mandatory blade retirement after a specific number of operating hours. Standard fuel capacity remained at 2363-litre (638 US gal) in two sponson tanks and, as was the case with the CH-53A, one to five 1136-litre (330-US gal) ferry tanks could be installed in the fuselage.

German giants

Seeking a replacement for the Sikorsky H-34s and Weserflug H-21s of the Heeresflieger, West Germany evaluated the Boeing Vertol CH-47 and Sikorsky CH-53 in 1966. Orders were placed in June 1968 for two Sikorsky-built

CH-53Gs through USN channels and 133 CH-53Gs to be built under licence by a consortium led by VFW. Production costs soon reduced the total requirement to 110 examples, which serve with three medium transport regiments.

Superior lifter

Seeking to improve the capabilities of the CH-53, modifications were made that included an additional centrally mounted third engine with intake and exhaust on the port side, a beefed-up transmission, and a seven-bladed main rotor with broader chord blades and increased diameter. Designated CH-53Es, the variant differed internally from the CH-53D in having a 1.88-m (6-ft 2-in) longer fuselage, a broader tailfin, a low-mounted tailplane, longer sponson housing that enabled internal fuel capacity to be increased from 2415 to 3850 litres (638 to 1,017 US gal), and provision for 2460-litre (650-US gal) pylon-mounted tanks for an inflight-refuelling probe.

The first production CH-53E was accepted by the USMC on

13 December 1980, following operational evaluation at MCAS Quantico, MCAS Cherry Point, NAS Norfolk, Fort Bragg and aboard an LPH. The improved variant demonstrated its superior lifting capability.

By February 1981 CH-53Es equipped five Marine squadrons operating in heavylift shore operations and in support of amphibious assault operations. In August 1990, during Operation Desert Shield, ship-based CH-53Es were among the first helicopters to reach the new troublespot. They provided a lifting capability not only for the USMC but also for the US Army and other coalition forces.

By the turn of the century, USMC CH-53Es were serving alongside the delayed OV-22 Osprey and are currently undergoing a major upgrade programme which has led to the introduction of the Hughes AN/AAQ-16 FLIR, Night Vision System and the adaptation of the cockpit to NVG-compatibility. The Sikorsky CH-53E is fulfiling a proud tradition, and is vital to US overseas operations.

HH-53 variants

'Super Jolly'

During Vietnam, the ageing HH-3 proved insufficient to the task of combat rescue – the USAF therefore turned to Sikorsky's H-53, which offered unparalleled power and superior range.

The addition of a refuelling probe set the HH-53 apart from its CH-53 progenitor. This fitment enables the 'Super Jolly' to loiter over potential rescue sites for longer periods of time.

Development of the HH-53B began in September 1966, prompted by the urgent need of the Aerospace Rescue and Recovery Service to supplement its HH-3Es with a more powerful combat rescue helicopter. Changes from the CH-53A were kept to a minimum, but as the main requirement was additional range, a retractable flight refuelling probe was fitted. A jettisonable fuel tank, able to carry 2460 litres (650 US gal), was added to each side and braced to the fuselage by two parallel struts. Three Miniguns and 544 kg (1,200 lb) of armour were added for self-defence.

The HH-53Bs were provided with a rescue hoist, mounted externally above the main door on the starboard side of the forward fuselage. A jungle penetrator and 76 m (250 ft) of steel cable enabled downed aircrews to be recovered in dense jungle areas without the need to land.

Preceded into USAF service by a pair of CH-53As borrowed from the Marine Corps to initiate crew training, the first HH-53Bs were flown on 15 March 1967. Barely five months later, two HH-53Bs were deployed to Southeast Asia to serve with the 37th ARRS at Udorn RTAFB, Thailand. They made their first rescue before the end of 1967 and quickly demonstrated their superiority over the HH-3Es when operating under hot and high conditions. Quickly supplemented by HH-53Cs and afterwards primarily assigned to CONUS-based units, HH-53Bs were operated until the late 1980s.

Super 'Super Jolly'

After rushing up the development of the interim HH-53Bs, Sikorsky refined the design of the Super Jolly to produce 44 HH-53Cs. With delivery to the Aerospace Rescue and Recovery Service commencing in August 1968, the new Super Jolly version was distinguished externally by the absence of parallel bracing struts between the fuselage and the boom supporting the external tanks. This change was made possible after the external tanks of the HH-53Bs resulted in unsatisfactory roll-handling and forced a shift to smaller tanks, with capacity reduced from 2460 to 1703 litres (650 to 450 US gal). Fortunately, the reduction in external tank capacity had no significant impact on mission radius and endurance as the HH-53C relied routinely on inflight-refuelling. A convincing demonstration of the

A rare picture shows water rescue operations from an HH-53C, with a swimmer dropping from the ramp during a low hover. Such operations ensure that the helicopter is in a dangerous position for as little time as possible.

▶

Seen here over Tower Bridge, London, this HH-53C is not in its normal combat environment. There has been a constant HH-53 presence in the UK for the past two decades, with HH-53Cs and, later, MH-53Js located at the USAF's Woodbridge, Bentwaters, Alconbury and Mildenhall bases.

type's remarkable endurance was given from 15–24 August 1970, when two HH-53Cs were refuelled 13 times by a pair of HC-130Ns and, with seven intermediate stops, were flown 14500 km (9,000 miles) from Eglin AFB, USA to Da Nang AB, Vietnam.

Other improvements incorporated during production included the installation of additional armour and the fitting of a more complete set of radios to facilitate communications between the 'Super Jolly' and HC-130 tanker/rescue command post aircraft, fighters providing fire support, and downed aircrews. Changes dictated by combat experience included the

introduction of an experimental RHAW system during the spring of 1972 and the subsequent installation of IR counter-measures pods. The lack of RHAW (radar homing and warning) gear had come to light in 1971 when the North Vietnamese started moving SAMs and radar-guided guns near the DMZ and along portions of the Ho Chi Minh Trail.

While most HH-53Cs were operated in the combat rescue role, those of the 55th ARRS flew in support of every Apollo space mission as their external cargo hook of 9072 kg (20,000 lb) capacity would have enabled them to retrieve the manned capsule in the event of an abort

shortly after launch. Others were assigned to the Air Force Flight Test Center at Edwards AFB and to three Test Squadrons (the 6512th at Edwards AFB, the 6514th at Hill AFB and the 6593rd at Hickam AFB) to recover drones and space capsules. In addition to operating its 'Super Jollies' in support of the military space programme, the Hawaii-based 6593rd Test Squadron also made good use of its HH-53Cs during rescue operations; for example, on 22 March 1979 it saved 19 Japanese fishermen from a vessel burning 128 km (80 miles) south of the island of Hawaii. HH-53Cs remained in USAF service until the late 1980s, when the last were modified as MH-53Js.

Special Forces superlative

Before the entry into service of the HH-53B, it had already become obvious to the USAF that combat rescue helicopters would have to be provided with night/all-weather capability to be able to recover downed aircrews as quickly as possible. Accordingly, a limited-capability Pave Low I system using low-light-level television (LLLTV) was tested at Eglin AFB and was fitted in November 1969 to a 'Super Jolly' of the 40th ARRS at Udorn RTAFB. Unfortunately, Pave Low I proved ineffective and a more reliable system did not become available until 1972. Although still far from being satisfactory under certain operating conditions, the revised system did prove its worth on 21 December 1972 when it enabled the crew of an HH-53C to make the first night combat rescue (the fortunate recipient being the pilot of an F-4J from VMFA-232 that had been shot down over Laos).

After the war ended in Southeast Asia, the ARRS continued to work with the Air Force Systems Command to obtain a more capable night/all-weather system for its 'Super

Jollies'. Designated Pave Low II, the improved package was fitted in June 1975 to a modified HH-53B (66-14433) which, redesignated YHH-53H, underwent system testing at Edwards AFB and operational evaluation by the 1550th ATTW at Kirtland AFB.

Successful evaluation of the YHH-53H Pave Low II led to that helicopter being upgraded to the HH-53H Pave Low III configuration and to the modification of eight HH-53Cs to the same standard. The work was performed at the Naval Air Rework Facility which had been handling overhaul and repair for all H-53s since the onset of the programme. Later, to replace two HH-53Hs lost in training accidents in 1984, two CH-53Cs were fitted with a flight refuelling probe and Pave Low III avionics to bring them up to HH-53H standard.

Delivered in 1979–80, these night/all-weather capable Pave Low III helicopters were fitted with a complex avionics fit, including a Texas Instrument AN/AAQ-10 FLIR, a Canadian Marconi Doppler navigation system, a Texas Instrument AN/APQ-158 TF radar, a Litton inertial navigation system, a computer-projected map display system, RHAW and chaff/flare dispensers. The designation of the Pave Low III helicopters was changed from HH-53H to MH-53H in 1986, when these special operations helicopters were upgraded under the Constant Green programme.

Pave Low III HH-53Hs were first assigned to the 67th ARRS at RAF Woodbridge in 1980, but were soon handed to the 20th SOS, 1st SOW, at Hurlburt Field, Florida. Transferred from TAC to MAC in March 1983, the 1st SOW began supplementing its Pave Low III MH-53H helicopters with Pave Low III Enhanced MH-53Js in late 1987. The Pave Low IV MH-53M, a modified MH-53J, has enhanced defensive capabilities.

Special ops and minesweeping

MH-53E/H/J

Representing the latest and most powerful of the venerable H-53 family is the MH-53 series of highly versatile Special Operations and mine-clearing helicopters in service with the USAF and US Navy.

In a USAF rebuild of two CH-53Cs and eight HH-53B/Cs, the Sikorsky HH-53H Pave (precision avionics vectoring equipment) Low III was fitted with night/all-weather search and rescue equipment. This included an inertial navigation system, Doppler, projected map display, infra-red and terrain-following radar. The HH-53H was a member of a family which had been in service since 1967 and which had, in a number of variants, served so well in Vietnam. However, in 1986, under the Constant Green programme, the Special Forces role was added to this variant and so it was redesignated the MH-53H. This was the first version of the H-53 family to be fully cleared for nocturnal operations, with the crew employing NVGs (Night Vision Goggles).

It was later decided to upgrade the MH-53Hs and several CH-53Cs to MH-53J standard. This was partly due to the poor performance of the Navy RH-53D helicopters in the unsuccessful Eagle Claw American hostage rescue mission, combined with less than total satisfaction with the HH-53H version. The Pave Low III Enhanced MH-53J helicopters are Special Forces aircraft with upgraded Pave Low III night and adverse weather capabilities. They are also fitted with integrated digital avionics for increased reliability. MH-53Js further differ from their predecessors in being fitted with a strengthened transmission to absorb the power of two 3266-kW (4,380-shp) T64-GE-415s, in possessing 454 kg (1,000 lb) of additional armour, and in having

their maximum take-off weight increased from 19050 kg (42,000 lb) to 22680 kg (50,000 lb). They first entered service in 1988.

Above: The US Navy's MH-53 performs the minesweeping role inherited from the RH-53D. The mirrors positioned forward of the cockpit allow the crew to monitor the sled as it is pulled through the water.

Top: A Mildenhall-based Special Forces MH-53J cruises over the English countryside. The advanced Pave Low III system allows the MH-53J to perform low-level flights, even at night or in bad weather, for covert infil/exfil missions into hostile territory.

MH-53s in combat
Since then, USAF MH-53Hs and MH-53Js of the 1st SOW took part in Operation Just Cause in Panama, dropping Navy SEALs ▶

into Panama City. Then in March 1990, they were transferred into the USAF's Special Operations Command.

During Operation Desert Storm, MH-53Js provided navigation and support for the US Army AH-64 Apaches which attacked Iraqi radar defence sites as part of Task Force Normandy on the opening night of the Gulf War. Later in the conflict, they were involved in the insertion of the SAS and US Special Forces teams which then went on to hunt the much-publicised Iraqi 'Scud' missile launchers.

The USAF planned to replace its MH-53Js with the new Bell-Boeing CV-22 Osprey tilt-rotor aircraft, although problems with congressional funding pushed back the entry into service date for that type until 2001. Nevertheless, the MH-53J was able to remain in service until then and even beyond.

Mine-hunter

By combining the airframe and powerplant of the three-engined CH-53E with the minesweeping gear of the RH-53D, Sikorsky created the MH-53E. The MH-53E offers a greatly improved capability as its increased power enables it to drag minesweeping gear through rougher seas than the RH-53D, and its more advanced avionics give it an all-weather capability.

Development of this variant began in 1980 and the prototype first flew a year later. Externally similar to the CH-53E, the MH-53E has been fitted with enlarged sponsons, which enable the internal fuel capacity to be raised from 3850 litres (1,017 US gal) to 12113 litres (3,200 US gal). This gives the MH-53E the ability to sweep for mines with a towed sled for some four hours, while operating 30 minutes from its base. What is more, the addition of an air-air refuelling probe enables the endurance of the helicopter to be extended even further. As with the RH-53D, the MH-53E can deal with mechanical, acoustic and magnetic mines.

MH-53J Pave Low III Enhanced

In 1995 this MH-53J was based at RAF Mildenhall with the 21st SOS 'Dust Devils', as part of the 352nd SOG. It has adopted the new low-IR signature overall grey finish, in place of the green 'European One' camouflage carried previously by AFSOC's MH-53J fleet.

Main rotor
The MH-53J has a 22.02-m (72-ft 3-in) diameter main rotor. The titanium and steel elastomeric rotor head can be folded for full shipboard capability.

External fuel tanks
Two 1893-litre (500-US gal) jettisonable fuel tanks are an almost permanent fixture on the MH-53J. Those MH-53Js converted from HH-53Bs retain the latter's braced external fuel tank installation.

MH-53 genesis
The first Pave Low was the HH-53B Pave Low I, which underwent limited trials in Vietnam towards the end of the US involvement. This experience motivated the Aerospace Rescue and Recovery Service, along with AFMC, to develop the Pave Low II, which first flew as the YHH-53H in 1975. Production HH-53Hs were equipped as Pave Low IIIs, with AAQ-10 FLIR, APQ-158 terrain-following radar (TFR), refuelling probes and many of the other systems fitted to today's MH-53Js. HH-53Hs became MH-53Hs in 1986, and the MH-53J Pave Low III Enhanced upgrade was initiated in 1987.

Armament
The Pave Low III Enhanced carries three guns; two are 7.62-mm (0.3-in) Miniguns which are mounted on either side of the fuselage, while mounted on the rear ramp is the tried and trusted 12.7-mm (0.5-in) heavy machine-gun. Although its rate of fire is less than that of the Minigun, the '50 cal' has a greater range and much greater weight of shot. Up to 450 rounds (including armour-piercing) can be carried.

Powerplant
The standard engines fitted to the MH-53J are two 3266-kW (4,380-shp) T64-GE-415s with an uprated transmission. This is a significant improvement over the 2125-kW (2,850-shp), T64-GE-6-equipped CH-53A, but is overshadowed by the three-engined CH-53E whose three T64-GE-614 provide a total power output of 9789 kW (13,140 shp).

Sikorsky H-60 Black Hawk/Seahawk

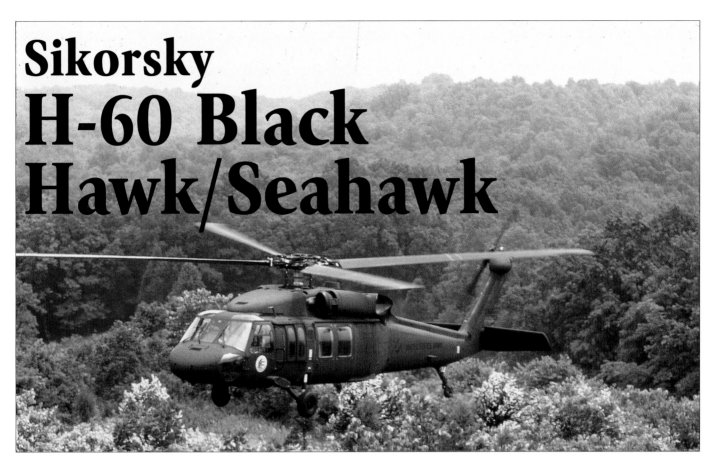

Sikorsky Black Hawks and Seahawks were among the unsung heroes of the Gulf War. Combining manoeuvrability, versatility and reliability, the 'Hawks' have revolutionised the deployment of helicopters over the battlefield.

Above: With over 1,000 aircraft now in service, the Black Hawk is the backbone of any US Army air assault. Flying low with cabin doors open, these UH-60As are seen on a training exercise in the United States.

The request for proposals (RFP) for the Utility Tactical Transport Aircraft System (UTTAS) was issued in January 1972. The new utility helicopter was required to carry squad-sized units like the UH-1 Huey, but had to be capable of doing so in high temperatures and/or at high altitude. It also had to be highly manoeuvrable, more reliable, and more easily maintainable than the UH-1. Experience gained in Vietnam emphasised improved crashworthiness and survivability, with main rotor blades capable of absorbing hits from 23-mm (0.9-in) shells, and internal fuel tanks able to absorb hits from 12.7-mm (0.50-in) shells. Further, the new UTTAS was required to be easily transportable, so that one could be airlifted in a C-130, two in a C-141, or six in a C-5 – preparation for air transportation

was to take no more than 6½ hours.

A winning design

For Sikorsky which, by the end of 1971, had already produced some 5,000 helicopters, winning the UTTAS competition was of the utmost importance. To do so, the Sikorsky design team adopted a strategy calling for a thorough understanding of US Army requirements and full compliance with RFP conditions; the company aggressively developed the 'right' technology, undertaking full-scale demonstrations of advanced technology systems and components. To undertake this testing, Sikorsky flew five technology demonstrators: three CH-53Ds, an S-67 and an S-61. Each was fitted with components that were to be utilised on Sikorsky's design. After extensive testing, the

The addition of the ESSS pylons to the Black Hawk allows the helicopter to carry either extra fuel or weapons. Up to 16 Hellfire missiles can be carried.

prototype UH-60A flew for the first time on 17 October 1974, in the event beating its rival, Boeing Vertol's YUH-61A, by one month. Although problems were encountered early on in the flight-test programme, the US Army was impressed enough

by the Black Hawk's performance to place an order for the helicopter on 23 December 1976. Minor structural changes were made to the Black Hawk's rear fin and rotor head to improve its handling in the hover.

HELICOPTERS

By far the most significant foreign operator in terms of sheer numbers of Black Hawks and Seahawks in service is Australia. Initially, S-70A-9s (foreground) served with the RAAF, but they were subsequently turned over to the army for the troop transport role. The S-70Bs (background) are equipped with RAN-specified equipment which includes an internally-mounted AQS-504 MAD system and other sonar-processing equipment.

In the army now

Deliveries of the Black Hawk to the Army began on 31 October 1978 and, following service trials and initial training of crews at Fort Rucker, Alabama, and maintenance personnel at Fort Eustis, Virginia, the UH-60As entered service with the 101st Airborne Division (Air Assault) in June 1979. Four aircraft were delivered for Force Development Test and Experimentation (FDTE) at Fort Campbell, Kentucky. The UH-60A was a far more capable combat helicopter than the UH-1H in terms of crew survivability in the event of a crash, and had a much improved performance in 'hot-and-high' conditions. With the addition of the External Stores Support System (ESSS) shoulder-mounted/fuselage-braced pylons to carry either fuel tanks or weapons, the fitting of Hover Infra-Red Suppressor Subsystem (HIRSS) to cool the engine exhaust and reduce IR detectability, the advent of the more powerful UH-60L variant, and the installation of upgraded countermeasures systems, the Army Black Hawk has evolved into the world's leading utility helicopter. It has also been supplied to a host of countries, many of which – such as Australia (Hawker de Havilland) and Japan (Mitsubishi) – have obtained permission from Sikorsky to build the Black Hawk locally under licence.

Although intended to fulfil the role of a utility helicopter, the potential of the Black Hawk saw the development of a number of Special Operations variants for both the US Army and USAF, the latter being keen to find a suitable helicopter for the CSAR role. Equipped with a nose-mounted IFR probe and sophisticated avionics, these MH-60G Pave Hawks and MH-60Ks are tasked with operating deep behind enemy lines in all weathers. During the Gulf War one Black Hawk, a UH-60A, was shot down during a rescue mission while trying to retrieve an F-16 pilot from Iraqi territory. Only three of the six crew were to survive and all were made PoWs, one of them – Flight Surgeon, Maj. Rhonda L. Cornum – holding the dubious distinction of becoming America's first female PoW.

By far the most high-profile role for the Black Hawk is that carried out by the USMC's HMX-1 at Quantico. Under the designation VH-60N, the two helicopters are configured for VIP transport for the President of the United States and his immediate aides.

Navalised variants

In response to the light airborne multi-purpose system (LAMPS) III requirement, Sikorsky proposed a navalised variant of the Black Hawk with an over-the-horizon search and strike capability for the latest ASW frigates and destroyers, partnering the Kaman SH-2 Seasprite which served on earlier vessels. Sikorsky was awarded the development contract for the Seahawk in September 1977. The Army's decision to adopt the UH-60 was seen as a major factor in influencing the Navy to choose the S-70B Seahawk.

The Seahawk retained an 83 per cent commonality with the UH-60A, but introduced some important features including anti-corrosion treatment on the airframe and

Black Hawks in the midst of the storm

The UH-60 saw widespread service during the Gulf War, with the US Army alone deploying approximately 400 Black Hawks to Saudi Arabia. The ground war began on 24 February 1991, the largest single lift in air assault history involving more than 300 aircraft, many of which were UH-60s. During the course of the war, three UH-60s were lost, although only one was due to ground fire. Also serving in the campaign were ship-based Seahawks from both the US and Australian navies.

engines. With these structural modifications came a host of avionics equipment dedicated to the detection of enemy submarines and, in a secondary role, a fuselage-mounted hoist for rescue operations. Entering front-line service in 1983, the Seahawk has since been steadily upgraded in parallel with the vessels it is intended to attack with its anti-ship missiles and depth charges.

A follow-on variant to the Seahawk, the SH-60F Ocean Hawk, entered service with the US Navy in 1991. Intended to operate from the US Navy's super carriers, the Ocean Hawk utilises a Bendix AQS-13F dipping sonar in place of air-dropped sonobuoys. Many of the components necessary for helicopter operations from small decks have been deleted to allow extra rescue equipment to be carried during air operations from the carrier deck.

Foreign/civilian service

Many countries' armed forces found themselves in a similar position to the United States, in that they were looking for a suitable utility helicopter to replace their ageing fleet. Sikorsky was therefore eager to market both the Black Hawk and Seahawk globally. Under the company designation S-70, Sikorsky sold the helicopter throughout the world, with many customers electing to obtain a licence to allow them to build the helicopter locally. Some countries, such as Japan, fitted a host of indigenous equipment to the Seahawks, to enable them to operate in the anti-submarine role. Other operators, such as Colombia and the Philippines, armed their aircraft for anti-drug operations. Similarly, the USCG, a long-time operator of the HH-60J Jayhawk, is currently proposing to arm its fleet for anti-narcotic operations.

The Black Hawk has been adopted by a number of countries for operation by both civilian and paramilitary organisations. Operators such as Turkey and the Republic of Korea have equipped their police forces with the S-70A and UH-60P, respectively.

Westland Commando and Sea King HC.Mk 4

Sea King assault versions

A land-based transport version of the Sea King was first projected in 1972, and it was soon named **Commando**. Egypt placed the first order for the type, which emerged in **Commando Mk 1** form as something of an interim type. It was, in reality, not a Commando as such, but a basic troop-carrying version of the initial Sea King HAS.Mk 1, with increased fuel capacity. The first Commando flew initially on 12 September 1973, and the aircraft were delivered from 29 January 1974.

Commando Mk 2 and 3

With strongest Commando sales prospects in the Middle and Far East, it became clear that the helicopter's performance would have to be maximised to cope with 'hot-and-high' conditions. Thus, Westland combined the airframe of the Commando with the H.1400-1 engines and six-

bladed tail rotor of the Sea King HAS.Mk 2 to produce the **Commando Mk 2**. The first Commando Mk 2 first flew on 16 January 1975 and was bought by Egypt. Qatar placed an order for three **Commando Mk 2A** helicopters in 1974, these being generally identical to the Egyptian machines. Qatar also ordered a VIP version, designated as the **Commando Mk 2C**. The **Commando Mk 2E** is a somewhat different machine, being a dedicated autonomous EW platform, equipped with the Italian Selenia/Elettronica IHS-6 integrated ESM/ECM system. Four were built for Egypt following a 1978 order.

The **Commando Mk 3** was intended to perform utility and ASV duties. The aircraft appear to carry Exocet ASMs as standard, but can carry a range of other weapons. The first Commando Mk 3 flew on 14 June 1982.

Sea King HC.Mk 4

It was not until 1978 that the Royal Navy asked Westland to study a Commando variant to replace its assault-transport Wessex HU.Mk 5s. The RN aircraft (designated **Sea King HC.Mk 4**) were based on the Sea King HAS.Mk 2 and retain folding main rotors and tail rotor pylons. The aircraft have the same extended cabin as other Commandos and SAR Sea Kings as well as the standard Commando Mk 2 undercarriage.

The Sea King HC.Mk 4 has seen the most action among Royal Navy Sea King variants and NAVSTAR GPS was added for Operation Granby, along with various defences. Door guns are routinely fitted.

The first Sea King HC.Mk 4 flew for the first time on 26 September 1979. Some 42 Sea King HC.Mk 4s were built. The first batch of 10 aircraft was available for use in the Falklands, along with some of the second-batch aircraft. The HC.Mk 4 has proved to be a popular test and trials platform.

SPECIFICATION	
Westland Commando Mk 2	maximum payload
Type: twin-engined medium-assault helicopter	**Weights:** operating empty 5620 kg (12,390 lb); maximum take-off 9752 kg (21,500 lb)
Powerplant: two Rolls-Royce Gnome H.1400-1T turboshaft engines each rated at 1238 kW (1,660 shp) for take-off and 1092 kW (1,465 shp) for continuous running	**Dimensions:** main rotor diameter 18.9 m (62 ft); length overall, rotors turning 22.15 m (72 ft 8 in); height overall 5.13 m (16 ft 10 in) with rotors turning; main rotor disc area 280.47 m² (3,019.07 sq ft)
Performance: never exceed speed 226 km/h (140 mph) at sea level; maximum climb rate 619 m (2,030 ft) per minute at sea level; range 396 km (246 miles) with	**Payload:** 28 fully equipped troops, or up to 3629 kg (8,000 lb) of freight

South Africa's Atlas CSH-2 Rooivalk was based on engineering elements of the AS330 Puma and developed over a long period of time as an adaptable, multi-role, all-weather attack and battlefield support helicopter.

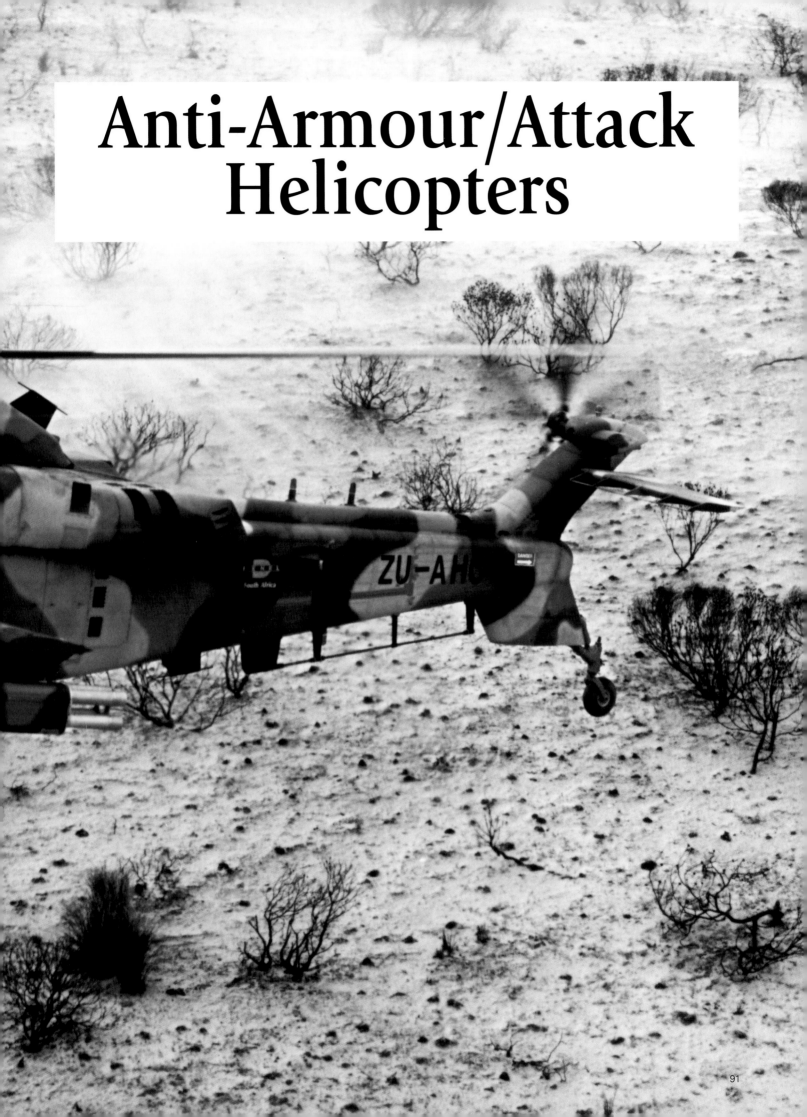

Anti-Armour/Attack Helicopters

Aérospatiale
SA 341 Gazelle

Armed scout

The Anglo-French Gazelle has proved a useful and popular light battlefield helicopter and this graceful aircraft has seen action in several conflicts, with only its fragility generating any real criticism.

Following the success of the Alouette II, Sud Aviation began work on a new helicopter that would be faster and more manoeuvrable than its predecessor. Turbomeca, the local turboshaft engine manufacturer, provided part of the formula with a more powerful engine but the Gazelle benefited most from a 1964 agreement with Bölkow of West Germany for joint development of a glass-fibre rotor blade and an associated rigid rotor head. A new development for the time, composite-material rotors ushered in a breakthrough in blade construction through their ability to combine lightness, with strength, resistance to damage, reduced maintenance requirements and an extended fatigue life.

A fenestron was chosen as the tail rotor while the Gazelle's cockpit was of a semi-monocoque frame. Alloy honeycomb panels are used liberally through the central and rear sections of the cabin, whereas the boom and tail are produced from sheet metal.

What was originally known as the Sud X-300 became the SA 340 by the time of its maiden flight on 7 April 1967. The aircraft became the Sud Gazelle in July 1969, but only until 1 January 1970 when Sud was absorbed into the new Aérospatiale. However, further problems meant that service entrance was delayed further.

French service

The first examples of the Gazelle entered Aviation Légère de l'Armée de Terre (ALAT) service in 1973 and these gradually began to replace the Alouette II. The original aircraft were of a basic design and were equipped with an Astazou III engine, limiting their take-of weight to 1800 kg (3,968 lb). However, later that year, Aérospatiale flew the prototype SA 342 and upon entry to service, the SA 342M (as it was designated in ALAT service) had an improved take-off weight of 1900 kg (4,189 lb) thanks to its Astazou XIVM engine. In 1985, Aérospatiale began delivering the further improved SA 342L.

The nimble and agile Gazelle exists in ALAT service today in many variants: the basic SA 341F Gazelle is used for training, VIP transport and scouting. The SA 341F2 Gazelle/Canon, with an M621 20-mm (0.79-in) cannon, is used for fire-suppression and anti-helicopter missions. The SA 342ML1 Gazelle ATAM (Air-To-Air Missile) is armed with four MATRA/BAe Dynamics Mistral AATCPs (Air-Air Très Courte Portée; short-range air-to-air). The anti-tank SA 342M Gazelle HOT is armed with four Euromissile HOT missiles able to destroy any armoured vehicles at a range of up to 4000 m (2½ miles). This variant will be totally withdrawn from service in the next two years and partially replaced by the Gazelle Viviane, the latest version of the proven Gazelle. The SA 342M1 Gazelle Viviane is fitted with a night-capable laser rangefinder/thermal imaging sight for the HOT missile and with Eurocopter Ecureuil rotor blades to compensate for the increased take-off weight. The Gazelles will start to be replaced in 2003, when the first Eurocopter Tigre helicopters are delivered. Their relatively low cost, simplicity, ease of maintenance and good characteristics have made the Gazelle a popular choice for several other countries, and this helicopter is still highly regarded by its crews, who praise its remarkable agility, its low visual, radar and infra-red signatures and the unrestricted field of view offered by the canopy.

ALAT Gazelles fought successfully in the Gulf War, firing HOT missiles at Iraqi armour.

British production

Under the terms of an 1967 agreement, Westland was granted a licence to build Gazelles. The first deliveries were handed over to the Army Air Corps in 1973 and by the time the production line finished in 1983 it had contributed 282 aircraft. All except 12 (10 for civilian use and two for the

SPECIFICATION

Aérospatiale (Westland) SA 342M Gazelle	**Weights:** empty 2935 kg (2,000 lb); loaded 2100 kg (4,620 lb)
Type: five-seat utility helicopter	**Dimensions:** main rotor diameter 10.50 m (34 ft 5 in); length 11.97 m (34 ft 3 in); height 43.15 m (10 ft 4 in); rotor disc area 86.5 m² (931 sq ft)
Powerplant: one 640-kW (860-hp) Turbomeca Astazou IIA turboshaft	
Performance: maximum speed 310 km/h (192 mph); climb rate 731 m (2,400 ft) per minute; service ceiling 4100 m (13,488 ft); range 670 km (415 miles)	**Armament:** 36-mm (1.42-in) rockets, 20-mm (0.79-in) cannon, AS.11, TWO, HOT, Mistrale and other missiles

An ALAT SA 342 pops above the treeline to fire a HOT missile. HOT is a Franco-German heavy anti-tank weapon, tube-launched and wire-guided.

Qatari police) were for home military use, including pilot training models for the FAA and RAF.

Today, the Gazelle's presence in the UK has markedly diminished, the RAF's examples have been replaced by AS 355F1 Twin Squirrels while in FAA and Army service, the Lynx has supplemented many of the Gazelle's former roles. Army and Royal Marine Gazelles were deployed to the Falklands Islands during the war. While their presence was invaluable, they proved vulnerable to small arms fire.

Gazelles abroad

Over 1,500 Gazelles were eventually built with some 40 countries and 29 armed forces receiving the type. Today, 21 nations including Serbia, Cameroon, Egypt, Ireland, Libya, UAE and Yugoslavia continue to operate the Gazelle.

Many have seen considerable service: Iraqi Gazelles were used against Iranian troops/armour during the first Gulf War, while Syrian Gazelles fought unsuccessfully against the Israelis during the 1982 invasion of Lebanon. Indeed, one Gazelle was captured by the Israelis and repainted in that nation's colours. Yugoslavia and Serbia had a number of Soko-built examples but after a decade of conflict, their exact number is hard to determine.

Despite its age, the Gazelle is still heavily represented in several significant air arms. It may no longer meet the standards of battleworthiness demanded from today's combat helicopters, but in all other aspects it is a highly regarded military aircraft.

Gazelle AH.Mk 1

The armies of France and the UK are still the principal operators of the Gazelle, both employing the type in the scout/observation role. This example was based at the Army Aviation Centre at Middle Wallop, where it was used for training by either the Basic Rotary Squadron or No.670 Squadron, its training role denoted by the Dayglo panels for high conspicuity. Today the task is undertaken by Squirrels.

Stores
In certain operational areas, stores would be carried on a boom counterbalanced across the helicopter. Equipment includes the Spectrolab SX-16 NightSun, a Canadair reconnaissance pod, 10.2-cm (4-in) flares and SNEB 68-mm (2.7-in) rocket pods.

Fenestron tail rotor
Thirteen light alloy blades make up the tail rotor, shrouded by the tail fin, and pitch change is obtained by movement of the blades. The disadvantage of the fenestron is that a great deal of power is used in the hover, but the flight safety advantage of the shrouded rotor was seen, at the time to outweigh this drawback.

Rear passenger seats
Bench-type seats for three people are provided; behind is additional kit stowage space. These can be removed and the left-hand forward seat stowed for the carriage of stretchers.

VHF/FM homer
The ARC 340 has twin dipole aerials for radio homing; direction indication is given in the cockpit on the attitude indicator. The same radio has a communications aerial under the tailcone.

Agusta
A129 Mangusta

Lightweight battlefield helicopter

Conceived in response to an Italian army requirement of the mid-1970s, the **A 129 Mangusta** (mongoose) was the first dedicated attack helicopter to be designed, built and deployed by a European country. It was also the first in the world to be built around an advanced MIL-STD 1553B digital databus, which allows a high degree of automation, considerably reducing the crew workload. The first A 129 prototype made its official maiden flight on 15 September 1983, at Cascina Costa.

Mangusta orders

The original Italian requirement had been for 100 Mangustas, in distinct anti-tank and scout versions, but as the threat of all-out war in Europe receded, the final order was cut back to 60 A 129s. In the event, a total of 45 A 129s was delivered to AVES (Aviazione Escercito – Italian army aviation) between October 1990 and 1992, when production was stopped. Later, funding problems, and changing operational needs forced the Italian army to re-evaluate its requirement for dedicated anti-tank helicopters.

The need for a more multi-role helicopter was reinforced when Mangustas were deployed on UN peacekeeping duties to Somalia between 1992 and 1995. Hence, the **Mangusta International**, whose most significant changes include an undernose 20-mm

Italy's Cavalleria Dell'Aria (air cavalry, as AVES became in 2000) may eventually operate an all-Mangusta International attack fleet.

(0.79-in) cannon and 1016-kW (1,362-shp) AlliedSignal LHTEC CTS800-2 turboshafts.

A long section of conduit, scabbed onto the port side of Mangusta International's fuselage, carriers the ammunition feed for the 20-mm (0.79-in) cannon.

SPECIFICATION

Agusta A 129 Mangusta
Type: two-seat lightweight anti-tank and scout helicopter
Powerplant: two Piaggio (Rolls-Royce) Gem 2-2 Mk 1004D turboshaft engines, each rated at 615 kW (825 shp)
Performance: maximum speed 259 km/h (161 mph) at sea level; radius 100 km (62 miles) for a 1-hour 30-minute patrol
Weights: empty 2529 kg (5,575 lb); maximum take-off 4100 kg (9,039 lb)

Dimensions: main rotor diameter 11.9 m (39 ft ½ in); wing span 3.2 m (10 ft 6 in); length overall 14.29 m (46 ft 10½ in) with rotors turning; main rotor disc area 111.22 m² (1,197.2 sq ft)
Armament: maximum weapon load 1200 kg (2,646 lb), including up to eight TOW-2A anti-tank missiles, 52 70-mm (2.75-in) rockets or 81-mm (3.19-in) SNIA-BPD Medusa rockets or 12.7-mm (0.5-in) gun pods

Bell **AH-1 HueyCobra** and **SeaCobra**

Attack helicopter

Above: This 'Whiskey Cobra' (AH-1W) carries a standard USMC weapon load of two four-round BGM-71 TOW missile launchers and a pair of LAU-68 rocket pods.

Right: Until the AH-1Z has entered service in sufficient numbers, the AH-1W remains the USMC's only attack helicopter. The Corps could find no funds to purchase Apache.

On 7 September 1965 Bell flew the prototype of the world's first dedicated attack helicopter. Based on the Model 204 utility helicopter, the **Model 209** introduced a new slim fuselage with a fighter-type cockpit. The pilot sits high in the rear with a co-pilot/gunner lower in the front directing the fire of a wide range of weapons mounted on lateral stub wings or under the nose. The **AH-1G HueyCobra** went into production in 1966 and over 1,000 were delivered in the first four years. The AH-1G saw extensive service in Vietnam.

Seacobra

The **AH-1J SeaCobra** was the first twin-engined version, for the US Marine Corps, with a 1343-ekW (1,800-shp) T400 installation; in 1974–75 a batch of 202 with TOW missiles was supplied to Iran. The **AH-1Q** was an interim US Army version with TOW missiles, produced by conversion of AH-1Gs, while the **AH-1S**, fitted with a 1343-ekW (1,800-shp) T53-703 engine, was a production HueyCobra with TOW capability and other improvements. A number of AH-1Qs was also modified to -1S standards, while AH-1S aircraft were themselves modified into a number of variants. In addition, the **AH-1P** was produced by conversion of AH-1S helicopters with flat-plate canopies and other revisions. This confusing situation was resolved in 1987, when all surviving US Army HueyCobras were updated to a common AH-1F standard.

The USMC's SeaCobra is today represented by the **AH-1W SuperCobra**. This Hellfire-toting machine will be upgraded in a similar manner to the USMC UH-1N fleet, to **AH-1Z** standard.

Below: Japan maintains a large force of AH-1S attack helicopters. The aircraft may be replaced in the future by an attack derivative of the indigenous Kawasaki OH-1 helicopter.

SPECIFICATION

Bell AH-1W SuperCobra
Type: two-seat close support, attack and anti-armour helicopter
Powerplant: two 1212-kW (1,625-shp) General Electric T700-GE-401 turboshafts; transmission limited to 1515 kW (2,032 shp) for take-off and 1286 kW (1,725 shp) for continuous running
Performance: maximum level speed 'clean' at sea level 282 km/h (175 mph); service ceiling more than 3660 m (12,000 ft); range 635 km (395 miles) with standard fuel
Weights: empty 4627 kg (10,200 lb); maximum take-off 6691 kg (14,750 lb)

Dimensions: main rotor diameter 14.63 m (48 ft); fuselage length 13.87 m (45 ft 6 in), height overall 4.32 m (14 ft 2 in); main rotor disc area 168.11 m² (1,809.56 sq ft)
Armament: one chin-mounted M 197 three-barrelled 20-mm (0.79-in) cannon; maximum ordnance 1119 kg (2,466 lb) including eight TOW or Hellfire ATGMs, seven- or 19-shot 70-mm (2.75-in) rocket pods, 127-mm (5-in) Zuni rockets, cluster munitions, napalm, AIM-9 and Stinger IR AAMs and drop tanks; qualified for AGM-65 Maverick AGMs

AH-1 Single-engined variants

The basic models of the AH-1 formed the backbone of US Army Aviation's combat units during the 1970s and the 1970s. Though the HueyCobra has now all but disappeared from US service, it continues to be a front-line type in several other countries.

AH-1G

The AH-1G was the first production variant of the HueyCobra. The 'G' suffix was applied by the Army which treated the AH-1 as simply a follow-on from existing UH-1 Iroquois variants. Two YAH-1G prototypes were built, an initial batch of 100 aircraft was ordered on 13 April 1966 and the type entered service in June 1967. The Army eventually acquired 1,119 AH-1Gs.

The AH-1G closely resembled the Model 209 prototype, but from the outset was built with a fixed skid landing gear. Power was supplied by a 1043-kW (1,400-shp) T53-L-13 turboshaft, derated to 819.5 kW (1,100 shp). A few early production aircraft had the tail rotor mounted to port, but the bulk of production aircraft had this position reversed. The helicopters had a distinctive rounded, conical nose which, in early versions, housed landing lights behind a transparent fairing. In later model AH-1Gs the lights were moved to retractable housings under the nose. Initially, the AH-1G was armed with an Emerson Electric TAT-102A turret, mounting a single GAU-2B 7.62-mm (0.3-in) Minigun and 8,000 rounds of ammunition. The turret could be slewed through a 230° arc, elevated to 25° or depressed to 60°.

The single-weapon TAT-102A was later replaced by the XM28 turret which  could house a GAU-2B, and an XM129 40-mm (1.57-in) grenade launcher with 300 rounds. Experience in Vietnam led, from 1969 onwards, to an increase in firepower through the addition of a podded M35 six-barrelled 20-mm (0.79-in) cannon under the port underwing pylon. Some AH-1Gs also employed 70-mm (2.75-in) rockets.

Seen firing a salvo of unguided rockets during armament tests, this AH-1G is an early production example with the clear nose cone.

The AH-1G had no sensor or target acquisition systems and was a daylight-only operations aircraft. Several trials sensor fits were flown by AH-1G testbeds, including the SMASH (Southeast Asia Multi-sensor Armament Sub-system for HueyCobra) system, which combined an early FLIR and moving target radar, and the CONFICS (CObra Night FIre Control System), which used a low-light level TV. A single JAH-1G went on to become an important testbed for new sensor and weapons systems, such as the Hellfire missile.

The AH-1G had a successful combat career in Vietnam and most surviving aircraft were later rebuilt to AH-1S, AH-1E or AH-1F standard. Between 1981 and 1986 a number of modified aircraft, stripped of all armament and armour, served with the US Customs Service. Known as 'Snakes', they were used to intercept drug-running aircraft. Despite the large numbers built, the only export customers for the AH-1G were Spain and Israel. The Spanish navy took delivery of eight M35-armed aircraft (known locally as Z.14s) in 1972 and they served until 1985. Israel took delivery of 12 aircraft, where were later replaced by AH-1Fs.

The first prototype differed from all other HueyCobras in having a retractable landing gear. Over a six-year career, the helicopter was up-graded to virtual AH-1G standard.

AH-1Q

The AH-1Q was derived from the AH-1G but had a significantly improved combat capability through the addition of the BGM-71 TOW missile. In 1973 the Army took delivery of eight pre-production AH-1Qs, modified to carry the nose-mounted M65 stabilised TOW sight and four-tube TOW launchers under each pylon. The AH-1Q retained the M28 chin turret and could also carry 70-mm (2.75-in) rocket pods. Just 85 production-standard AH-1Qs were delivered, beginning in June 1975, before the introduction of the AH-1S.

Improved AH-1S

The AH-1S became the definitive late-model Cobra variant and has itself spawned a confusing number of subvariants. The addition of new weapons and systems to the AH-1Q had left it seriously underpowered so the most important change to the AH-1S was the installation of an uprated 1341-kW (1,800-shp) T53-L-703 engine. A single YAH-1R prototype was built to test the new engine, the prototype later being redesignated YAH-1S.

The AH-1Q/S was intended to bridge the gap between the cancellation of the Lockheed AH-56 Cheyenne and the introduction of the AH-64 Apache. The first service version was the AH-1S Improved (also known as the AH-1S Modified). All remaining AH-1Qs and 198 AH-1Gs were converted to this standard, and the type entered service in 1974. The AH-1S Modified/Improved airframe had several changes over the AH-1Q, including extra cooling scoops over the main engine intake and RWR antennas. Aircraft also usually carried the 'sugar-scoop' IR-suppressant shroud above the engine exhaust. As other versions of the AH-1S were introduced, these first aircraft became known simply as AH-1Ss.

AH-1S (Production) – later AH-1P

The 100 new-build AH-1S Production-standard Cobras delivered to the US Army between 1977 and 1978 featured several small changes to the Improved/Modified aircraft. Most important of these was the addition of flat-plate cockpit canopies that reduced reflected glint off  the aircraft. These aircraft retained the M28 turret, TOW missiles and associated M65 sight. They featured improved flight systems and avionics that better enabled them to undertake low-level nap-of-the-earth (NoE) flying. From the 67th aircraft onwards the AH-1S Production was fitted with tapered Kaman K-747 main rotor blades. In 1998 the AH-1S Production became the AH-1P.

Turkish Army Aviation operates approximately 30 (of 36 delivered in 1992) AH-1Ps alongside its twin-engined AH-1Ws, as part of the attack helicopter battalion based at Ankara-Güvercinlik. In 1994 Bahrain took delivery of 14 Cobras, believed to be AH-1Ps (but also reported as AH-1Es), including some dual control aircraft. They form a single squadron of the Bahrain Amiri Air Force based at Shaikh Isa AB.

AH-1S ECAS (Enhanced Cobra Armament System)/Up-Gun AH-1S – later AH-1E

The second phase of the new-build AH-1S programme added a new M197 three-barrelled 20-mm (0.79-in) cannon in an undernose Universal turret, replacing the M28. The M197, based on the M61 Vulcan cannon, was equipped with 750 rounds of ammunition. The Up-Gun aircraft had a small but distinctive bulge housing a 10-kVA alternator in the inlet for the port engine. Most aircraft also gained wire-strike protection cutters above and below the cockpit. Ninety-eight AH-1S ECAS aircraft were delivered between 1978 and 1979. In 1988, when the whole AH-1 designation system was reorganised, the AH-1S Up-Gun became the AH-1E.

AH-1S Modernized – later AH-1F

The final stage of the US Army's AH-1S upgrade programme resulted in 99 new-build AH-1S Modernized aircraft, plus 50 for the Army National Guard and 378 rebuilt from AH-1Gs. Deliveries took place between 1979 and 1986. The Modernized aircraft included all the improvements of previous versions, plus a new cockpit HUD, better IR suppressor, new IFF, ALQ-144 IR-jammer and a Marconi air-data sensor arm mounted on the starboard fuselage side. Many aircraft were fitted with the AN/AVR-2 laser-warning system. A bulged fairing for a laser-spot tracker, which was never actually fitted, was added to the leading-edge of the rotor mast sail.

The AH-1S Modernized/AH-1F has become the most widely exported single-engined Cobra variant. Today it is in service in Israel, Japan, Jordan, Pakistan, South Korea and Thailand. Japan is unique among export Cobra operators as its aircraft were built under licence. Fuji Heavy Industries has supplied 89 AH-1Fs to the Japan Ground Self Defence Force, and two AH-1Ss were also acquired directly from Bell.

In Israeli service the Cobra is known as the *Tsefa* (viper) and 64 aircraft have been delivered to the IDF/AF since 1981. They are believed to be in service with Nos 160, 161 and 162 Sqns, based at Palmachim and

TAH-1S – TAH-1F

Dual controls were fitted to 41 AH-1Gs upgraded to AH-1S Modernized standards, for use as pilot trainers at the Army Aviation School, Fort Rucker. When the Cobra designations were changed in 1988 these aircraft became known as TAH-1Fs. They were most readily identifiable by large high-visibility red panels on the side of the fuselage (common to all US Army training helicopters) and white three-character codes. All TAH-1Fs have now been withdrawn from use.

Hatzerim ABs. The Royal Jordanian Air Force took delivery of 24 aircraft, from 1985, which are currently based at Amman with Nos 10 and 12 Sqns. Pakistan's Army Aviation Corps acquired 20 AH-1Fs in 1984 and they fly with Nos 31 and 32 Sqns, at Multan. The Republic of Korea Army operates a mix of approximately 68 AH-1F HueyCobras and AH-1J SeaCobras. The AH-1Fs were delivered from 1988 onwards, joining the AH-1Js that had been in service since 1978. Since 1990, the Royal Thai Army Air Division has operated four AH-1Fs from its main base at Lop Buri.

TH-1S 'Surrogate'

To train AH-64 Apache crews to operate the Apache sensor system, 15 early-model and unarmed AH-1Ss were fitted with the AH-64's PNVS (Pilot's Night Vision System) FLIR above the nose. These aircraft entered service at Ft Rucker in 1984/85, but have now all been retired.

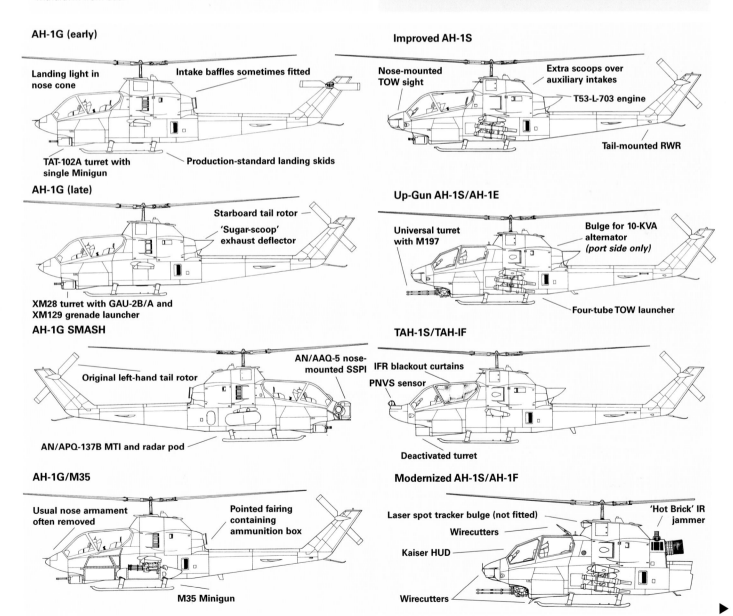

AH-1G (early)

Landing light in nose cone

Intake baffles sometimes fitted

TAT-102A turret with single Minigun

Production-standard landing skids

AH-1G (late)

Starboard tail rotor

'Sugar-scoop' exhaust deflector

XM28 turret with GAU-2B/A and XM129 grenade launcher

AH-1G SMASH

Original left-hand tail rotor

AN/AAQ-5 nose-mounted SSPI

AN/APQ-137B MTI and radar pod

AH-1G/M35

Usual nose armament often removed

Pointed fairing containing ammunition box

M35 Minigun

Improved AH-1S

Nose-mounted TOW sight

Extra scoops over auxiliary intakes

T53-L-703 engine

Tail-mounted RWR

Up-Gun AH-1S/AH-1E

Universal turret with M197

Bulge for 10-KVA alternator *(port side only)*

Four-tube TOW launcher

TAH-1S/TAH-IF

IFR blackout curtains

PNVS sensor

Deactivated turret

Modernized AH-1S/AH-1F

Laser spot tracker bulge (not fitted)

'Hot Brick' IR jammer

Wirecutters

Kaiser HUD

Wirecutters

AH-1 twin-engined variants

Developed to meet the needs of the US Marine Corps in the late 1960s, the original twin-engined AH-1 has been constantly developed over the years, the main benefactor being the original customer.

AH-1J SeaCobra

As originally envisaged, the AH-1J was to have been a single-engined aircraft, similar to the AH-1G but with a rotor brake (deemed essential for shipborne operations), US Navy standard avionics and heavier armament, as well as better corrosion protection. The AH-1G was already in limited service with the USMC, and the logistic and political advantages of a common American powerplant initially overrode the Marines' traditional desire for a twin-engined machine. The 1968 Tet Offensive generated the need for massive attrition-replacement helicopter orders, and the Marines were given the go-ahead to replace their single-engined Hueys and Cobras with twin-engined machines, albeit that the engine was Canadian.

This allowed the Marines to procure a much more capable aircraft, with a Pratt & Whitney Canada T400-CP-400 (PT6T-4) turboshaft engine and a three-barrelled M197 cannon in a new undernose turret. The new weapon was basically a lightened version of the well-known six-barrelled M61, and came with an internally-mounted ammunition box containing 750 rounds. The gun had a nominal rate of fire of 750 rpm, but individual bursts were limited to 16 rounds.

The T400-CP-400, also used by the UH-1N and the Bell 212, consisted of a pair of PT6s driving a single shaft through a common gearbox. The new powerplant was appreciably more powerful than the original Lycoming T53, but its main advantage lay in the fact that it offered genuine twin-engine reliability. Since the rotor system was unchanged, the AH-1J produced more power than could be used (1141 kW/1,530 shp max continuous), but this gave a useful engine-out hover capability.

The first AH-1J was handed over in October 1969, and four were sent to Patuxent River for evaluation in July 1970. The first AH-1Js were sent to Vietnam in February 1971, where they quickly proved their worth under combat conditions. During their subsequent service, the Marines' AH-1Js were cleared to carry a wider variety of ordnance than Army Cobra variants, and all now have revised wing pylons and a new canopy-ejection system. Some surviving AH-1Js were modified to carry the AIM-9 Sidewinder, and were to have received the AGM-114A Hellfire (the latter having been abandoned). The J continued to fly with Marine Reserve units into the 1990s but have now been retired. Reserve AH-1J units were activated and sent to the Gulf.

Model 309 KingCobra

Following the cancellation of the Lockheed AH-56 Cheyenne, Bell developed the Model 309 KingCobra. Two were built, the first a 'Marine' demonstrator powered by the same T400-CP-400 powerplant as the standard AH-1J, but with a strengthened drivetrain allowing the full 1332 kW (1,800 shp) to be used, and the second a single-engined 'Army' demonstrator powered by the Lycoming T55-L-7C, flat-rated at 1492 kW (2,000 shp).

The twin-engined aircraft made its maiden flight on 10 September 1971. The type differed from the AH-1J as its airframe was strengthened, while the tail boom was lengthened and fitted with a ventral fin to improve directional stability and to allow a larger diameter (14.6-m/48-ft) main rotor to be fitted. The single-engined 309 was

AH-1J International

When the Shah of Iran decided to order AH-1s for his army, he specified a TOW-compatible AH-1J derivative which incorporated many features previously tried and tested by the Model 309. The $704-million contract, the biggest single export programme ever undertaken by Bell, was signed on 21 December 1971, and covered the sale of 287 Model 214 utility helicopters and 202 AH-1Js.

The 'Iranian J', as it was sometimes dubbed, was powered by an uprated T400-WV-402, with a new transmission system derived from that of the Model 211 HueyTug flying crane. This gave the J International much improved hot-and-high performance, with a rating of 1248 kW/1,673 shp (maximum continuous). South Korea was the only other user of the AH-1J International, taking delivery of eight TOW aircraft in 1978.

AH-1T Improved SeaCobra

The AH-1T was the first production Cobra variant with a new fuselage, necessitated by the upgraded powerplant and transmission system. Developed for the US Marine Corps, who wanted a TOW missile-capable Cobra, the AH-1T Improved SeaCobra used the 1470-kW (1,970-shp) Pratt & Whitney Canada T400-WV-402 twin-pac and a virtually unmodified Bell 214 transmission system. To absorb the extra power, the AH-1T was also given a new, 48-ft (14.6-m) diameter rotor, with blades whose chord had been increased from 69 cm (27 in) to 84 cm (33 in). The hub was strengthened, and given Lord Kinematics Lastoflex Elastomeric and Teflon-faced bearings. Swept tips were incorporated for reduced noise and to improve high-speed performance. The increased diameter of the main rotor made it necessary to lengthen the tailboom, and to provide a more powerful tail rotor with increased diameter and larger tail surfaces. To maintain the centre of gravity the forward fuselage was also stretched, making room for an additional avionics bay and 181 kg (400 lb) more fuel. Longer undercarriage skids were also used.

The adoption of the T400-WV-402 engine gave the AH-1T a dramatic increase in available power, allowing heavy payloads to be carried even with full internal fuel and giving the new variant, despite its much greater empty weight, a really impressive performance. The promise shown by the AH-1T was such that only 67 of the planned 124 AH-1Js were delivered, production switching to the AH-1T.

The last two AH-1Js built served as AH-1T prototypes, the first flying in its new guise on 20 May 1976. They were followed by 57 production aircraft. TOW compatibility was not provided from the start on the first 33 aircraft, due to budgetary constraints, but the survivors were given a retrofit programme including a nose sight, Sperry Univac helmet sights for both crew, and a recoil compensator to allow the TSU to be used with the M197 gun. This programme has given them compatibility with the TOW missile, and other modifications were to have allowed them to use the newer Hellfire. The second batch of 24 AH-1Ts was built with full TOW compatibility.

similar, except for its engine pack, and indeed commonality was sufficient for the twin-engined aircraft to be rebuilt with a single engine after the original single-engined 309 was destroyed in an accident. The main rotor featured a new, very broad chord, high-lift blade with forward-swept tips and an asymmetric section. The original AH-1G-style nose was soon replaced by a longer unit housing an electro-optical or 'Visonics' sensor package, including a FLIR, a low-light TV, the TOW missile tracker and a laser rangefinder. The pilot had his own independent LLTV system mounted at the front of the rotor fairing, and this allowed him to fly in total darkness, even when the FLIR was being used by the gunner. Although not produced, KingCobra technology did find its way back into other AH-1 and UH-1 programmes.

AH-1T+

The AH-1T+ began its life as a paper proposal to Iran for a further enhanced SeaCobra incorporating the General Electric T700-GE-700 engines and transmission system of the Bell Model 214ST, which was to have been produced under licence in Iran. The new aircraft offered 75 per cent more power than the AH-1J then in Iranian service, with 25 per cent better fuel burn. It was to have had sand filters, better recoil compensation for the gun and enhanced avionics. It was also intended to demonstrate a top speed of 173 kt (319 km/h; 199 mph). The overthrow of the Shah deprived Bell of its intended customer, and the Marines made no secret of the fact that they wanted some AH-64s and did not want another 'warmed-over' Cobra. Work on the new aircraft continued, however, and an AH-1T was flown with the 938-kW/1,258-shp (max continuous) General Electric T700-GE-700 in April 1980.

4BW

The last production AH-1T (161022), previously the AH-1T+ and AH-1W prototype, was converted by Bell with the all-composite, bearing-free, Model 680 four-bladed rotor, first test-flown on a Bell 222. The new rotor is much simpler to make and maintain, and has a much longer life, as well as giving the SuperCobra improved manoeuvrability, increased top speed (by 20 kt/37 km/h; 23 mph) and less vibration. It is much stealthier than existing rotors, and Bell hopes to demonstrate an ability to withstand direct hits by AAA of up to 23-mm (0.9-in) calibre. Known only as the 4BW (Four-Bladed Whiskey), the former AH-1T+ demonstrator aircraft was also fitted with new tail surfaces, positioned further aft by some 152 cm (60 in), and with end-plate fins. The aircraft also incorporated a digital flight-control system and the night-targeting sights and Doppler-based navigation system under consideration for the AH-1W. With USMC evaluations complete, the 4BW prototype aircraft has reportedly been returned to stock AH-1W configuration and given back to the USMC. Many of the features tested on the 4BW will appear on the AH-1Z.

AH-1W SuperCobra

In 1981, Congress refused to grant any funds for a Marine procurement of the AH-64; instead, Bell was given a $4.1-million contract to qualify the T700-GE-401 in the AH-1T. Bell then proceeded to add a host of new improvements and updates to the AH-1T+ prototype (161022), which was given prominent exhaust suppressors and bulged 'cheek' fairings which marked the relocation of TOW electronics previously carried in the tailboom. Sidewinders, Hellfire and TOW were all carried by the prototype, which was also given an AN/ALQ-144 IRCM set and AN/ALE-139 chaff/flare dispensers. The first production aircraft was redesignated AH-1W. An initial order was placed for 44, plus a single TAH-1W trainer, and the USMC eventually received a total of 179 newly-built helicopters. The 43 remaining AH-1Ts were modified to AH-1W configuration. Approximately 190 were in service in January 1999.

Export customers include Turkey, who received 10 of the Marines allocation. Bell is currently proposing the AH-1W KingCobra to meet a Turkish requirement for 145 locally-produced attack helicopters. Taiwan procured 42 examples between 1993 and 1997. Ambitious plans for Romania to licence-build an initial batch of 96 'Whiskey'-based AH-1RO Draculas may come to fruition.

The USMC plans to upgrade its AH-1Ws (and UH-1Ns) in a programme which will eventually see the 'Whiskey' become the AH-1Z.

AH-1Z

After abandoning the Integrated Weapons System and the Marine Observation and Attack Aircraft programme in 1995, a two-phase improvement of the AH-1W was ordered. The first phase involved the fitting of the Night Targeting System (NTS) for dual TOW/Hellfire day, night and adverse weather targeting, while the second, more radical phase involves fitting the Bell 680 four-bladed rotor, new wing assemblies, and glass cockpits. AH-1Ws updated to Phase II standards will be re-designated AH-1Zs. First flight of an AH-1Z was conducted in late 2000, while remanufacture began in 2003. A total of 180 AH-1Zs are expected to be produced for the Marine Corps light helicopter units.

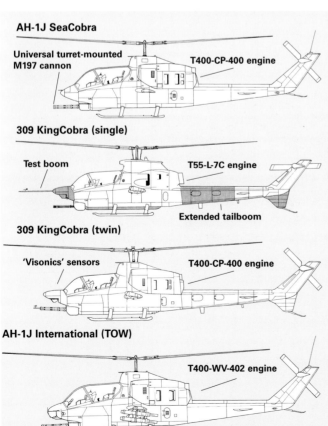

AH-1J SeaCobra
Universal turret-mounted M197 cannon — T400-CP-400 engine

309 KingCobra (single)
Test boom — T55-L-7C engine — Extended tailboom

309 KingCobra (twin)
'Visonics' sensors — T400-CP-400 engine

AH-1J International (TOW)
T400-WV-402 engine — TOW missiles

AH-1T SeaCobra
New rotor hub — Lengthened tailboom

AH-1T+
Compatibility with Hellfire missiles — T700-GE-700 in distinct nacelles

AH-1W SuperCobra
Enlarged 'cheek' fairings — Reconfigured engine nacelles

AH-1 4BW
Digital 'glass cockpit' — Four-bladed composite rotor

Boeing/Sikorsky
RAH-66 Commanche
Stealth helicopter

Left: In keeping with its stealth requirements, the Commanche has been designed with angular panels similar to those of the F-117 Nighthawk.

Below: The YRAH-66 made its maiden flight on 4 January 1996, with IOC scheduled for 2006.

In 1982 the US Army announced its ambitious **LHX (Light Helicopter Experimental)** programme for an armed multi-role helicopter. The aircraft was to replace the UH-1 Iroquois, AH-1 HueyCobra, OH-6 Cayuse and OH-58 Kiowa helicopters. As the complexity of the programme and its real cost became clear, however, the procurement total was gradually whittled down and the definitive programme finally emerged in 1995. This called for two prototypes, six 'early operational capability' helicopters with reconnaissance equipment but no armament for trials from 2001, a production decision in 2003, the establishment of the first operational unit in 2007, and production encompassing 1,292 helicopters. These machines will fly in the attack and scout roles only.

Boeing/Sikorsky

A Boeing/Sikorsky team was selected to develop the new aircraft in April 1991. The engine for the new helicopter had been selected in October 1988 as the LHTEC (Allison/Garrett, now Allison/ AlliedSignal) T800. In 1990 the LHX designation was changed to **LH**, and in April 1991 the designation and name **RAH-66 Comanche** was selected, the prototype and test helicopters then being designated **YRAH-66**.

Development of the Comanche was slowed by technical considerations as well as political antipathy in several quarters and then the downturn in the funding of advanced US military programmes.

The Comanche has a 'stealthy' airframe offering a minimum of reflective surfaces and built largely of composite materials. The five-bladed main rotor is of composite construction with cuffed swept-tip blades. The T-tail has a vertical surface inclined to starboard and includes an eight-bladed, shrouded anti-torque rotor. The landing gear is retractable, while weapon stowage is internal, with a bay on each side of the lower fuselage. The very advanced avionics include dual triplex fly-by-wire control systems and a nav/ attack system with GPS update and FLIR.

SPECIFICATION

Boeing/Sikorsky RAH-66 Comanche
Type: two-crew reconnaissance, attack and air combat helicopter
Powerplant: two LHTEC T800-LHT-801 turboshaft engines each rated at 1165 kW (1,563 shp)
Performance: (estimated) maximum speed 324 km/h (201 mph) at 1220 m (4,000 ft); initial vertical climb rate 432 m (1,418 ft) per minute; range 2334 km (1,450 miles) with drop tanks; endurance 2 hours 30 minutes with standard fuel
Weights: (estimated) empty 3522 kg (7,765 lb); maximum take-off 7896 kg (17,408 lb)
Dimensions: main rotor diameter 11.90 m (39 ft ½ in); length overall, rotors turning 14.28 m (46 ft 10¼ in); height 3.37 m (11 ft ¾ in); main rotor disc area 111.21 m² (1,197.04 sq ft)
Armament: one three-barrelled 20-mm (0.79-in) cannon, plus up to six Hellfire or Stinger missiles carried internally, or eight Hellfires or 16 Stingers and fuel tanks carried externally on a detachable stub wing

Denel **CSH-2/AH-2A** Rooivalk

South Africa may have a long-term requirement for up to 36 Rooivalks.

South African attack helicopter

The **Denel** (formerly **Atlas**) **Rooivalk** (red kestrel) is the first operational result of a development programme launched in 1981 for an indigenous South African attack helicopter. Although it looks like an entirely new machine, the Rooivalk is based on a degree of reverse engineering of the Aérospatiale Puma using the same engines (albeit in slightly uprated form) and the same main rotor. The stepped tandem cockpits for the pilot and co-pilot/gunner (rear and front respectively) have dual controls, as well as three CRT displays and a HUD in each cockpit. A gyro-stabilised turret at the nose contains an automatic target detection and tracking system which incorporates a laser rangefinder, FLIR and TV camera, and the two crewmen each have a helmet-mounted sight system.

In service

The full production standard Rooivalk, of which the SAAF ordered an initial 12 operational helicopters, differs from the prototypes in a number of important respects. These include improved IR exhaust suppressors and enlarged sponson cheeks housing avionics and ammunition. A pair of external seats can be fitted to these cheeks, allowing a Rooivalk to pick up the crew of a downed helicopter, or to transport special forces soldiers. No. 16 Sqn, the SAAF's first Rooivalk unit, received its first **AH-2A** (as the aircraft is officially known in service) in May 1999, with ongoing upgrades increasing the helicopter's firepower.

No. 16 Squadron SAAF has become the only regular Rooivalk unit. Efforts to find export customers have so far drawn a blank.

SPECIFICATION

Atlas CSH-2 Rooivalk
Type: two-seat attack helicopter
Powerplant: two Atlas Topaz (locally-upgraded Turbomeca Makila 1A2) turboshaft engines each rated at 1491 kW (2,000 shp)
Performance: maximum cruising speed 278 km/h (172 mph) at optimum altitude; initial climb rate 671 m (2,200 ft) per minute; service ceiling 6095 m (20,000 ft); hovering ceiling 5545 m (18,200 ft) in ground effect and 5030 m (16,500 ft) out of ground effect;

range 940 km (584 miles)
Weights: empty 5910 kg (13,029 lb) maximum take-off 8750 kg (19,290 lb)
Dimensions: main rotor diameter 15.58 m (51 ft 1½ in); length overall 18.73 m (61 ft 5½ in) with rotors turning; height 5.19 m (17 ft ¼ in); main rotor disc area 190.64 m² (2,052.15 sq ft)
Armament: one 20-mm (0.79-in) trainable forward-firing cannon, and up to 1563 kg (3,446 lb) of disposable stores

Eurocopter
EC 665 Tiger/Tigre
Battlefield helicopter

The **EC 665**, known in France as the **Tigre** and in Germany as the **Tiger**, was planned to meet French and German requirements for an advanced multi-role type for battlefield operations in the typical European scenario. It originated from a 1984 memorandum of understanding and after much deliberation Eurocopter received a contract to build five prototype and development helicopters in November 1989. Three were to be unarmed aerodynamic testbeds and the other two armed prototypes for the basically similar Tiger/Tigre anti-tank variants required by Germany and France (one prototype), and for a French escort helicopter variant.

Tiger described

The basic type is of typical attack helicopter configuration with an airframe built largely of composite materials and optimised for high survivability over the modern battlefield. The first prototype made its maiden flight in April 1991. Three versions are being developed in

Tigre HAP (above) and Tiger UHT (below) differ in role and configuration. HAP is designed as a battlefield escort and support aircraft, able to escort assault helicopters and to engage in air-to-air combat. Tiger UHT is a more conventionally configured anti-armour helicopter. It is similar to Tigre HAC.

two basic layouts. The ALAT requires 100 **HAC** (**Hélicoptère Anti-Char**) anti-tank helicopters, while the German army needs 212 **UHT** (**Unterstützungshub-schrauber Tiger**) anti-tank/multi-role support helicopters. Both HAC and UHT share a common mast-mounted TV/FLIR/laser rangefinder sighting system, nose-mounted FLIR for the pilot and Trigat missile armament. UHT may later be fitted with a turret-mounted 30-mm (1.18-in) Mauser cannon. The **Tigre HAP** (**Hélicoptère d'Appui et de Protection**) is being developed for the French army, which

requires 115 examples for the escort and fire-support roles. HAP carries a chin turret-mounted 30-mm (1.18-in) GIAT M30/781B cannon, STRIX roof-mounted sight and a disposable armament of rockets and Mistral AAMs. In June 1999 French and German governments signed a production contract for an initial batch of 160 helicopters. Deliveries of the first Tigers and Tigres for Germany and France began in the closing months of 2003. In addition, Australia and Spain have both signed Tiger orders.

SPECIFICATION	
Eurocopter Tiger HAC/UHT	maximum take-off 6100 kg (13,448 lb)
Type: two-seat anti-tank and close support helicopter	**Dimensions:** main rotor diameter 13 m (42 ft 7¾ in); length 15.8 m (51 ft 10 in) with the rotors turning; height 5.2 m (17 ft ¾ in) to top of mast-mounted sight; main rotor disc area 132.73 m² (1,428.76 sq ft)
Powerplant: two MTU/Turbomeca/Rolls-Royce MTR 390 turboshaft engines each rated at 958 kW (1,285 shp) for take-off	
Performance: maximum speed 269 km/h (167 mph) at optimum altitude; initial climb rate 642 m (2,106 ft) per minute; range 800 km (497 miles) with standard fuel; endurance 3 hours 25 minutes	**Armament:** (primary) up to eight HOT 2/HOT 3 ATMs (later Trigat 2); plus four Stinger 2 (UHT) or Mistral (HAC) short-range AAMs; additional options include unguided rockets or podded guns
Weights: empty 3300 kg (7,275 lb);	

Kamov **Ka-50** and **Ka-52 'Hokum'**
Close-support helicopter

The Ka-50's cannon is installed on the starboard side of the fuselage, below the wing root, as close as possible to the helicopter's centre of gravity. This is also the strongest and most rigid location and so minimises the effect of recoil and maximises accuracy.

The **Ka-50 Chernaya Akula** (black shark) **'Hokum'** began life in 1977 and was planned as a rival to the Mi-28 in the competition to provide the Soviet armed forces with a new attack helicopter. Kamov used its standard superimposed pair of contra-rotating co-axial rotors for the aircraft, employing a single crew member to save weight that could then be used for more armour, more powerful armament and a greater number of more advanced sensors. The first of an eventual three **V-80** prototypes made its maiden flight on 17 June 1982, and there were also two **V-80Sh-1** pre-production prototypes, the suffix indicating **Shturmovik-1** (single-seat assaulter). The competitive evaluation ended in October 1986 with the selection of the Ka-50 in preference to the Mi-28.

Weapons system

The core of the Ka-50's weapon system is the tube-launched Vikhr ATGM, of which 16 are carried. These can be complemented by AS-12 'Kegler' ASMs, up to 80 S-8 unguided rockets, and a variety of bombs. A 30-mm (1.18-in) cannon is also fitted.

Combat survivability is enhanced by IR-suppressed exhausts, cockpit armour capable of withstanding 20-mm (0.79-in) fire, foam-filled self-sealing fuel tanks, a high degree of systems redundancy, and chaff/flare dispensers in wingtip pods. In the event of a catastrophic hit, the pilot can use his K-37 ejection seat, whose departure sequence begins with automatic explosive separation of the two rotors' six blades. The Ka-50's avionics, including provision for third-party target acquisition, are optimised to ease the pilot's workload. However, a later emphasis on night capability led to a reassessment of the Ka-50. The revised **Ka-50N** was subsequently flown in 1997.

The Ka-50 was chosen over the Mi-28 as a result of its greater agility, longer stand-off missile range, heavier ammunition load, more extensive armour and greater accuracy of weapons delivery.

SPECIFICATION

Kamov Ka-50 Chernaya Akula 'Hokum-A'
Type: single-seat battlefield air-combat and close-air support helicopter
Powerplant: two Klimov TV3-117VK turboshaft engines each rated at 1635 kW (2,193 shp)
Performance: maximum speed 300 km/h (186 mph) at optimum altitude; cruising speed 270 km/h (168 mph) at optimum altitude; maximum vertical rate of climb 600 m (1,969 ft) per minute at 2500 m (8,200 ft); service ceiling 5500 m (18,040 ft); hovering ceiling 4000 m (13,125 ft) out of ground effect; range 540 km (279 miles); endurance 1 hour 40 minutes with standard fuel
Weights: empty 7800 kg (17,196 lb); maximum take-off 10800 kg (23,810 lb)
Dimensions: rotor diameter, each 14.50 m (45 ft 7 in); length 16 m (52 ft 6 in) with the rotors turning; height 4.93 m (16 ft 2 in); rotor disc area, total 330.26 m² (3,555 sq ft)
Armament: one 30-mm (1.18-in) 2A42 semi-trainable forward-firing cannon, plus up to 3000 kg (6,614 lb) of ordnance

McDonnell Douglas
AH-64 Apache

Regarded as the world's premier attack helicopter, the AH-64 Apache's crowning glory came in Operation Desert Storm. Undertaking the first attack missions of the war, Apaches were instrumental in the destruction of Iraqi positions.

The AH-64 Apache gives an army on the battlefield all of the advantages of a helicopter combined with the firepower of a heavily-armed combat aircraft. Like an infantry soldier, the AH-64 uses agility to exploit its fighting prowess. It can hide, duck, rise, and fight in a fluid, fast-changing situation but, unlike the foot soldier, the AH-64 can also reach out over great distances with its weapons. When put into action as part of an integrated battle plan with assistance from E-8 J-STARS aircraft, the Apache can become the decisive weapon in a military engagement.

Anything but beautiful, with its bug-like silhouette, the AH-64

makes up for its ungainly appearance with Hellfire missiles, Hydra rockets and a M230 Chain Gun. This arsenal is directed by a high-tech array of sensors. These electronic and infra-red systems can be difficult to maintain in good running order but, when operating properly, they pinpoint the enemy by day or night.

Apache was conceived and developed in the Cold War years because the West needed an answer to that most fearsome of weapons, the main battle tank. Almost forgotten today is the challenge that faced NATO leaders when they pondered an assault on the plains of Europe by tens of thousands of Soviet

Despite recent improvements to their avionics, Apaches are able to operate in the most primitive conditions. These examples are seen in Germany where, a few years ago, they would have been tasked with halting a Russian armoured advance.

and Warsaw Pact tanks. The Apache was optimised to detect tanks and to kill them, fighting in a highly mobile way using terrain and vegetation as a shield. When ready to lash out, the Apache pops up over the horizon and launches deadly missiles without ever coming within range of the tank's weapons. And if things go wrong, the Apache is well armed for fighting at close quarters.

Apaches perform their task of killing targets with finesse, despite certain limitations. Most of those in service today lack global-positioning (GPS) and terrain-following systems for navigation on long missions. As a product of the 1970s, the Apache is an analog, not a digital warrior. Mission planning for any Apache mission is arduous because every eventuality must be foreseen, sketched out and planned on paper before the aircraft are in the air. Apaches fight as a team and, if the cohesion of that team is lost, so is the mission. Apache crews know the truth of Clausewitz's maxim that 'no plan survives contact with the enemy'. Communication of new ideas or intelligence is nearly impossible after launch, so

Apache crews have to fly and fight in a stressful combat environment hoping that all the answers have been worked out before the shooting starts.

The long, slender Apache with its gunner and pilot in a two-seat, tandem cockpit offers excellent handling and flying characteristics and good visibility. The helicopter responds well to a skilled hand at the controls and performs as well as any battlefield helicopter in service anywhere. On the ground, its wheeled undercarriage affords easy movement for maintenance.

The Apache is a formidable weapon. But it was not the first of its kind. As a combat aircraft for army use, it was preceded by the Bell AH-1 HueyCobra from the Vietnam years.

An ambitious programme to improve the fleet of Apaches in service in half a dozen nations is underway. The aim of the programme is to update this 1970s helicopter by means of modern-day radar and digital instruments. Once viewed purely as a helicopter to confront and halt oncoming tanks, the AH-64 Apache has evolved into a powerful multi-role battlefield warrior for the 21st century.

Above: Required to operate at low level over the battlefield to avoid hostile fire, the agility of the Apache is superb, although its ability to perform dramatic manoeuvres is reduced when carrying a large weapon load. Such is the strength of the Apache's performance that it was decided that the helicopter would have a limited air-to-air role. To perform these missions, Stinger air-to-air missiles are mounted on the stub wings. British Apaches will be equipped with the Shorts Starstreak/Helstreak air-to-air missile.

Above: An Apache attack would start with the helicopter being positioned out of the range of enemy small arms fire. Despite the vast array of high-tech weapons carried by the AH-64, unguided rockets have proved to be highly effective against so called 'soft' targets. A variety of warheads can be installed on the rockets ranging from high-explosives to white phosphorous.

Left: Apaches wear an overall scheme of chemically-resistant polyurethane Aircraft Type 1 Green. Squadron markings are kept to a minimum, much to the crews' annoyance, who are often left with the impression that army flying is viewed as a second-rate force. Colourful squadron markings have recently been making a return.

AH-64 development

The Hughes (later McDonnell Douglas) Apache had a lengthy development history as it encountered troubles, both technical and financial. During this time, however, it matured into the most effective attack helicopter in service today.

In August 1972, the official Request for Proposals (RFP) for the US Army's Advanced Attack Helicopter (AAH) was announced. The AAH was a replacement for the AH-1 HueyCobra, which had proven the value of a dedicated attack helicopter in the closing stages of the Vietnam War. The new AAH was intended to fight at night, in strength, on a future European battlefield. Five competing submissions were made for the new helicopter – from Bell, Boeing-Vertol (teamed with Grumman Aerospace), Hughes, Lockheed and Sikorsky. Bell Helicopter Textron, not surprisingly, saw itself as the front-runner. It had amassed the most relevant experience of any of the competitors and its resultant YAH-63 (Bell Model 409) had the appearance of a thoroughbred. Hughes's designers developed the angular and awkward-looking Model 77 which, to the US Army, became the YAH-64.

AAH fly-off

On 22 June 1973, the US Department of Defense announced that the Bell YAH-63 and Hughes YAH-64 had been chosen as the AAH competitors. This launched Phase 1 of the competition, whereby both firms would build and fly two prototypes, plus a Ground Test Vehicle (GTV), for a competitive fly-off. By June 1975, Hughes had begun ground tests with AV-01 (Air Vehicle-01), the prototype. This aircraft would be tasked with all the preliminary power tests, but AV-02 would be the first to fly. In fact, AV-01 never flew and served as Hughes's *de facto* GTV. In contrast, Bell had already run a dedicated YAH-63 GTV in April of that year and its apparent lead in the programme forced Hughes to hurriedly accelerate its work. The first YAH-64 succeeded in beating the YAH-63 into the air by one day, on 30 September 1975.

An intensive flight test programme was undertaken, first by the manufacturers and then by the US Army. During this period, the TOW missile armament originally planned for the AAH was replaced by the Rockwell Hellfire (HELicopter-

Above: This view of prototype AV-03 shows dummy Hellfire missiles, but also clearly illustrates the actuated trailing edge originally fitted to the AH-64's stub wings. This complicated feature was later deleted.

Top: AV-02, the second YAH-64 prototype, can be seen here on an early test flight – note the original shape of the nose and canopy.

Launched, FIRE-and-forget), a laser-guided anti-tank missile which promised effective engagement ranges in excess of 6 km (3.7 miles).

On 10 December 1976, having reviewed the evaluation results, the Secretary of the Army announced that the Hughes YAH-64 was the winner of the AAH competition. There had been some problems during the Phase 1 evaluation and the rotor system had had to be redesigned. The mast was lengthened and the blade tips were swept back. The weight of the prototype also had to be

reduced and this was achieved by redesigning the tail unit and by introducing lightweight Black Hole IR-suppressors.

The Phase 2 contract called for the building of three production-standard AH-64s, conversion of the two prototypes and GTV to this standard also, and complete weapons and sensor system integration. The first flight of the modified AV-02, now in production configuration, took place on 28 November 1977. Hellfire tests began in April 1979. Two competing TADS/PNVS (Target Acquisition

Hellfire testing began in 1980 and the extra stand-off range provided by the new missile made a huge contribution to the Apache's survivability on the modern battlefield. Initial testing did reveal some problems with the laser-guided Hellfire, however, particularly in fog, smoke, dust or rain – each of which could conspire to hinder the laser.

and Designation Sight/Pilot's Night Vision Sensor) systems were installed on the AH-64 prototypes; AV-02 carried Martin-Marietta's system and AV-03 carried Northrop's. The last of the Phase 2 batch of three aircraft, AV-06, flew on 16 March 1980. This final aircraft was the first to fly with the definitive 'stabilator' design and extended tail rotor. In April 1980 a crucial landmark in the AAH story was reached with the selection of the Martin-Marietta TADS/PNVS for production.

Sadly, 1980 ended on a tragic note. On 20 November, AV-04 departed on a routine tail incidence/drag test, accompanied by a T-28D photo chase plane. Flying in close formation, the two collided, and only the pilot of the T-28 survived.

In May 1981, AV-02/-03/-06 were handed over to the US Army, in preparation for the AH-64's final Operational Test II (OTII) evaluation at Ft Hunter-Liggett, which was successful. One element of fall-out from OTII was the decision to move to an uprated version of the T700 engine, the T700-GE-701, rated at 1259 kW (1,690 shp). It was then, during the final stages of AAH Phase 2 testing, late in 1981, that the name 'Apache' was adopted.

Apache go-ahead

It was not until 15 April 1982 that full-scale go-ahead for Apache production was finally given. The US Army had increased its Apache requirement to 536 aircraft, but was then forced to cut this back to 446. On this basis, Hughes estimated the total programme cost would be $5,994 million. The US Army had always accepted that the unit cost would creep up from $1.6 million (in 1972 dollars), but was now faced with a price per aircraft of over $13 million (rising to $16.2 million later that year). The AAH was faced with serious political opposition, however – the Apache had powerful friends. A letter dated 22 July 1982, from General Bernard C. Rogers NATO Commander-in-Chief Europe to the Apache's chief detractors in the Senate, spelled out the threat to Europe posed by the Warsaw Pact, and the urgent need for a counter. It ended with the words, 'we need the AH-64 in Europe now and cannot afford the luxury of another trip to the drawing board'.

Handover

The first Apache for the US Army was rolled out in a ceremony held at Mesa, ahead of schedule, on 30 September 1983 – eight years to the day of the first flight. The stated price of the aircraft, its 'over-the-fence' cost according to the-then Project Manager Brigadier Charles Drenz, was $7.8 million in 1984 terms or $9 million in real-year terms. This equated to a unit cost of approximately $14 million when development costs were included. Hughes planned to accelerate production to a peak of 12 per month by 1986, with purchases of 144 AH-64s in FY85, followed by a projected 144 in FY86 and 56 in FY 87.

PV-01 made its 30-minute maiden flight on 9 January 1984, and, by then, the prototype fleet had logged over 4,500 hours in the air. This noteworthy event was obscured in the headlines by the announcement on 6 January 1984 that Hughes Helicopters was about to become a subsidiary of McDonnell Douglas.

Into service

The first handover of an Apache to the US Army took place on 26 January 1984, although this was only a formality since the heavily-instrumented aircraft concerned, PV-01, would remain with Hughes/McDonnell Douglas and, in fact, it was not until the delivery of PV-13 that a US Army crew could fly an Apache away and call it their own.

Initial deliveries were made to US Army Training and Doctrine Command bases at Ft Eustis, Virginia (home of the Army logistics school), and Ft Rucker, Alabama (the US Army's centre of flying training). Apache acquisition ultimately amounted to: 138 (FY85), 116 (FY86), 101 (FY87), 77 (FY88), 54 (FY89), 154 (FY90) and a follow-on batch of 10 (FY95), for a grand total of 827 AH-64A Apaches (including six prototypes and 171 acquired in the first half of the 1980s). The first Apache unit was the 7th Battalion, 17th Cavalry Brigade, which began its 90-day battalion-level conversion training in April 1986. The last of 821 AH-64As destined for the US Army was delivered on 30 April 1996.

The official handover ceremony of the first AH-64A to the US Army, in September 1983, was held at the massive Mesa, Arizona factory, specially built to handle Apache production.

AH-64A Apache

This AH-64A Apache was one of those delivered to the 6th Cavalry Brigade (Air Combat), at Fort Hood Army Air Field, Texas, in 1987. The 6th Cavalry Brigade fielded three AH-64A battalions between 1986 and 1988. In 1988, one of these units (2-6 CAV) was deployed to West Germany, marking the first overseas deployment of the Apache. Today, the '6th Cav' has Apache units forward deployed in South Korea.

Rotor system

The Apache's rotor head is fully articulated, allowing the blades to 'hunt' (lead and lag) individually. The blades themselves have stainless steel cores, surrounded by Nomex honeycomb and glassfibre, making them resistant to direct hits from 23-mm (0.9-in) anti-aircraft shells. Above the rotor head is the Apache's air data sensor, known as the Pacer system, which monitors air temperature pressure and velocity and is vital for the correct operation of the flight instruments and fire control system.

Cockpit

The front cockpit is occupied by the CPG (co-pilot/gunner), with the handling pilot sitting behind in the stepped rear seat. The two pilots sit in crash-resistant Kevlar armoured seats and the tandem cockpits are separated by a transparent acrylic blast barrier and protected by lightweight boron armour shields. This shielding reduces the risk of both pilots being incapacitated by a single hit to the cockpit area. The canopy also incorporates armoured glass windscreen panels, further ensuring the protection of crew members.

Chain Gun

Technically, the Apache's lethal 30-mm (1.18-in) M230E1 cannon is designated as the aircraft's 'secondary area weapon', owing to its short range. The M230E1, more commonly known as the Chain Gun (on account of the one-piece metal chain that feeds ammunition to the barrel), is very accurate, but is used chiefly for suppressive fire 'to keep heads down'. The Chain Gun is slaved to the CPG's and pilot's helmet-mounted sights and so will follow the crew's line-of-sight – tracking and firing upon targets they are looking at. During Operation Desert Storm, the Chain Gun's standard M789 HE armour-piercing/explosive shells proved powerful enough to destroy Iraqi T-55 tanks on their own.

Black Hole IR-suppressor

A battlefield helicopter is most at risk from IR-guided shoulder-fired missiles (such as the Russian SAM-7 or SAM-14). The Apache was expressly designed to have as low an infra-red 'signature' as possible and, to achieve this, Hughes designed the revolutionary Black Hole exhaust shrouds in large box fairings around the engines. The Black Hole system draws in outside air to cool the exhaust and uses special heat absorbent materials to cut down the Apache's exhaust plume.

Hellfire missile

The Rockwell AGM-114 Hellfire missile was developed as the primary weapon of the AH-64. The Hellfire combines accurate laser-guidance with the longest range of any in-service helicopter-launched anti-tank missile, plus a devastatingly powerful warhead capable of destroying any battlefield target with a single shot. The exact range of the Hellfire is classified but it is almost certainly in excess of its quoted range of 8000 m (26,248 ft). The latest model of the missile to enter US Army service is the AGM-114K Hellfire II, which was developed as a result of Gulf War experience. The Hellfire II has an improved laser-seeker head, a new autopilot and a redesigned warhead. The warhead of a standard Hellfire missile comprises a shaped explosive charge, wrapped around a copper core. When the missile hits a target (such as a tank), the shaped charge compresses the copper 'slug' and shoots it as a jet of molten metal into the tank, destroying it completely. The Hellfire II uses two of these warheads, arranged in tandem, with a new steel core replacing the copper one.

Tail rotor design

The Apache's tail rotor is unusual, as the blades are offset to each other (at 60° and 120°) rather than being arranged symmetrically. This configuration reduces the noise signature of the tail rotor, a major contributing factor to the overall noise 'footprint' of any helicopter. The space-saving shape also allows the AH-64 to be loaded aboard a C-141 transport without having to remove its tail rotor.

Keith Fretwell.

Air-to-air missile armament

During the 1980s, several trials were conducted in the USA to give the Apache an air-to-air combat capability. Test firings were conducted with the AIM-9 Sidewinder and the Air-to-Air Stinger (ATAS),with the smaller Stinger missile emerging as the most likely option. However, trials have been conducted more recently with the British Starstreak missile (in its helicopter-launched Helstreak form) and this missile has proved to be extremely accurate and effective. It is probable that British WAH-64Ds will become the first operational Apaches with a dedicated air-to-air weapon (Helstreak) and this weapons option may then be taken up by the US Army.

Self-defence systems

The Apache is fitted with AN/APR-39(V)1 radar warning receivers, with antennas situated around the airframe on the nose and tail fin. An AN/ALQ-136 radar jammer can also be fitted. Near the end of the tail boom, the Apache can be fitted with a 30-round M130 chaff/flare launcher, to defeat IR- and radar-guided missiles. Below the main rotor mast is an AN/ALQ-144(V) 'Disco Light' IR jammer.

Wing-mounted weapons

AH-64s typically operate with a mix of AGM-114 Hellfire missiles and rocket pods, allowing them maximum operational flexibility against a range of targets. The full load of 16 Hellfires – known to the crews as a 'heavy Hellfire' configuration – would be carried for a dedicated anti-armour mission. However, there are few targets (such as a main battle tank) that justify the killing power (or the expense!) of a Hellfire and the Apache's 70-mm (2.75-in) rockets are capable of dealing with most battlefield targets, albeit at a shorter range than that of the Hellfire.

▶

AH-64 Apache
Briefing

This Apache is one of those operated by the US Army's 1st Aviation Training Brigade, located at Ft Rucker, Alabama – the home of US Army aviation. All training helicopters based at Ft Rucker wear large white identification codes. Students who have graduated onto the AH-64 from basic training join the 1-14 AVN for the 12-week conversion.

AH-64A Apache

Cutaway key
1 Night systems sensor scanner
2 Pilot's Night Vision System (PNVS)
3 Electro-optical target designation and night sensor systems turret
4 Target Acquisition and Designation System (TADS) daylight scanner
5 Azimuth motor housing
6 TADS/PNVS swivelling turret
7 Turret drive motor housing
8 Sensor turret mounting
9 Rear-view mirror
10 Nose compartment access hatches
11 Remote terminal unit
12 Signal data converter
13 Co-pilot/gunner's yaw control rudder pedals
14 Forward radar warning antenna
15 M230E1 Chain Gun barrel
16 Fuselage sponson fairing
17 Avionics cooling air ducting
18 Boron armoured cockpit flooring
19 Co-pilot/gunner's 'fold down' control column
20 Weapons control panel
21 Instrument panel shroud
22 Windscreen wiper
23 Co-pilot/gunner's armoured windscreen
24 Head-down sighting system viewfinder
25 Pilot's armoured windscreen panel
26 Windscreen wiper
27 Co-pilot/gunner's Kevlar armoured seat
28 Safety harness
29 Side console panel
30 Engine power levels
31 Avionics equipment bays, port and starboard
32 Avionics bay access door
33 Collective pitch control lever
34 Adjustable crash-resistant seat mouldings
35 Pilot's rudder pedals
36 Cockpit side window panel
37 Pilot's instrument console
38 Inter-cockpit acrylic blast shield
39 Starboard side window entry hatches
40 Rocket launcher pack
41 Starboard wing stores pylon
42 Cockpit roof glazing
43 Instrument panel shroud
44 Pilot's Kevlar armoured seat
45 Collective pitch control lever
46 Side console panel
47 Engine power levers
48 Rear cockpit floor level
49 Main landing gear shock absorber mounting
50 Linkless ammunition feed chute
51 Forward fuel tank: total fuel capacity 1419 litres (312 Imp gal)
52 Control rod linkages
53 Cockpit ventilating air louvres
54 Display adjustment panel
55 Grab handles/maintenance steps
56 Control system hydraulic actuators (three)
57 Ventilating air intake
58 UHF aerial
59 Starboard stub wing
60 Main rotor blade
61 Laminated blade-root attachment joints
62 Vibration absorbers
63 Blade pitch bearing housing
64 Air data sensor mast
65 Rotor hub unit
66 Offset flapping hinges
67 Elastomeric lead/lag dampers
68 Blade pitch control rod
69 Pitch control swashplate
70 Main rotor mast
71 Airturbine starter/auxiliary power unit (APU) input shaft
72 Rotor head control mixing linkages
73 Gearbox mounting plate
74 Transmission oil coolers, port and starboard
75 Rotor brake
76 Main gearbox
77 Gearbox mounting struts
78 Generator
79 Input shaft from port engine
80 Gearbox mounting deck
81 Tail rotor control rod linkage
82 Ammunition magazine
83 Stub wing attachment joints
84 Engine transmission gearbox
85 Air intake
86 Engine integral oil tank
87 General Electric T-700-GE-701 turboshaft
88 Intake particle separator
89 Engine accessory equipment gearbox
90 Oil cooler plenum
91 Gas turbine starter/auxiliary power unit
92 Starboard engine cowling panels/fold-down maintenance platform

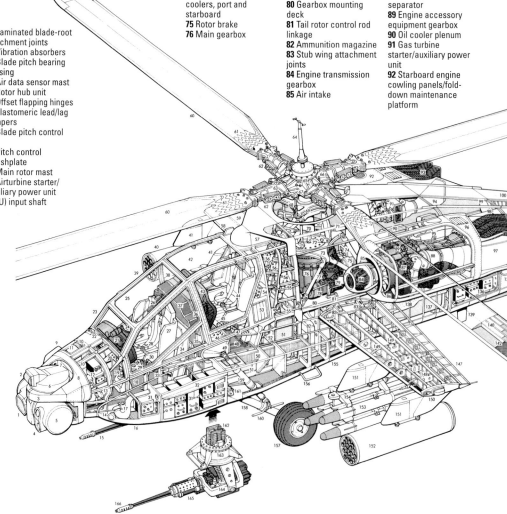

The Apache's performance during Operation Desert Storm persuaded several nations, such as Greece, the UK and the Netherlands, to finally accelerate their search for a new attack helicopter – while existing customers (such as Saudi Arabia and the UAE) came back for more. Over 200 Apaches have now been exported.

SPECIFICATION

AH-64A Apache (unless otherwise noted)

Dimensions

Fuselage length including both rotors turning:
17.76 m (58 ft 3⅛ in)
Main rotor diameter: 14.63 m (48 ft)
Tail rotor diameter: 2.79 m (9 ft 2 in)
Height over tail rotor: 4.30 m (14 ft 1¼ in)
Total height AH-64D: 4.95 m (16 ft 3 in)
Main rotor disc area: 168.11 m² (1,809.5 sq ft)
Tail rotor disc area: 6.13 m² (66 sq ft)
Wingspan: 5.23 m (17 ft 2 in)
Tailplane span: 3.4 m (11 ft 2 in)
Wheelbase: 10.59 m (34 ft 9 in)
Wheel track: 2.03 m (6 ft 8 in)
Main rotor ground clearance (turning): 3.59 m² (11 ft 9¼ in)

Powerplant

Two 1265-kW (1,696-shp) General Electric T700-GE-701 turboshafts, each derated for normal operations or, from 604th helicopter, two General Electric T700-GE-701C turboshafts, each rated at 1409 kW (1,890 shp)
AH-64D: two General Electric T700-GE-701C turboshafts, each rated at 1342 kW (1,800 shp)

Weights

Empty: 5165 kg (11,387 lb)
AH-64D: 5352 kg (11,800 lb)
Normal take-off for primary mission: 6552 kg (14,445 lb)
Design mission weight: 8006 kg (17,650 lb)
Maximum external stores: 772 kg (1,700 lb)
Maximum take-off: 9525 kg (21,000 lb)

Fuel and load

Internal fuel: 1157 kg (2,550 lb)
External fuel (four Brunswick tanks): 5980 kg (2,712 lb)

Performance

Maximum level and cruising speed: 158 kt (293 km/h; 182 mph)
AH-64D: 141 kt (261 km/h; 162 mph)
Never-exceed speed: 197 kt (365 km/h; 227 mph)
Maximum rate of climb at sea level: 990 m (3,240 ft) per minute
AH-64D: 942 m (3,090 ft) per minute
Maximum vertical rate of climb at sea level: 762 m (2,500 ft) per minute
AH-64D: 474 m (1,555 ft) per minute
Service ceiling: 6400 m (21,000 ft)
Service ceiling, one engine out: 3290 m (10,800 ft)
Hovering ceiling: 4570 m (15,000 ft)
AH-64D: 4115 m (13,500 ft)

Range

Maximum range, internal fuel only: 260 nm (482 km; 300 miles)
AH-64D: 220 nm (407 km; 253 miles)
Ferry range, max internal and external fuel in still air: 1,024 nm (1899 km; 1,180 miles)

Armament

Maximum ordnance: some 771 kg (1,700 lb) of ordnance can be carried by the Apache. One McDonnell Douglas M230 30-mm (1.18-in) Chain Gun is located between the mainwheel legs in an underfuselage mounting. Normal rate of fire is 625 rds/min of HE (high-explosive) or HEDP (high-explosive, dual-purpose) ammunition, with a maximum load of 1,200 rounds. There are four underwing hardpoints, upon which can be carried 16 Rockwell AGM-114A Hellfire anti-tank missiles or up to 77 70-mm (2.75-in) FFAR (folding fin aircraft rockets) in their launchers, or a combination of Hellfires and FFAR. The co-pilot has responsibility for firing the gun and missiles, but the pilot can override his controls in the event of an emergency.

93 Starboard engine exhaust ducts
94 APU exhaust
95 Pneumatic system and environmental control equipment
96 Cooling air exhaust louvres

109 All-moving tailplane
110 Tail rotor gearbox housing
111 Right-angle final drive gearbox
112 Fin tip aerial fairing
113 Rear radar warning antennas

126 Fin/rotor pylon attachment joint
127 Chaff and flare dispenser

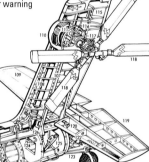

97 Particle separator exhaust duct/mixer
98 Black Hole infra-red suppressors
99 Hydraulic reservoir
100 Gearbox/engine bay tail fairings
101 Internal maintenance platform
102 Tail rotor control rod
103 Spine shaft housing
104 Tail rotor transmission shaft
105 Shaft bearings and couplings
106 Bevel drive intermediate gearbox
107 Fin/rotor pylon construction
108 Tail rotor drive shafts

114 Tail navigation light
115 Cambered trailing-edge section (directional stability)
116 Tail rotor pitch actuator
117 Tail rotor hub mechanism
118 Asymmetric (noise attenuation) tail rotor blades
119 Tailplane construction
120 Tailplane pivot bearing
121 Castoring tailwheel
122 Tailwheel shock absorber
123 Tailwheel yoke attachment
124 Handgrips/ maintenance steps
125 Tailplane control hydraulic jack

128 Tailboom ring frames
129 Ventral radar warning aerial
130 Tailcone frame and stringer construction
131 UHF aerial
132 ADF loop aerial
133 ADF sense aerial
134 Access hatch
135 Handgrips/ maintenance steps
136 Radio and electronics equipment bay
137 Rear fuel tank
138 Reticulated foam fire suppressant tank bay linings
139 VHF aerial
140 Main rotor blade stainless steel spars (five)
141 Glassfibre sparlinings
142 Honeycomb trailing-edge panel

143 Glassfibre blade skins
144 Trailing-edge fixed tab
145 Swept-blade tip fairing
146 Static discharger
147 Stub wing trailing-edge flap
148 Stub wing rib construction
149 Twin spar booms
150 Port navigation and strobe lights
151 Port wing stores pylons
152 Rocket pack: 19 x 70-mm (2.75-in) FFAR rockets
153 Rockwell Hellfire AGM-114 anti-tank missiles
154 Missile launch rails

155 Fuselage sponson aft fairing
156 Boarding step
157 Port mainwheel
158 Main landing gear leg strut
159 Shock absorber strut
160 Boarding steps
161 Main landing gear leg pivot fixing
162 Ammunition feed and cartridge case return chutes
163 Gun swivelling mounting
164 Azimuth control mounting frame
165 Hughes M230E1 Chain Gun 30-mm (1.18-in) cannon
166 Blast suppression cannon muzzle

Above: The Apache offers unparalleled manoeuvrability. Its maximum rate of roll touches 100°/sec, a figure that likens its performance more to that of a fighter than to that of a helicopter. The ability to pull up to 3.5g (unlike a normal helicopter's 2g) means that a pilot could make a potentially life-saving manoeuvre or position himself to make a vital shot while in combat without fear of an airframe failure.

Left: The US Army arms its AH-64s with 70-mm (2.75-in) Hydra 70 rockets, fired from 19-round M261 pods (illustrated). WAH-64Ds destined for the British Army will be armed with CRV-7 70-mm (2.75-in) rockets.

Right: The first combat deployment for the Apache was made by the 82nd Airborne Division's 1st Aviation Batallion, participating in Operation Just Cause in Panama in December 1989. Apaches of the 101st Airborne Division, operating as Task Force Normandy, later fired the opening shots of Operation Desert Storm. On the night of 17January 1991, eight AH-64As crossed into Iraq to destroy early-warning radar sites and open a path for Coalition strike aircraft on their way to their first night targets.

AH-64 Apache systems

COCKPIT

With Vietnam experience fresh in US Army planners' minds, the cockpit of the Apache was designed so that crew safety was of paramount importance. As well as extensive cockpit armour and individually-armoured and crash-worthy seats, the Apache undercarriage was designed to be able to absorb the impact of a very severe crash. The glint of sunlight from rounded canopies can reveal a helicopter's position from many miles away; accordingly, the canopy glazing of the Apache is constructed from flat panels to minimise reflected glare. The US Army is now investigating fitting air bags to its Apaches, to further protect the crew in the event of a crash.

APACHE SENSOR SYSTEMS

The TADS/PNVS (Target Acquisition and Designation System/Pilot's Night Vision System) is a crucial element of the overall Apache design – without it, the AH-64 is incapable of carrying out its mission. The AAQ-11 PNVS is a Forward-Looking Infra-Red (FLIR) system, located in a turret above the nose, which the pilot uses for night/bad weather flying when visibility is poor. The AN/ASQ-170 TADS is made up of two independently-moving turrets, mounted in a 'ball' beneath the nose. To the left (as seen here) is a large FLIR, equivalent to the PNVS system, but used by the co-pilot/gunner to locate targets. In the right-hand turret, arranged one above the other (like traffic lights) are an optical telescope, a magnifying TV system and the Apache's laser designator – which marks targets for Hellfire missiles.

M230E1 CHAIN GUN CANNON

The 30-mm (1.18-in) Chain Gun is a unique invention, pioneered by Hughes as an integral part of the Apache's weapons system development. The name derives from the ammunition feed mechanism which uses a one-piece metal chain to feed linkless shells from a central magazine. The Apache can carry approximately 1,200 rounds, 1,100 in the magazine and 100 in place on the chain feed of the gun. The cannon is also linked via the pilot's IHADSS helmet sight system, and can be traversed up by 11°, down by 60° and up to 100° off the aircraft centreline.

CURRENT AND FUTURE WEAPONS

Today, the combination of the Apache's AGM-114 Hellfire armament and its TADS/PNVS system make it by far the most deadly battlefield helicopter in the world. When the AH-64D Longbow Apache is introduced, it will be equipped with a new version of the Hellfire, the AGM-114L. This version, the Longbow Hellfire, will be guided by the Longbow MMW radar, enabling it to be launched from behind trees or around hillsides – unlike the current Hellfire which must be able to 'see' an uninterrupted straight line to the laser spot on its target.

APACHE POWERPLANTS

The original AH-64A was powered by the 1265-kW (1,696-shp) General Electric T-700-GE-701 turboshaft. From the 604th production aircraft this was replaced by the more powerful -701C engine, uprated to 1409-kW (1,890-shp). All the US Army's upgraded AH-64Ds will be fitted with the newer engine, but Britain's WAH-64Ds will be powered by the 1566-kW (2,210-shp) Rolls-Royce Turbomeca RTM322.

AH-64D Longbow Apache
Briefing

The AH-64D Longbow Apache represents the culmination of America's most important attack helicopter programme. US Army pilots have described the Longbow as a helicopter from the next generation.

Since the earliest days of AH-64A operations, there have been attempts to upgrade the helicopter. In the mid-1980s, McDonnell Douglas began studies of the Advanced/Apache Plus, which was later referred to, unofficially, as the 'AH-64B'. The AH-64B would have had a revised, updated cockpit with a new fire control system, Stinger air-to-air missiles, and a redesigned Chain Gun. Aimed exclusively at the US Army, the programme was abandoned before it reached the hardware stage.

With new technologies becoming available, there was now the possibility of transforming the already formidable Apache into something of even greater capability. Operational limitations with the AH-64A became apparent during Desert Storm and provided the stimulus for developing an improved attack variant.

New technology

One of the 'new' Apache's most significant developments was the mounting of a Longbow radar above the rotor head to provide millimetre-wave (MMW) guidance for specially-developed AGM-114L Hellfire missiles. When this was fully integrated into the helicopter's systems, the AH-64D was renamed the Longbow Apache.

Largely impervious to atmospheric interference, the

Seen as a quantum leap over the AH-64A Apache, the Longbow is able to detect up to 1,024 potential targets. Of these, 128 can be classified, with attack priority being given to those 16 which have the highest threat value.

mast-mounted Longbow radar system allows the AH–64D to fire-and-forget all 16 AGM-114L Hellfire missiles, while remaining hidden behind a tree-line. Thus, in wartime, the Longbow Apache can stay concealed while attacking targets, thereby increasing its chances of surviving retaliation from AAA or shoulder-launched SAMs.

The AH-64D is equipped with a totally new avionics system. Four dual-channel MIL-STD 1553B data buses combine with new processors and an uprated electrical system to greatly increase and revolutionise the capabilities of the AH-64D

compared to the AH-64A. The dials and 1,200 switches of the AH-64A cockpit have been replaced by a Litton Canada multi-function up-front display, two 6-in (15-cm) square Allied Signal Aerospace colour CRT displays and just 200 switches. Improved helmet-mounted displays, an upgraded Plessey AN/ASN-157 Doppler navigation system, and Honeywell AN/APN-209 radar altimeter

The mast-mounted Longbow radar allows the AH-64D to acquire, designate and destroy targets in all weathers, by day or night, amid hazards such as thick smoke.

have also been incorporated. In service the AH-64D will have a dual embedded GPS and inertial navigation (EGI) fit plus AN/ARC-201D VHF/FM radios. The helicopter's improved navigation

*Right: With its mast-mounted
radar, the AH-64D can remain
completely concealed while
searching for potential targets,
so reducing its vulnerability.*

suite gives it near all-weather
capability compared to the
adverse-weather capability of
the AH-64A. The larger volume
of avionics in the AH–64D
Longbow has forced the
expansion of the Apache's cheek
fairings, to become known as
EFABs (Enhanced Forward
Avionics Bays).

Combat communication

The fluid nature of the battlefield
has seen communication
between friendly forces play an
increasingly important role.
Incorporating a data transfer
module (DTM), the AH-64D is
able to talk not only to other
AH-64Ds, and OH-58Ds, but
also to USAF assets such as the
Rivet Joint (RC-135) and
J-STARS E-8. Target information
can be supplied to the Longbow
Apache crew on a secure
frequency, allowing them to
transfer to the assigned 'killing
zone'. Once the attack has
begun, the Longbow radar can
catalogue targets, designating
those that are deemed to be the
most threatening.

Performance and power

The Apache's current General
Electric GE T700-GE-701
turboshafts are to be completely
replaced by uprated 1,285-kW
(1,723-shp) T700-GE-701C
engines. The -701C has already
been fitted to existing AH-64As
from the 604th production
aircraft (delivered in 1990), and
has proved to offer a marked
increase in performance.

The US Defense Acquisition
Board authorised a 51-month
AH-64D developmental
programme in August 1990. This
was later extended to 70
months to incorporate the AGM-
114L Hellfire missile. Full-scale
production of 232 Longbows
was authorised on 13 October

*Right: Six AH-64D prototypes
were built, the first flying on
15 April 1992, and the last on
4 March 1994. The US Army has
ordered a total of 232 new-build
Longbow Apaches.*

1995, with the complete US
Army AH–64D contract also
calling for 13,311 AGM-114L
missiles. The first AH-64Ds
were delivered in March 1997,
with the first front-line unit
expected to be operational in
July 1998. Longbow Apaches
will transform the composition
of US Army aviation battlefield
units. They will help to prove the
advanced technologies that will
be introduced by the RAH-66A
Commanche. Should the latter
enter widespread service, the
two helicopters will be able to
communicate with new levels of
efficiency across the 21st
century's 'digital battlefield'.
Deliveries of the Longbow
Apache are likely to continue
until 2008.

Lethal Longbow

In answer to its critics, the AH-
64D Longbow received
spectacular validation in a series

of field tests. Between 30
January and 9 February 1995, at
China Lake, a joint team of AH-
64As and AH–64Ds undertook
gunnery trials involving some of
the most complex exercise
scenarios ever devised.

The test results were
staggering. The AH-64Ds
achieved 300 confirmed enemy
armour kills, whereas the AH-
64As notched up just 75. Four

AH-64Ds were shot down, as
opposed to 28 AH-64As. One
test official stated, "In all my
years of testing, I have never
seen a tested system so
dominate the system it is
intended to replace."

Both the Netherlands and the
UK have followed the US Army's
lead in ordering the AH-64D,
with the Netherlands ordering
30 aircraft and the UK some 67.

*The advent of the AH-64D
Longbow Apache heralds the
rejuvenation of the Apache
helicopter, although its high
price has led some customers to
opt for the AH-64A.*

AH-64 Apache operators

With the role of the dedicated battlefield helicopter steadily increasing in importance, it came as no surprise to McDonnell Douglas to find that, despite its initially high purchase price, the Apache would attain a respectable list of overseas operators.

The awesome capabilities of the AH-64 Apache were demonstrated to the world during the Gulf War. Following the conflict, McDonnell Douglas received a flood of requests from countries interested in purchasing fleets of new Apaches to reinforce their attack forces, with a view to operating them in emerging localised low-intensity conflicts.

European operators

Constant tension between Greece and Turkey over territorial violations led Greece to upgrade its attack helicopter fleet. On 24 December 1991, Hellenic Army Aviation finalised its order for 12 AH-64As, with an option for eight more examples, which could then be increased by a further four. Delivered by sea in June 1995, a total of 20 Apaches is now in service with 1 Tagma Epidolkon Elikopteron (attack helicopter battalion), based at Stefanovikion. US sources have indicated that a further 24 examples are actively being sought.

Greece was the first European export customer for the AH-64 Apache, initially ordering 12 examples.

Filling a requirement for a multi-role armed helicopter to undertake escort, reconnaissance, protection and fire-support missions, the Apache proved to be the clear choice for the Netherlands. Despite objections from economic affairs advisers, the Netherlands announced its decision in favour of the AH-64D Apache on 24 May 1995, and so became the first export customer of this variant. Thirty examples are expected to be delivered during 1998, although the RNLAF AH-64Ds will not be equipped with the mast-mounted Longbow radar. The Apaches will form the centrepiece of the newly-evolving Dutch rapid deployment Air Mobile Brigade.

Middle East customers

A host of Arab clients have also placed orders for the AH-64 Apache, following its performance in the Gulf War. With cost being of little concern to these oil-rich states, the United Arab Emirates Air Force received its first AH-64 Apache at a handover ceremony in Abu Dhabi on 3 October 1993, with deliveries continuing throughout the year. A total of 20 examples are based at Al Dhafra, and a further 10 aircraft are on order.

Saudi Arabia received 12 AH-64As in 1993 for its Army Aviation Command, based at King Khalid Military City. The Apaches operate alongside Bell 406CS Combat Scouts in hunter-killer teams, but it is not known whether Saudi Arabia received AGM-114 Hellfire missiles.

Egypt received a substantial arms package ($318 million) from the US in March 1995. This included 36 AH-64As, four spare Hellfire launchers, 34 rocket pods, six additional T700 engines, and one spare optical and laser turret – an additional 12 Apaches were also requested. All aircraft were to be of the latest US Army standard, with embedded GPS, but with a localised radio fit. The Egyptian Apaches are believed

Israel's Apache fleet has been particularly publicity-shy. Despite the substantial number of the aircraft that have been delivered over the years, only one squadron has been acknowledged to any extent by the Israelis. Although not officially identified, this is known to be No. 113 'Wasp' Squadron (badge seen opposite). The AH-64A Apache is known as the Peten (cobra) in IDF/AF service. It has been used extensively against the terrorist group, Hizbollah, operating alongside Hughes 500MDs.

to have been allocated to the air force's single attack helicopter regiment.

Combat operations
Reformed on 12 September 1990, Israel's No. 113 Squadron

became the country's first operational Apache unit. In August/ September 1993, Israel received a further 24 AH-64As (plus two UH-60As) from surplus US Army Europe stocks, as a 'thank you' for support during Operation Desert Storm. All

were delivered by C-5 from Ramstein AFB. The arrival of these aircraft led to the establishment of the IDF/AF's second AH-64 squadron. During November 1991, Israel became the first foreign AH-64 operator to use its aircraft in combat,

when Hizbollah targets in southern Lebanon were attacked.

Future operators
Kuwait's requirements for a new attack helicopter led to its decision to acquire the AH-64 Apache. At present, however, the deal seems unlikely following the purchase of Hellfire-capable Sikorsky UH-60L Blackhawks.

Bahrain and the Republic of Korea have both expressed interest in the AH-64, although both deals have fallen through.

AH-64A APACHE

Israel became an AH-64A Apache operator in September 1990, since when its AH-64As have seen combat on the Israeli front line of southern Lebanon. On 16 February 1992, for

example, a pair of AH-64As carried out an ambush on the convoy carrying Hizbollah's Secretary-General, Abbas Musawi, along the mountainous road from Jibchit to Sidon.

The precision of the Apache's Hellfire system is greatly valued in attacks on small terrorist targets, which are frequently surrounded by civilian buildings and infrastructure.

IDF/AF AH-64A markings
Unlike any other of its combat helicopters, the IDF/AF's Apaches are painted in an (IR-suppressive) olive drab finish. Squadron badges (in the case of No. 113 Sqn at least) are regularly seen. For operations in southern Lebanon, aircraft carry an IR-reflective 'V' identification marking on the rear of the fuselage.

Weapons pylons
The Apache's external stores pylons are articulated to provide the desired elevation for various fire control modes and for aerodynamic/handling purposes. When an Apache lands, the pylons automatically translate to ground stow mode, so that they are parallel with level terrain.

Audio warning system
In addition to visual cues, critical threat warning and aircraft malfunctions are relayed as aural warnings through the crew's headsets. The crew members also receive a tonal signal to indicate that they are transmitting in secure radio mode.

Wire strike protection
Wire cutters are located forward of the nose turret, below the rotor hub, in front of the gun, and on both main landing gear legs. These have proved highly effective when operating over urban areas.

Main landing gear
The Apache's main landing gear has shock struts to absorb impact and a kneeling facility to allow for air transportation. Each landing strut has a one-time, high-impact absorbing capability, so reducing injury to the crew in the event of a forced landing.

Chaff/flare fit
The Apache can carry removable 30-round M130 chaff dispensers on a mounting to the rear of the tail boom, to starboard. The M130 can fire M1 chaff cartridges to defeat radar-guided weapons.

Post-Desert Storm combat operations

Armed with Hellfire missiles and Hydra-70 rocket pods, an AH-64A from the United Arab Emirates Air Force's 69th ACG lifts off on a policing mission in Kosovo. The UAE's Apaches were airlifted to Skopje in Macedonia by chartered Il-76 transports.

Since the end of the 1991 Gulf War, US Army Apaches have been involved in three UN/NATO peacekeeping efforts. Meanwhile, Israel's AH-64s have regularly been in action against guerrilla factions in Lebanon and Palestine.

In the immediate aftermath of Desert Shield, during which the US Army's Apache had distinguished itself, the type was called back into action to support UN peacekeeping efforts in northern Iraq. As part of Operation Provide Comfort, the operation to protect Iraq's Kurd population from Saddam Hussein's army following an abortive uprising, AH-64As were deployed from the 6/6 CAV 'Sixshooters' to Turkey. On 24 April 1991 the Apaches air-deployed from their base at Illesheim in Germany, achieving some 23 hours of flight time on the way. They were then used to provide armed escort for UN transport helicopters flying supplies in to Kurdish refugee camps in the mountains of northern Iraq, and were particularly useful in deterring Iraqi army operations at night.

When the US Army finally entered the Balkans theatre in December 1995, the deployment of the 1st Armored Division from its German bases was spearheaded and protected by AH-64As from the 2-227th and 3-227th Attack Helicopter Battalions, normally based at Hanau. The Apaches deployed ahead of the main force, first to Taszar in Hungary where the US force was assembling, and then on to Zupanje in Croatia, in order to protect engineers building a pontoon bridge over the River Sava. Finally, the Apaches settled at Tuzla.

As the lead element of IFOR (Implementation Force), the 1st Armored Division was involved in separating the warring factions in Bosnia. The Apaches were busy flying border patrols along the Zone of Separation in order to deter any infringements, and also escorted transport helicopters and ground convoys. They were used to provide security during many operations, including VIP

The AH-64 was designed for rapid deployment, either by air (in this case a C-5 Galaxy), by ship or under its own power. External tanks can be carried for long-range ferry flights.

visits. At the end of 1996, with Bosnia stable, the Apaches returned to Germany.

Task Force Hawk

When NATO launched Operation Allied Force against Yugoslavia on 24 March 1999, there were no official plans to deploy Apaches. On 4 April, however, the Pentagon announced that the attack helicopter would be

deployed. Much fanfare surrounded this announcement, as many commanders and politicians had been calling for the type's use since the first days of the war. However, the deployment of Task Force Hawk, as the Apache force was known, was to be something of a PR disaster.

Twenty-four AH-64As were deployed from the 11th Aviation

Right: After operating from Camp Able Sentry in Macedonia for some months, the Kosovo policing Apache force moved forward into the region itself, setting up at Camp Bondsteel (illustrated).

Below: Apaches from the 1st Battalion, 1st Aviation Regiment are seen during Kosovo operations. As well as pre-planned missions, the Apache force kept two aircraft on ground alert.

Regiment's 2/6 CAV and 6/6 CAV at Illesheim. Supporting them were 26 UH-60L Black Hawks and CH-47D Chinooks (the latter to provide forward air refuelling points), and a massive force of armour and troops to ensure the Apache's protection on the ground. One source at the time suggested it would take 115 missions by C-17 to airlift the entire Task Force Hawk to its base at Rinas in Albania.

Deployment got under way on 14 April, but the Apaches were held up at Pisa in Italy for some days, before the first arrived at Tirana on 21 April. By 26 April the Apaches were finally all in-country, but on that day one was lost when it hit a tree during a daylight training sortie. On 4 May a second was lost, this time at night. The two-man crew was killed, and represented the first NATO fatalities of the campaign. Training continued, but the Allied Force air operations ceased on 9 June without the much-heralded Task Force Hawk having ever fired a shot in anger.

Aerial policing

However, on the following day, a dozen 6/6 CAV Apaches

deployed forward as Task Force 12 to Camp Able Sentry, Petrovec in Macedonia, in preparation for Joint Guardian, the operation to occupy Kosovo following the Serb withdrawal. On 12 June, the Apaches were the first NATO helicopters to cross into Kosovo, scouting ahead and then escorting British Pumas and Chinooks taking in the first troops. Escort and policing missions were flown throughout the short duration insertion operation.

Apaches took centre-stage in the operations which followed. In several instances, Albanian terrorists gave themselves up when confronted with a hovering Apache. In December 1999 the force moved to Camp Bondsteel in Kosovo. By this time the original 6/6 CAV aircraft had been replaced by eight from B Co, 1/1 AVN 'Wolfpack', and also six aircraft from the UAE Air Force's 69th Air Combat Group.

In late 2000, Apaches

The UAE Apaches shared policing duties in Kosovo with the US Army aircraft. The deployment provided the UAE personnel with valuable experience of operations.

embarked on another peacekeeping operation, marking the first operational deployment for the AH-64D, and the first for the Apaches of the Royal Netherlands Air Force. Four aircraft were deployed from Gilze-Rijen to the French colonial outpost of Djibouti, from where they are assisting UN forces in policing the uneasy ceasefire between Ethiopia and Eritrea. Operations in Afghanistan (Enduring Freedom) and Iraq (Iraqi Freedom) showed that the Apache, designed to destroy enemy armour from a safe distance, could be vulnerable to ground fire in certain circumstances. In Afghanistan, about 80 per cent of the Apaches deployed were damaged to some extent, and during the second Gulf War many were damaged by close-range small arms fire while operating in urban areas.

The grapes of wrath

By far the most active of the Apache users has been Israel, where the Apache is known as the Peten (Cobra) In 1996

Operation Grapes of Wrath was launched, a major anti-guerrilla offensive into southern Lebanon. Apaches led off the assault with a precision strike against a Hizbollah headquarters in southern Beirut, and were heavily used throughout the fighting.

In early 2000 this simmering conflict flared up again in advance of the Israeli withdrawal from southern Lebanon. Again Apaches were in the thick of the action, attacking Hizbollah forces which had been firing over the border into Israel, and flying missions in support of the Israel-backed South Lebanon Army. On 24 May the last Israeli troop left Lebanese soil.

However, the Peten fleet has subsequently seen continued employment on retaliatory strikes across the border. During 2001, AH-64s were also employed in retaliatory attacks flown into Palestine (in the former West Bank area). Targets such as Palestine Authority police stations were singled out and, due to their urban locations, they required pinpoint attacks to minimise collateral damage.

Mil Mi-24/25/35 'Hind'

The ferocious-looking Mi-24 'Hind' became the symbol of the Soviet Union's involvement in the Afghanistan war, performing countless ground-support missions. The type was also exported to a host of client states, seeing extensive combat throughout Asia and the Middle East.

Above: The Indian air force operates the export sub-variants of the Mi-24, known as the Mi-25 and Mi-35. They serve with No. 104, No. 116 and No. 125 Units at Pathankot in northern India.

The Mil Mi-24 'Hind' has become one of the most widely-known assault helicopter gunships in the world. Its impressive firepower and the vast numbers available meant that it was the backbone of first-line assault helicopter regiments of the former Warsaw Pact nations. It was therefore of major concern to NATO planners who estimated that, in the event of war, Allied forces would encounter hundreds of 'Hinds' over the European front lines during the opening stages of an armoured assault.

Although now regarded as an assault helicopter, the 'Hind' entered service with the Soviet armed forces as the 'Hind-A', which was viewed by Western analysts as no more than an armed transport. Soviet interest in armed helicopters had really been kindled as a result of watching US involvement in Vietnam, when the advantages of such a machine in the assault role became clear. Mil Mi-4 'Hounds' were hastily modified with racks for rocket pods and air-to-surface missiles, or were fitted with machine-guns. The development of dedicated attack and escort helicopters by the Americans was watched with great interest and, in the late 1960s, the Mil Design Bureau was told to develop a similar machine. The project commenced under the leadership of Mikhail Mil himself.

The Mil Mi-24 was developed from the tried and tested, combat-proven Mil Mi-8 'Hip' assault transport. The 'Hind' utilised the basic power-train and dynamic system of the 'Hip', its five-bladed main rotor redesigned with a smaller diameter, and the tail rotor moved to the port side of the tail boom. A new fuselage was designed, with a narrower cross-section which minimised drag and the target area presented to enemy air defences.

The new helicopter was first seen by the West at East German airfields in 1974. It was dubbed the 'Hind', but it was then realised that there was a pre-production version with simpler horizontal wings without the missile launchers, so the standard version was called the 'Hind-A' and the pre-production type was termed the 'Hind-B'. The name 'Hind-C' was then

Seen undergoing maintenance at the Syrzan Air Force Academy, Volga Military District, are these 'Hind-D' trainers. The nose gun and ammunition doors are faired over and the air data sensor boom is deleted. The majority of training 'Hinds' were converted from standard attack 'Hind-Ds' and 'Hind-Es'.

A pair of East German 'Hind-Ds' on patrol. East Germany used its 'Hinds' on border patrols, especially along the Berlin Wall. In the event of a European war, NATO planners foresaw hundreds of Mi-24s being used in the initial opening assault.

given to a supposed model without the nose gun and chin sight. Only a few of these early 'Hinds', if any, remain in service, and those that do serve as trainers or squadron hacks. Few examples were exported, but those operated by Afghanistan, Algeria, Libya and Vietnam undertook combat patrol missions along each nation's borders.

Operational experience with the initial Mi-24s soon showed that the original concept was slightly flawed. The type's ground-attack potential was clearly reduced when carrying troops, and it was realised that this role was better suited to

less agile helicopters like the Mil Mi-8. As the Mi-24's transport role declined, its attack capability became progressively more important. It soon became apparent that the greenhouse canopy of the 'Hind-A' gave less than perfect all-round visibility, and offered the crew little protection. The solution was to redesign the Mi-24 with an entirely new nose, with heavily-armoured tandem cockpits for the pilot (rear) and gunner (front). These were covered by bubble canopies, with bulletproof armoured glass windscreens. The pilot's cockpit canopy incorporated a large door which opened to starboard,

while the front canopy hinged sideways to port. The new arrangement gave a much smaller frontal area, improved visibility and reduced drag.

Under the nose was fitted a stabilised turret housing a completely new four-barrelled YakB 12.7-mm (0.5-in) Gatling gun. Beside the new gun turret were a missile guidance pod and a laser rangefinder. The cabin itself retained its seats, but came to be regarded as a space for stowing AT-2 'Swatter' anti-tank missiles. Designated 'Hind-D' by NATO, the new gunship model was produced at a rate of 15 examples per month at its peak, with hundreds being exported to the Warsaw Pact and client states.

But it was the Soviet army that first undertook combat operations with the new gunship model, in Afghanistan. Operating alongside the Sukhoi Su-25 'Frogfoot', the 'Hind-Ds' quickly became one of the Soviet weapons most feared by the *mujaheddin*. Providing close air support and convoy escort capabilities, the 'Hinds' were able to pursue the enemy to their hide-outs. Only the introduction of the American shoulder-launched Stinger SAM by the CIA affected the abilities of the Mi-24. Other operators were quick to exploit the capabilities of Mil's new attack helicopter; the war between Iran and Iraq saw 'Hinds' engaging in air-to-air combat, with Iraqi examples downing Iranian Cobra gunships and even F-4 Phantom IIs.

Spurred on by combat experience in Afghanistan, the 'Hind-F' saw the introduction of a larger-calibre cannon. With the nose turret deleted and a GSh-30-2 twin-barrelled 30-mm (1.18-in) cannon mounted on the starboard side of the forward fuselage.

In recent years, at least two 'Hind' reconnaissance variants have been produced for the Russian army. Identified by NATO as the 'Hind-G', the Mil-24RKR is charged with NBC reconnaissance, picking up soil samples to ascertain the spread of nuclear fallout. The other reconnaissance variant, the Mi-24K or 'Hind-G2', serves as an artillery fire correction platform. Equipped with a large camera mounted in the cabin, it serves only in limited numbers with the Soviet armed forces.

The abolition of the Warsaw Pact has meant that examples of the Mi-24 have found their way into NATO hands. The reunification of Germany saw large numbers of former East German Mi-24s being absorbed into the air force but, after being thoroughly evaluated, all examples were retired to comply with limits set by the CFE (Conventional Forces in Europe) Treaty. Shrinking Russian defence budgets have led to the production of de-militarised 'Hind' variants for service with Russia's police force. Russian army aviation now awaits the introduction of pure gunships, namely the Kamov Ka-50 'Hokum' or Mil Mi-28 'Havoc'.

To celebrate the 20th anniversary of the Czech Air Force's 51st Helicopter Regiment at Prostejov (which disbanded in October 1994), a Mi-24 'Hind-D' from the 1st Letka was painted in a smart 'tiger' colour scheme. It appeared at a number of air shows throughout Europe as one half of the unit's two-ship display team.

▶

Mi-24D 'Hind-D'

This heavily-armed 'Hind-D' is part of a Soviet assault helicopter squadron which belonged to the 16th Air Army, Group of Soviet Forces, based in East Germany during the early 1980s. The 'Hind' gave Soviet commanders a dedicated anti-armour and attack capability that had been lacking since the withdrawal of Ilyushin's World War II-vintage Il-2 *Shturmovik*. As the most important helicopter to enter Soviet service during the Cold War period, the Mi-24 arrived in Germany in force in 1974. These early 'Hind-As', along with a small number which may have been delivered in 1973, were divided between two regiments at Parchim and Stendal. The 'Hind-D' began to reach the front-line units in 1976 and was supplanted and eventually all but replaced by the Mi-24V 'Hind-E' from 1979. By 1989, a handful of 'Hind-Ds' remained with the Soviet forces in Germany, and just eight were on charge at the time of the Soviet withdrawal in 1992. This withdrawal, in the wake of German reunification, marked the end of a massive Soviet presence in East Germany which, in 1990, had reached a total of 363,690 military personnel, 5,880 tanks, 9,790 armoured vehicles, 4,624 artillery pieces, 625 combat aircraft and 698 combat helicopters.

Cabin
When the 'Hind-A' entered service, it was thought that the aircraft would have an important role in the rapid movement of troops on the battlefield. With the type in service, it soon became clear that this was a task better suited to transport-dedicated helicopters such as the Mi-8 and, with the major re-design that created the 'Hind-D' from the 'Hind-A' came a shift in mission priority towards the anti-armour and attack roles.

Retractable undercarriage
With high-speed flight an important Mi-24 capability, a retractable undercarriage was a necessity. The main units retract backwards, with the wheels swivelling to lie within bulged fairings on the lower fuselage sides, while the nosewheel retracts backwards to a partially-covered position.

AT-2 'Swatter' ATGMs

An endplate at the tip of each stub-wing carries two launch rails for the AT-2 ATGM (anti-tank guided missile). This second-generation anti-tank weapon (illustrated) may have been introduced in wire-guided form, but was used exclusively in radio command-guided form by the Mi-24. Having entered service in the 1960s, the AT-2 was approaching obsolescence when replaced by the 9M114 Shturm (AT-6 'Spiral') from 1978. 'Spiral' has since become the standard 'Hind' guided missile and, while it shares the radio-command guidance of the earlier AT-2, the AT-6 is tube-launched and has increased range and penetrative power. It seems likely that the AT-6 has a limited air-to-air capability, a factor which makes the 'Hind' a formidable anti-helicopter aircraft, especially in its 'Hind-F' form with 30-mm (1.18-in) cannon.

Tractor tail rotor

Both early 'Hind-As' and pre-production 'Hind-Ds' had their tail rotors mounted on the starboard side of the tailboom. In this case, the tail rotor acted as a pusher unit, pushing against the torque generated by the main rotor and keeping the helicopter laterally stable. Production 'Hind-Ds' and late 'As' featured a tractor tail rotor mounted to port. This pulls against main rotor torque and the revised location leads to improved yaw control (especially in the hover) and eliminates an early problem of aerodynamic masking of the tail rotor by its pylon.

UV-32-57 rocket pods

A total of four 16-round 57-mm (2.24-in) rocket pods can be carried, one on each of the underwing pylons. The rocket is a highly effective area weapon, backing up both the 'Hind's' cannon and guided-missile armament to give it a high degree of versatility and combat persistence over the battlefield. Experience in Afghanistan soon revealed that the four-barrelled 12.7-mm (0.5-in) machine-gun of the 'Hind-D' lacked the 'punch' for some targets, while rockets or guided missiles represented an expensive case of overkill. The solution was therefore found to be a gun of higher calibre and Mil produced two answers to the requirement. Both the Mi-24P 'Hind-F' with its twin-barrelled 30-mm (1.18-in) GSh-30-2 cannon mounted on the fuselage side, and the less successful Mi-24VP with a turret-mounted GSh-23 23-mm (0.9-in) cannon, have seen service.

Mi-24 'Hind'

Briefing

In addition to its normal underwing load of rocket pods and guided-missiles, the 'Hind' is capable of carrying a variety of stores including bombs, napalm tanks and fuel tanks, as illustrated by these Czech 'Hind-Es'.

Mi-24RCh & -24K 'Hind-G1 & G-2'

Cutaway key
1 Remotely-controlled camera (Mi-24K) mounted beneath nose cannon barbette
2 Hinged lens cover
3 Low-speed precision airflow sensors
4 Air data sensor boom
5 IFF antenna
6 Armoured windscreen panel
7 Windscreen wiper
8 Gunsight
9 Pitot heads
10 Turret mechanism
access doors
11 Ammunition feed mechanism
12 Four-barrelled 9-A-624 12.7-mm (0.50-in) rotary machine-gun with 1,470 rounds
13 Gun turret; ±20° traverse and +20°/-60° elevation/depression
14 Radar warning antenna
15 Retractable landing lamp
16 Boarding step
17 Kick-in steps
18 Oxygen bottle
19 Weapons Systems Officer (WSO) hatch
20 Collective pitch
control column, flying controls duplicate in front cockpit
21 WSO's seat
22 Safety harness
23 Side console panel
24 WSO's hatch, open position
25 Cabin-mounted camera pallet (Mi-24K)
26 Hinged lens aperture, replaces starboard cabin door
27 Film magazine
28 Cabin-mounted data-link console (Mi-24RCh)
29 Pilot's entry door
30 Armoured windscreen panel
31 Windscreen wiper
32 Head-up-display
33 Instrument panel shroud
34 Cyclic pitch control column
35 Yaw control rudder pedals
36 Underfloor control linkages
37 Search light
38 Nosewheel leg door and indicator light
39 Levered suspension axle beam
40 Aft-retracting twin nosewheels
41 Conditioned air ducting (ammunition magazine on starboard side)
42 Nosewheel bay (semi-retracted housing)
43 Cockpit section armoured skin panelling
44 Cyclic pitch control lever
45 Fuel cocks
46 Circuit-breaker panel
47 Oxygen bottle
48 Rear view mirror
49 Pilot's seat
50 Engine air intake vortex-type dust/debris extractors
51 Debris ejection chute
52 Intake cowling
53 Generator cooling air intake
54 Starboard engine cowling/hinged work platform
55 Engine bay dividing firewall
56 Accessory equipment gearbox

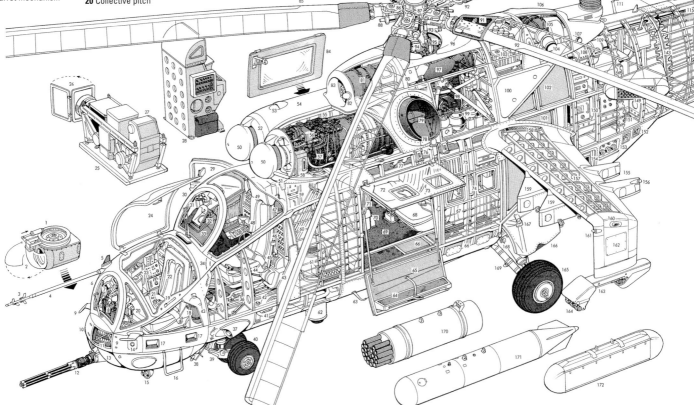

SPECIFICATION

Mi-24D 'Hind-D'

Dimensions

Length overall, rotors turning: 19.79 m (64 ft 11 in)
Fuselage length (excluding rotors and gun): 17.51 m (57 ft 5½ in)
Main rotor diameter: 17.30 m (56 ft 9 in)
Tail rotor diameter: 3.91 m (12 ft 10 in)
Height overall, rotors turning: 6.50 m (21 ft 4 in)
Height to top of rotor head: 4.44 m (14 ft 6¾ in)
Main rotor disc area: 235 m² (2,529.52 sq ft)
Tail rotor disc area: 11.99 m² (129.12 sq ft)
Wingspan: 6.54 m (21 ft 5½ in)
Tailplane span: 3.27 m (10 ft 9 in)
Wheel base: 4.39 m (14 ft 5 in)
Wheel track: 3.03 m (9 ft 11½ in)
Maximum rotor disc loading: 51.05 kg/m² (10.46 lb/sq ft)

Powerplant

Two 1640-kW (2,200-shp) Klimov (Isotov) TV3-117 Series III turboshafts

Weights

Empty: 8400 kg (18,519 lb)
Normal take-off: 11000 kg (24,250 lb)
Maximum take-off: 12500 kg (27,557 lb)

Fuel and load

Internal fuel: 1500 kg (3,307 lb) or 2130 litres (469 Imp gal) plus provision for 1000 kg (2,205 lb) or 850 litres (187 Imp gal) of auxiliary fuel in an optional cabin tank
External fuel (with auxiliary internal tank removed): 1200 kg (2,646 lb) in four 500-litre (110-Imp gal) drop tanks
Maximum ordnance: 2400 kg (5,291 lb)

Performance

Maximum level speed 'clean' at optimum altitude: 168 kt (310 km/h; 192 mph)
Maximum cruising speed at optimum altitude: 140 kt (260 km/h; 162 mph)
Maximum rate of climb at sea level: 750 m (2,461 ft) per minute
Service ceiling: 4500 m (14,765 ft)
Hovering ceiling (out-of-ground effect): 7,220 ft (2200 m)

Range

Maximum range, internal fuel only: 405 nm (750 km; 466 miles)
Combat radius with maximum military load: 86 nm (160 km/99 miles)
Combat radius with two drop tanks: 135 nm (250 km/155 miles)
Combat radius with four drop tanks: 155 nm (288 km/179 miles)

Armament

One four-barrelled 12.7-mm (0.5-in) YakB-12.7 Gatling-type machine-gun in remotely-controlled undernose USPU-24 turret, plus four 9M17P Skorpion (AT-2 'Swatter') radio-guided anti-tank missiles, and four UV-32 rocket pods each containing 32 S-5 57-mm (2.24-in) unguided rockets; or four twenty-round B-8V-20 80-mm (3.15-in) S-8 rocket pods; or four five-round B-13L 130-mm (5.12-in) S-13 rocket pods; or four 240-mm (9.45-in) S-24B rockets. Possible underwing stores also include UPK-23-250 gun pods containing one GSh-23L twin-barrelled 23-mm (0.9-in) cannon; GUV gun pods containing one four-barrelled 12.7-mm (0.5-in) machine-gun or two four-barrelled 7.62-mm (0.3-in) 9-A-622 machine-guns or one 30-mm (1.18-in) AGS-17 Plamia grenade launcher; bombs, mine dispensers and napalm tanks

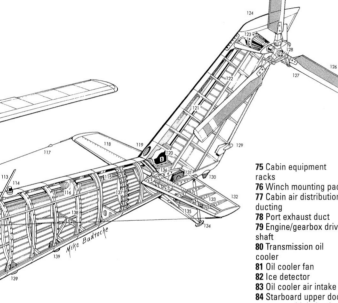

The Mi-24DU 'Hind-D' trainer saw extensive use in the Soviet Union, for training both Soviet pilots and those of client nations, almost all of whom sent their students to the USSR. These helicopters belonged to the Syzran Air Force Academy.

57 Klimov TV3-117 turboshaft engine
58 Engine oil tank
59 Starboard side avionics equipment racks
60 Flight control rods
61 Cabin air filtration system equipment
62 Cabin air intake
63 Ventral aerial mast
64 Boarding step
65 Cabin lower door segment
66 Underfloor fuel tanks Nos 4 and 5, total internal fuel capacity 1940 litres (427 Imp gal)
67 Cabin equipment consoles
68 Observer's seat
69 Main cabin floor panelling
70 Starboard side data-link console (Mi-24RCh)
71 Door interconnecting linkage
72 Tactical navigator's seat
73 Upper door segment
74 Cabin rear window panels

75 Cabin equipment racks
76 Winch mounting pads
77 Cabin air distribution ducting
78 Port exhaust duct
79 Engine/gearbox drive shaft
80 Transmission oil cooler
81 Oil cooler fan
82 Ice detector
83 Oil cooler air intake
84 Starboard upper door segment with bulged observation window (Mi-24RCh)
85 Five-bladed main rotor
86 Blade root hinge joints
87 Titanium rotor head
88 Hydraulic drag dampers
89 Hydraulic reservoir
90 Blade root cuffs
91 Blade spar crack indicator (pressurised nitrogen-filled)
92 Electric leading-edge de-icing
93 Blade pitch control rods
94 Swash plate mechanism
95 Rotor head actuating linkage
96 Rotor head fairing
97 Main reduction gearbox
98 Gearbox mounting struts
99 Fire extinguisher bottles

100 Fuel system equipment access
101 Main fuselage tank No. 3
102 Collector tanks Nos 1 & 2
103 Rotor head control hydraulic module
104 APU exhaust
105 AI-9V auxiliary power unit
106 Hinged access panels
107 Air system vent
108 Auxiliary equipment gearbox
109 Generator
110 L-166V-11E Ispanka, microwave-pulse infra-red jammer
111 Aerial lead-in
112 UHF aerial mast
113 VHF aerial
114 Anti-collision light
115 Tail rotor transmission shaft
116 Transmission shaft bearings
117 HF aerial cable
118 Starboard all-moving tailplane
119 Gearbox cooling air intake
120 Bevel drive gearbox
121 Tail rotor drive shaft
122 Tail pylon construction
123 Final drive right-angle gearbox
124 Pylon tip fairing
125 Three-bladed tail rotor
126 Aluminium alloy tail rotor blades

127 Electric leading-edge de-icing
128 Blade pitch control mechanism
129 Tail navigation light
130 Lower IFF antenna
131 Flight recorder
132 Port all-moving tailplane
133 Tailplane rib construction
134 Tail bumper
135 Aft-facing camera mounting
136 Tailplane spar pivot mounting
137 Tail assembly joint frame
138 Tailcone frame and stringer construction
139 Radar altimeter antennas
140 Signal cartridge firing unit
141 Short-wave aerial cable
142 DISS-15D gyromagnetic compass units
143 Tailcone joint frame
144 Hollow D-section titanium blade spar
145 Honeycomb trailing-edge panels
146 Glass-fibre skin panelling
147 Fixed blade tab
148 Leading-edge anti-erosion sheath
149 Chaff-flare dispensers, port and starboard
150 Rear avionics equipment bay

151 Ventral access hatch
152 Ground power socket
153 Pneumatic system around connectors
154 Battery bay, both sides
155 Wing pylon tail fairings
156 Radar warning antenna
157 Stub wing rib and spar structure
158 Stub wing attachment joints
159 Port stores pylons
160 Port navigation light
161 Radar warning antenna
162 Stub wing endplate pylon fairing
163 'Clutching-hand' ground sample collector
164 Hydraulically-operated scoops, three per side
165 Port mainwheel
166 Mainwheel leg door
167 Mainwheel leg aft pivot mounting
168 Shock absorber strut
169 Undercarriage indicator light
170 UV-32A-24 rocket launcher
171 PTB-450 500-litre (110-Imp gal) auxiliary fuel tank
172 Container store

Right: With its manoeuvrability, power and speed, the 'Hind' is a spectacular air show performer. With the help of Western sponsorship, Russia's Berkut (Golden Eagles) team flew a mix of Mi-24V, Mi-24P and Mi-24VP aircraft in a formation routine. The 'Hinds' used modified rocket pods to produce smoke during their display.

Left: The close confines of a woodland clearing emphasise the bulk of this Soviet 'Hind-E'. The 'Hind' is considerably larger than the majority of dedicated attack helicopters to have emerged from the West. While the 'Hind-A' was probably designed as a dual-role helicopter from the outset, later variants (from the 'Hind-D' onwards) were optimised more for the attack role, but retained some assault capability.

Below: In addition to playing host to large numbers of Soviet-based Mi-24s, Poland operated its own fleet of Mi-24D 'Hind-Ds'. In 1998, Poland had a strong attack helicopter force, with some 32 Mi-24D 'Hind-Ds'

'Hind' in service

Afghanistan
During the USSR's long drawn-out involvement in Afghanistan, around 60 'Hind-As' and 'Ds' (illustrated) were delivered to the Afghan air force for use against *mujaheddin* rebels. It is likely that Soviet aircraft also flew in Afghan markings.

Angola
Angola received its 'Hind-Ds' (illustrated) in 1983 and these have since been joined by a number of 'Hind-Es'. Around 20 'Hinds' remain in service, flying alongside Mi-8 assault helicopters. It is unlikely that the Mi-24s were used against South African forces.

East Germany
Some 50 'Hinds' (38 Mi-24Ds, 12 Mi-24Ps) were supplied to East Germany. With the reunification of Germany, the aircraft were retired from service, although the Luftwaffe's test squadron still lists the Mi-24D/P as part of its experimental inventory.

Libya
Traditionally on good terms with Moscow, Libya was an early recipient of the 'Hind-A' (illustrated). Today, the air force flies around 21 Mi-24s, consisting of the Mi-24D 'Hind-D' and Mi-24P 'Hind-E'. The first of Libya's 'Hinds' was delivered in 1978.

▶

'Hind' at war

The war in Afghanistan has continued since the Soviet withdrawal in 1988. Various warlords tore the Afghan air force apart in the 1990s, using its assets against each other. This Mi-24, seen to the north of Kabul in 1997, was being flown by the Taliban militia.

There has never been a helicopter like the 'Hind'. Combining speed with firepower, it was known as 'The Devil's Chariot' to the Afghan Mujahideen – but to its crews, it was always the 'Krokodil'.

Although some 'Hinds' in Afghanistan are still serviceable, most have been grounded by the lack of spares and skilled personnel able to maintain the complex machines.

The 'Hind' first saw action in Somalia early in 1978. Flown by Cuban pilots, 'Hinds' spearheaded General Siad Barré's drive into neighbouring Ethiopia. The 'Hinds' proved highly effective, and were to go on to play a full part in the fighting endemic in the Horn of Africa over the next decade.

In December 1979, the President of Afghanistan was murdered, and the puppet government which 'took office' on the same day invited the USSR to crush opposition. The whole event had been planned in advance, but what had been miscalculated was the Afghan people's will to resist.

The Soviet invasion took place with great efficiency, but rather than crushing the opposition it was the start of a decade-long war, which for all its military might, Moscow was unable to win.

Afghanistan

The Afghan War was like Algeria 20 years before: a hardy but ill-equipped people fighting a major military power, over rugged and completely undeveloped terrain. Frontal Aviation (FA), the Soviet tactical air force, played a major role in the war. Most of the FA regiments in Afghanistan were fixed-wing units, tasked with the punitive bombing of Afghan towns and villages. However, the most numerous single type was the Mil Mi-24 'Hind'.

Air power cannot occupy and rule an area as can ground troops. However, it can winkle out pockets of resistance, and the 'Hind' was one of the best weapons in that process.

By day and night the Mi-24s continually succeed in pinning down even individual Afghans who were then captured by the helicopter's own infantry or by ground forces summoned by radio. A typical technique was to land eight troops, wait until their advance met resistance and then mount a devastating assault with rockets or anti-tank missiles – the latter being very effective against caves and rock crevices.

Rising losses

Initially, the Mujahideen had little answer to the 'Hind', though several Mi-24s were lost in the early days to accurate fire from high-powered rifles. The big helicopters generally operated in pairs within larger flights of four or eight, attacking targets with guns, rockets, bombs and fuel-air explosives. They also flew escort missions for road convoys, and operated by night as 'Hunter' teams. However, the increasing use of shoulder-launched SAMs meant that losses began to rise, and 'Hinds' were increasingly used to escort transport aircraft into and out of Afghan bases.

Eventually, the Soviet government realised that there was no way to win the war, and in 1988 the Soviet army was pulled out. Over 300 'Hinds' had been lost in combat or on operations in the testing hot and high conditions.

Iraqi 'Hinds'

Even as Frontal Aviation was becoming embroiled in the Afghan mountains, another long-lasting war was to see extensive use of 'Hinds' in combat. During the Iran-Iraq war, Iraqi Mi-24s were used for a variety of close-support and interdiction tasks, occasionally dogfighting with Iranian AH-1J SeaCobras. The Iraqis had slightly the better of the exchanges, though the result of the battle often depended on who saw his opponent first.

After the initial invasion of Kuwait, Iraqi 'Hinds' saw little action during the Gulf War. However, before the war they had been used in Saddam Hussein's genocidal suppression of Kurdish rebels, and after the war saw similar use against Shi'ite rebels in southern Iraq.

Worldwide Combat

The 'Hind' has been widely exported, and it has probably seen more combat than any other military aircraft in service since the 1970s. Libyan Mi-24s were active in the long and bloody civil war in Chad, being used to support Goukouni Oueddi's rebels against the government of Hissen Habre.

'Hinds' have cast their shadows over countless regional flash points in the former Soviet Union. This Mi-24V is seen approaching a mortar post on the Tadjik-Afghan border during the struggle against Islamic insurgents in 1996.

Libyan 'Hinds' helped Oueddi's forces capture the capital of N'djamena in October 1980, but over the next seven years government forces gradually drove the Libyan-backed rebels into defeat.

In 1982, Syrian 'Hinds' achieved some success against Israeli tank forces in the Lebanon. In the mid-1980s, Angolan Mi-24s flown by Cuban and East German pilots, were used by the Marxist MPLA against Jonas Savimbi's UNITA guerrillas, and in 1987 and 1988 inflicted heavy losses on South African troops operating against SWAPO guerrilla bases in the south of the country.

Asian battles

Vietnam took delivery of 'Hinds' in the mid-1980s, and used them in operations against the Khmer Rouge in Cambodia. Indian 'Hinds' were first used against Pakistani troops in 1987, during a border dispute over the Siachin Glacier. Later that year, Indian peacekeepers in Sri Lanka used 'Hinds' to hunt down and kill 'Tamil Tigers' as over the next two years the Indian government tried to bring an end to the Sri

Lankan civil war. The Sri Lankan government acquired its own 'Hinds' in 1995, and the powerful helicopters were used to considerable effect against the Tamils, though three out of the six delivered were shot down or damaged by Stinger missiles and ground fire.

Latin America

A batch of Mi-25Ds were delivered to Nicaragua in 1983 and 1984. They were used by the Sandinista government as attack aircraft and to engage light aircraft being operated by the Contra rebels. When the civil war came to an end in 1990, the Nicaraguans sold their aircraft to the Peruvian government, who used the 'Hinds' in the war against the Maoist 'Shining Path' Guerrillas and the drugs cartels.

A single 'Hind', operating alongside gunship versions of the Mil Mi-17 Hip, made a considerable impact in the confused civil war in Sierra Leone. Initially operated for the government by Belarussian contract personnel, they were later taken over by the South African company Executive Outcomes. EO accomplished

more against the Revolutionary United Front in a week than the government had done on four years, forcing the RUF rebels to call for a (short-lived) cease fire.

Former Soviet Wars

The most extensive use of 'Hinds' in recent years has been in the series of ethnic and regional conflicts which have followed the break-up of the Soviet Union. Even before the break-up, 'Hinds' were used in an attempt to put down the fighting in Nagorni Karabakh. Control of this area had long been disputed by Azerbaijian and Armenia, and after the collapse of the USSR open war broke out between the two countries, with Russian forces being drawn into the conflict.

Similar fighting erupted in Georgia, where first the territory of South Ossetia began to fight for independence, followed by a similar outbreak of fighting in Abkhasia. Russian Mi-24s primarily flew escorts for transport helicopters, but were occasionally called upon to extricate Russian road convoys. In 1992, the trouble in South Ossetia spread to North Ossetia, part of the Russian Federation, and Federal troops were called in to restore order. In the same year Tadjikistan was added to the list of former Soviet republics where 'Hinds' saw action.

The most extensive use of 'Hinds' in recent years has been

in Chechnya. In 1994, four 'Hinds' flown by pro-Russian opposition forces were used against the separatist government of General Dzhokhar Dudayev. In December of that year, the Russian Federation began an all-arms offensive to regain control of the rogue state, which turned into a full-scale war which was to last for at least 18 months.

Two squadrons of Mi-24s were deployed to Chechnya, though they were little used in the street fighting for Grozhnii, the capital. However, they saw a great deal of action in the south, where crews often flew five or six sorties per day. Generally, operations were much more limited than they had been in Afghanistan – logistics problems meant that supplies of fuel and weaponry were limited.

The Balkans

The most recent use of 'Hinds' has been in the Balkans. Croatian 'Hinds' were used in the Yugoslav civil war in 1993 and 1994, while Serbian 'Police 'Hinds' were filmed by news crews attacking positions in Kosovo in 1998. From 1997 Ukrainian Army Mi-24Ps and Mi-24Ks operated in United Nations colours over Osijek and Vukovar in Croatia, patrolling the demilitarised zone between Serb and Croat forces. Macedonian 'Hinds' have been used extensively against Albanian rebels and infiltrators. ▶

Although 'Hinds' gained most of their notoriety for their use in Afghanistan, they have seen conflict all over the world in the last 25 years. Big, fast and hard-hitting, in trained hands they have proved to be fearsome counter-insurgency weapons.

Export variants of the Mi-24 'Hind-F' are known as Mi-35Ps. These probably represent the ultimate derivative of the Mil assault helicopter. Loaded with B-8 rocket pods and AT-6 'Spiral' ATGMs, the 'Hind-F' combines agility with a formidable weaponload.

Mil Mi 24 Missions and weapons

Equipped with a nose-mounted gun and an arsenal of air-to-ground missiles, the 'Hind' is able to unleash an array of weapons directly over the heads of friendly troops. Improvements in anti-tank missiles have seen the 'Hind' emerge as a deadly force over the battlefield.

The Mil Mi-24, dubbed *Gorbatov* (hunchback) by its crews, and known as the 'Devil's Chariot' by Afghan *mujaheddin* guerrillas, is perhaps the best-known dedicated attack helicopter in the world, and certainly one of the most widely used. It is also fundamentally misunderstood, since it differs so dramatically from its Western counterparts.

The ability of the Mi-24 to carry a formidable array of offensive weapons, while being fitted with an internal troop- or cargo-carrying cabin, has led many to misunderstand the aircraft. Some early Western intelligence analyses suggested that the aircraft could fly in the close air support or anti-armour roles, while carrying a full squad of infantry and their weapons, or, more significantly, could land troops and then provide them with fire support. In fact, as might be imagined, weight limitations mean that the Mi-24

is capable of carrying troops, or weapons, but not the two together. When operating in the air assault role, the Mi-24 can carry a partial, but fairly limited, offensive weaponload, and can use these weapons to suppress enemy defences if attempting to land at a 'hot LZ' (landing zone), though generally such tactics went out with the end of the Vietnam War. Most significantly, whatever its mission, the aircraft retains its cannon armament, and has a useful self-defence capability.

Although it has a capacious (if rather low-roofed) cabin, capable of seating eight, the Mi-24 is

First introduced on the 'Hind-D', the nose-mounted gun was reintroduced on later Mi-24 variants, as seen on this Russian army 'Hind-G'. The twin-barrelled GSh-23L 23-mm (0.9-in) cannon is mounted in a USPU-24 power-operated remotely-controlled turret.

seldom used in the transport role. In Russian service, this is normally the responsibility of the Mi-8s (or Mi-17s), alongside which the Mi-24 is inevitably deployed. The Mi-24's high speed, agility and suitability for NoE (Nap of the Earth) flight did make it more suitable than the Mi-17 for certain transport tasks, including the insertion of *Spetsnaz* special forces teams, and missions requiring flight

close to the front line, or at very high speed. Generally, however, the Mi-24's cabin is used to transport the crew's equipment and spares during deployments, and is left empty on operational missions. The cabin also has other uses, even when empty, enabling the flight engineer to move about rapidly, and keep a watch around the helicopter. Moreover, if the wingman is shot down, the Mi-24 pilot can

easily land and pick up any survivors. This instant-response capability was often used in Afghanistan.

But while the Mi-24 is seldom used for simple transport duties, it is extraordinarily well equipped for the role. Rapidly reconfigurable with seats or stretchers, the Mi-24 has sturdy rails running below each window, to which are attached sliding articulated mounts for the passengers' (or crew's) personal weapons (usually AK-47, -74, or AKMS sub-machine-guns). Thus, an Mi-24 can easily be something of a 'porcupine' to any unsuspecting attacker, with its own gun, and up to eight personal weapons firing from the cabin.

The Mi-24's main role is as a gunship or fire-support platform. Although well equipped for anti-armour duties, the Mi-24 is not as narrowly specialised as the AH-64 or TOW Lynx, but instead is designed to attack a wide range of targets. This is in contrast to the primary role of Western attack helicopters, which is the combating of

enemy armour – attacks on non-armoured targets constituting a secondary role, with the aircraft tending to rely on rockets for such missions. Most Russian (and formerly Soviet) concepts of operations see the Mi-24 as supporting the deployment of special forces by helicopter, reacting to and suppressing any enemy threats, rather than specifically going out to kill tanks. Thus, it is routine for the Mi-24 to carry a spectrum of weapons suitable for use against a variety of targets, with four anti-tank guided missiles (ATGMs) under the wingtips, augmented by unguided rockets, free-fall bombs, cluster munitions or gun pods.

Any examination of the Mi-24's missions would be incomplete without reference to two highly-specialised reconnaissance versions of the aircraft. The Mi-24RKR, known to NATO's Air Standards Co-ordinating Committee as 'Hind-G1', is a dedicated battlefield NBC reconnaissance aircraft, with air- and soil-sampling equipment and some onboard analysis capability. The

For ground-support missions, four UV-32-57 rocket pods can be mounted under the stub wings. These proved highly effective against guerrilla strongholds during combat operations in Afghanistan.

aircraft is also fitted with a device below the tailskid designed for planting marker flags. The Mi-24RKR is in surprisingly widespread use, with some six deployed with every attack helicopter regiment of the Russian army, giving a stark indication of the former USSR's preparedness (and perhaps willingness) to fight on a nuclear-, chemically- or biologically- contaminated battlefield.

The second reconnaissance version of the Mi-24 is the closely related Mi-24K. Usually deployed in mixed squadrons beside the Mi-24RKR, the

Mi-24K is a dedicated artillery fire correction platform, with secondary stand-off reconnaissance capabilities. The Mi-24K is fitted with a massive A87P camera in the forward part of the cabin, with a 1300-mm (51.2-in) focal length f8 lens mounted to take starboard oblique imagery, probably at a fixed angle.

Mi-24 variants have also been produced for minesweeping, internal security and even ecological survey, but the majority of the estimated 2,500 produced are used for close air support, anti-armour and assault roles.

Above: Late-model 'Hinds' now carry the Igla AAM although, as yet, this is operated on an experimental basis only. Mounted on the inboard pylon is a B-8V-20 rocket pod. Each pod carries up to twenty 80-mm (3.15-in) S-8 rockets which have proved to be well suited to attacking 'soft' targets on the battlefield.

Right: Introduced on the 'Hind-F' was the GSh-30-2 twin-barrelled 30-mm (1.18in) cannon. This followed combat experience in Afghanistan where the turreted 12.7-mm (0.5-in) machine-gun was found to be ineffective against certain types of target.

Mi-24 'Hind'
Early variants

The awesome 'Hind', once so feared by NATO ground forces, has progressed steadily since its conception. The original variants bear little resemblance to their descendants, which are in operational service with forces worldwide.

Mil V-24 Prototype ('Hind-B')

The Mi-24 prototypes were powered by a pair of 1250 kW (1,700-shp) TV2-117A turboshaft engines, as used on the Mil Mi-8 'Hip'. The aircraft were fitted with a modified version of the Mi-8's five-bladed main rotor, and a three-bladed pusher tail rotor mounted to starboard. The V-24s had provision for detachable stub wings which may have had underslung weapons pylons. No nose gun was fitted and no provision was made for missile guidance. It is believed that the cabin doors were split vertically and hinged outwards, instead of being split horizontally and opening upwards and downwards.

Mil Mi-24A 'Hind-A'

Testing of the 'Hind-B' revealed it was too cramped to accommodate the Raduga-F semi-automatic command line-of-sight (SACLOS) guidance system and the fast-firing machine-gun installation. Thus, two prototypes were converted by cutting off the cockpit section and grafting on a new forward fuselage. The new nose was slightly longer and had a more pointed profile, with more sharply raked upper windshield segments to reduce drag. The car-type pilot's door was replaced by a sliding bubble window to give the pilot some downward vision, and the A-12.7 machine-gun was fitted. A small teardrop fairing for the command link transmitter antenna was located immediately forward of the nose gear.

In this form, the helicopter entered production in Arsen'yev in 1970 as the Mi-24A, aka izdeliye 245. It was in this form that the Mi-24 was seen by NATO for the first time, resulting in the reporting designation designation 'Hind-A' being allocated to this more developed model. Early-production Mi-24As had the tail rotor on the starboard side, as on the Mi-8; when seen from the hub, the tail rotor turned clockwise so that the forward blade went with the main rotor downwash. However, due to poor directional control in some flight modes, in 1972 the tail rotor was relocated to port. The tail rotor still turned clockwise, meaning that the forward blade now went against the main rotor downwash, increasing tail rotor efficiency dramatically. The APU exhaust was also extended and angled downwards to prevent rain getting in.

More than 240 Mi-24As had been built when production ended in 1974. Once again, the seemingly illogical Soviet practice of launching full-scale production even before the aircraft had been officially phased in had paid off, allowing flight and ground crews to familiarise themselves with the helicopter by the time the thumbs-up from the Air Force came. Initially, the Mi-24A was operated by independent helicopter regiments but, later, the helicopter equipped independent combat control helicopter regiments. When the Army Aviation was formed within the Soviet armed forces, Mi-24s equipped independent helicopter squadrons within mechanised infantry divisions. The Mi-24A was also exported (e.g., to Afghanistan, Libya and Vietnam) and has seen action in the Afghan war and various African conflicts.

Mil Mi-24B 'Hind-A'

As the Mi-24A entered production, the Mil OKB continued improving the helicopter's armament. The Mi-24B, or izdeliye 241, featured a USPU-24 powered chin turret with a 12.7-mm (0.5-in) Yakoushev/Borzov YakB-12.7 four-barrelled Gatling-type machine-gun. This was slaved to a KPS-53AV sighting system which automatically made corrections for the helicopter's movement. The system featured an analog computer receiving input from the helicopter's air data sensors.

The manually-guided 9M17M Falanga-M anti-tank missiles gave way to an upgraded version, the 9M17P Falanga-P. The missiles were controlled by the Raduga-F SACLOS guidance system which increased kill probability three to four times. The targeting part of the system comprised low light-level television (LLLTV) and forward-looking infra-red (FLIR) sensors in a slab-sided ventral housing offset to starboard ahead of the nose gear, with twin protective metal doors covering the sensor window. The system was gyro-stabilised, enabling the helicopter to manoeuvre vigorously to avoid ground fire while targeting. The guidance part of the system (the command link antenna) was located symmetrically in a small egg-shaped fairing offset to port which could traverse as the missile manoeuvred, since the antenna dish was fixed.

The Mi-24B full-scale mock-up was probably rebuilt from the original 'Hind-B' mock-up, since it had no wing anhedral and featured the tested-and-failed detachable missile launchers on the fuselage sides. The real thing, however, was converted from several early-production Mi-24As with starboard-side tail rotor. The Mi-24B successfully passed the manufacturer's trials in 1971-72 but was eventually abandoned.

Mil A-10

During 1975, it was revealed that a Soviet helicopter designated A-10 had captured eight world records. Powered by Isotov TV-2-117A engines, the aircraft was a stripped-down early 'Hind-B', with its stub wings removed and was flown by a female civilian crew. The record-breaking flights, conducted between 16 July 1975 and 26 August 1975, included a record 342.6km/h (212.9 mph) over 15 and 25 km (9.32 and 15.53 miles), 334.44 km/h (207.82 mph) over a 100-km (62.13-mile) closed circuit, 332.62 km (206.69 mph) over 1000 km (621.40 miles), a time to climb record of 3000 m (9,843 ft) in two minutes and 33.5 seconds and an altitude record of 6000 m (19,685 ft) (achieved in 7 minutes and 43 seconds).

Mil Mi-24U 'Hind-C'

The Mil Mi-24U was a dedicated trainer version of the 'Hind-A' stripped of all armament but retaining stub wings and equipped with dual controls. Small numbers were supplied to Soviet forces (mainly to second-line training units) and a handful may have been exported alongside 'Hind-As', to Afghanistan, Algeria, Libya and Vietnam. No Mi-24Us are believed to currently be in service.

'Hind' variants

V-24 Prototype

Low-set rotor hub with balance weights

Rear SRO-2M 'Odd Rods' IFF antenna

Doppler behind flush dielectric fairing

No gun

'Hind-B'

No gun

Swept antenna for R-860 UHF

No anhedral stub wing

'Hind-A'

Tail rotor to port

A-12.7 machine-gun

Camera gun in fairing at root of port pylon

SRO-2M 'Odd Rods' IFF antenna

'Hind-C'

R-860 UHF antenna

Gun removed

Strap on chaff/flare dispensers

'Hind-D'

R-860 UHF antenna

Four-barrelled 12.7-mm (0.5-in) machine-gun

U-section antenna for R-828 Eucalypts UHF

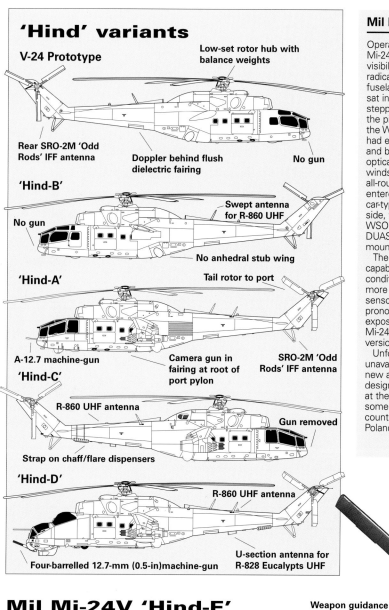

Mil Mi-24D 'Hind-D'

Operational experience with the Mi-24A showed that cockpit visibility was poor, leading to a radical redesign of the forward fuselage in early 1971. The crew sat in separate cockpits in a stepped-tandem arrangement, the pilot sitting above and behind the WSO. The narrow cockpits had extensive armour protection and bubble canopies with large optically-flat bulletproof windscreens that gave far better all-round visibility. The pilot entered via a rearwards-opening car-type door on the starboard side, while the port half of the WSO's cockpit canopy hinged open to starboard. A long air data boom with DUAS-V pitch and yaw vanes offset to starboard and the IFF aerials were mounted on the WSO's canopy frame.

The redesign, besides improving visibility for the crew, also enhanced the capabilities of the Raduga-F LLLTV/FLIR sensors and the operating conditions for the missile guidance antenna. However, this in turn called for more changes. To ensure adequate ground clearance for the LLLTV/FLIR sensor fairing, the nose gear unit was lengthened, giving the helicopter a pronounced nose-up attitude on the ground. The nosewheels were semi-exposed when retracted, so the bulged twin nosewheel doors of the Mi-24A gave way to single door linked to the oleo strut. The dual-cockpit version was allocated the designation Mi-24V.

Unfortunately, its intended armament of Shturm-V ATGMs was still unavailable, forcing the Mil OKB to develop a hybrid – a combination of the new airframe with the 'old' armament system. This stop-gap version was designated Mi-24D or izdeliye 246. In 1973 the Mi-24D entered production at the Progress Aircraft Factory and the Rostov Helicopter Factory, and some 350 had been built when production ended in 1977. A number of countries including Algeria, Azerbaijan, Bulgaria, Cuba, Germany, Hungary, Poland and Russia still operate the type.

Mil Mi-24V 'Hind-E'

This shark-mouthed Polish air force 'Hind-E' belongs to the 56th PSB at Inowroclaw. In Polish service, the 'Hind-E' is known as the Mi-24W, rather than as the Mi-24V. Poland received 16 Mi-24Ws and the one aircraft that was lost in service was replaced.

Weapon guidance
The standard undernose electro-optical package is carried to starboard with a new, fixed Shturm V guidance antenna in a fixed fairing with hemispherical radome to port.

Powerplant
The Mil Mi-24V is powered by a pair of Isotov TV-3-117V turboshaft engines, which provided greater power and endowed superior high-altitude performance. The Mi-24V designation may derive from the engine designation.

Markings
This aircraft is painted in standard Soviet ground forces aviation camouflage, with serial numbers applied in small white characters to the tailboom, and with the national marking on the rear fuselage sides.

Defensive systems
The Mi-24V can carry an L-166V-1AE Ispanka IR jammer above the rear fuselage, with 32-round ASO-2V chaff/flare launchers in triple clusters below the tailboom or scabbed onto the fuselage sides. This aircraft like most current Mi-24Vs and Mi-24Ws has prominent pylon-mounted L-006 Beryoza RHAWS antennas below the sides of the gunner's canopy.

Armament
The 'Hind-E' is armed with a four-barrelled 12.7-mm (0.5-in) machine-gun with 1,470 rounds of ammunition. Also carried are four AT-6 'Spiral' launch tubes in pairs on the endplate pylons, with gun pods on the inboard underwing pylons. These gun pods each contain a GSh-23L 23-mm (0.9-in) cannon.

Late 'Hind' variants

The later Mi-24 variants, beginning with the Mi-24V, introduced new engines and improved anti-tank missiles in the light of operational experience.

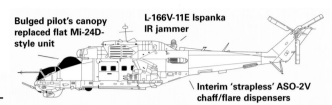

Bulged pilot's canopy replaced flat Mi-24D-style unit

L-166V-11E Ispanka IR jammer

Interim 'strapless' ASO-2V chaff/flare dispensers

Mi-24V 'Hind-E'

Developed in parallel with the Mi-24D, the Mi-24V features the definitive airframe/engine/missile combination. The Mi-24V first flew in 1976, but Shturm missile development problems delayed service introduction until 1979 (two years after the Mi-24D). Early Mi-24Vs differed little from the Mi-24D, lacking PZU engine intake filters and having much the same avionics fit and antenna configuration. The only visible changes were the new fixed Shturm-V guidance antenna pod for the 9M114 Shturm (AT-6 'Spiral') missile, and the addition of attachment points for the new missile's launch rails. The Mi-24V rapidly began to replace the Mi-24D in Soviet service, and it is possible that some of the earlier versions were recycled through the factory prior to export, or for upgrade to the later standard. As the major Soviet service variant, the Mi-24V was subjected to many improvements. It is believed that the first Mil Mi-24Vs retained the same engines as the Mi-24D, and that the improved TV-3-117V was introduced during production. New downward-pointing engine exhausts and associated IR suppressors were almost certainly developed for later production batches of the new variant, and then applied to the earlier Mi-24D and later Mi-24Ps. From 1985, reports emerged of Mi-24Vs

carrying extra 9M114 launch tubes under the outboard underwing pylons, bringing the total number of missiles carried to eight. The Mi-24V introduced provision for carrying external fuel tanks underwing, all four pylons being 'plumbed' for the carriage of PTB-450 500-litre (110-Imp gal) drop tanks. New weapons for the Mi-24V included the B-8V20A rocket pod, containing 20 unguided S-8 80-mm (3.15-in) rockets, the KMGU-2 sub-munitions dispenser, and the UPK-23/250 23-mm (0.9-in) cannon pod (with 250 rounds of ammunition). Weapons cleared for use on the Mi-24V as a result of Afghanistan war experience included the 9-A-669 GUV universal gun pod containing a 12.7-mm (0.5-in) four-barrelled machine-gun with 750 rounds, flanked by two four-barrelled 7.62-mm (0.3-in) machine-guns with 3,400 rounds. The same pod could be configured with a 213-PA grenade launcher and 300 30-mm (1.18-in) rounds. Later 'Hind-Es' introduced new defensive avionics, with L-006 Beryoza RHAWS antennas. The original SRO-2 IFF set was replaced by the 62-01, a triangular blade antenna replacing the old 'Odd Rods'.

Mi-35 'Hind-E'

For many years the 'Hind-E' was simply unavailable for export, except to selected Warsaw Pact allies. Eventually the 9M114 Shturm missile and its associated guidance equipment were cleared for wider export, as were some of the Mil Mi-24V's advanced defensive systems. As a result, the Mil Mi-35 was born as a slightly downgraded export variant. Confirmed Mil Mi-35 operators include Afghanistan (current status unknown), Angola, and India (illustrated).

Mi-35 'Hind-E' trainer version

Trainer versions of frontline Mi-24 variants exist, even though operationally capable aircraft can themselves be used for training, with rudimentary 'foldaway' flying controls in the front cockpit. The Mi-24U 'Hind-C' and Mi-24DU 'Hind-D' were dedicated trainers, with full dual controls and minus gun armament. Trainer versions of the 'Hind-E' also exist, albeit only for the export market. Whether the Indian aircraft illustrated was built as a trainer or converted remains uncertain.

Mi-24P 'Hind-F'

Early experience in Afghanistan revealed that there were targets against which a 12.7-mm (0.5-in) machine-gun was ineffective, but against which unguided rockets or guided missiles were too expensive. Mil began work on two 'Hind' variants (derivatives of the Mi-24V) armed with different calibre cannon. One of these was the Mi-24P. This was designed around the twin-barrelled 30-mm (1.18-in) GSh-30-2. Since this weapon was too large to be housed in the existing nose turret, the weapon was fitted to the starboard forward fuselage, aimed simply by pointing the helicopter itself. The type was first identified in the West during late 1982. Mi-24Ps were exported to East Germany. Like the 'Hind-E', the Mi-24P front cockpit is fitted with an emergency control column. This can be used by the gunner if the pilot is incapacitated, or by an instructor supervising a pupil in the rear seat. The front cockpit also has a fold-away collective lever and yaw pedals.

Mi-35P 'Hind-F'

The Mi-35P designation is applied to export versions of the 'Hind-F', and was unknown until a Mi-35P visited the Helitech exhibition at Redhill during 1989, the first public appearance in the West of the 'Hind'. This aircraft's H-370 code was assumed to be a Paris air show code, but may in fact have been an Angolan air force serial number. Angola and Iraq are believed to be the only current export customers of the Mi-35P, since Germany's aircraft were understood to retain the Mi-24P designation, and Afghan Mi-35Ps (if they were Mi-35Ps and not Mi-24Ps borrowed from the Soviet air force) are almost certainly now out of service.

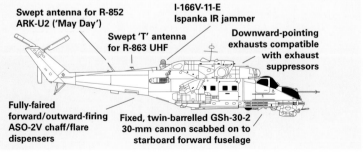

Swept antenna for R-852 ARK-U2 ('May Day')

I-166V-11-E Ispanka IR jammer

Swept 'T' antenna for R-863 UHF

Downward-pointing exhausts compatible with exhaust suppressors

Fully-faired forward/outward-firing ASO-2V chaff/flare dispensers

Fixed, twin-barrelled GSh-30-2 30-mm cannon scabbed on to starboard forward fuselage

Mi-24VP

As a means of increasing the Mi-24's firepower, a need dramatically demonstrated by combat experience in Afghanistan, the Mi-24VP was designed as an alternative to the Mi-24P. A derivative of the Mi-24V, it used a turret-mounted twin-barrelled GSh-23L 23-mm (0.9-in) cannon instead of the Mi-24P's fuselage-mounted, fixed 30-mm (1.18-in) cannon. The larger size of 23-mm rounds compared to 12.7-mm (0.5-in) rounds means that the number of rounds carried is much reduced, and that the ammunition stowage and carriage system (which has to fit into the same space) has had to be completely redesigned. There are reports that an experimental Mi-24VP was flown with a fenestron tail rotor, and that another flew with a narrow 'X' (delta H) tail rotor like that fitted to the Mi-28 and AH-64 Apache. Production of the Mi-24VP was

limited, the new ammunition feed system proving troublesome and unreliable. The *Berkuty* (Eagles) display team, drawn from the helicopter training centre at Torjok, included at least one Mi-24VP (illustrated), which was painted with the logo of an English sponsor.

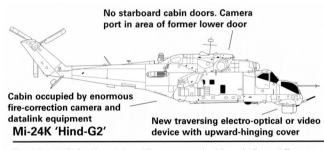

Pitch/yaw vanes retained

No camera gun on endplate/wing junction

Unidentified 'letterbox'-type aperture

Mi-24RCh Hind-G1'

'Clutching hand' mechanisms on endplates consist of three finger 'buckets' on the end of a downward-hinging arm

The Mil Mi-24RCh (RCh for Razvedchik, or reconnaissance/chemical) is a dedicated NBC detection/reconnaissance aircraft, optimised for the gathering of soil and air samples for analysis. The variant is believed to be a production version, and not produced by conversion of Mi-24Vs, though this cannot be entirely discounted. The cockpits and cabin are hermetically sealed, and a huge air filter is installed in the cabin floor, projecting below the port lower fuselage ahead of the cabin door. Despite this, all four crew (pilot, gunner, flight engineer and analyst) normally wear full NBC kit in flight. Soil samples are gathered using 'grabs', three of which are carried in a claw-like fitting below the endplate pylon. Some Mi-24RCh helicopters have also been seen with a further fitting mounted on the tail bumper. This may be a device for dropping or firing some kind of ground marker. Air samples are sucked

through an aperture behind the port cabin door, and fed via a prominent orange-coloured pipe to the analysis equipment. A massive datalink console occupies most of the front of the cabin, allowing the analyst to pass preliminary results to the tasking authority.

The Mi-24RCh cannot carry ATGMs, so has no underfuselage guidance pod. The underfuselage optical sighting system housing is also deleted, leaving only the gun turret, which is retained, although the front cockpit also includes dual flying controls. Operational Mi-24RCh aircraft are often seen carrying underwing rocket pods. The cabin window arrangement is changed slightly, with the twin windows in the starboard entry door replaced by a single blown observation window. Some aircraft have the late-standard fully faired-in chaff/flare dispensers, and others have the cruder framework-mounted units. PZU intake filters and late-style downward exhausts seem to be standard.

Large, bulged observation window replaces normal windows in upper part of starboard cabin door

Optional marker (flag/flare) launcher scabbed on to tailskid

No starboard cabin doors. Camera port in area of former lower door

Cabin occupied by enormous fire-correction camera and datalink equipment

Mi-24K 'Hind-G2'

New traversing electro-optical or video device with upward-hinging cover

The Mi-24K (K for Korrektirovchik, or correction) is a dedicated fire-correction helicopter, a modern equivalent to the artillery spotter. It uses a massive fully automated camera installed in the cabin, with a

1300-mm/f8 lens for observing the fall of shot. Access to the film magazine is through the port cabin doors, while the starboard cabin door is sealed, its windows removed and replaced by a single lower window through which the lens points. Beside this is a smaller aperture for the exposure meter. It is reported that the Mi-24K does not have dual controls. Like the Mi-24RCh, the Mi-24K cannot carry ATGMs and lacks the command/guidance pod under the port forward fuselage. It does, however, have a fairing below the starboard side of the nose, beside the gun turret. This appears to be a swivelling device whose forward end can be covered by a hinged fairing when pointing forward. When this is hinged out of the way, a circular aperture is revealed. Whether this serves a video camera or an electro-optical or infra-red sensor is uncertain. The aircraft can be armed with underwing rocket pods. Some Mi-24Ks have the late-standard fully faired-in chaff/flare dispensers; others have the cruder framework-mounted units.

Mi-24 environmental research version

A 'Hind-E/F' sub-variant was shown at an international ecology and earth resources exhibition at Nizhny Novgorod (now renamed Gorky). Reportedly designed for monitoring surface oil pollution, flooding, air pollution and the like, the aircraft was fitted with comprehensive data processing equipment, and a datalink to relay information to ground stations. The aircraft had an unusual sensor in the nose (possibly retractable) taking the form of a broad, flat 'tongue' projecting horizontally forward from the base of the gunner's windscreen. Apart from this, the aircraft had a box-like pod on the starboard outboard

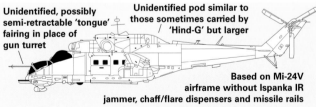

Unidentified, possibly semi-retractable 'tongue' fairing in place of gun turret

Unidentified pod similar to those sometimes carried by 'Hind-G' but larger

Based on Mi-24V airframe without Ispanka IR jammer, chaff/flare dispensers and missile rails

underwing pylon. This pod was reportedly developed by the 'Polet' scientific production association and the scientific research radiophysics institute.

Mi-35M

An upgraded, night-capable, version of the Mi-24/35, the Mi-35M is an export equivalent of the Mi-24M offered to the Russian Army (now proposed in the form of the more modestly upgraded Mi-24VP). The Mi-35M features the main and tail rotor assembles and transmission of the Mi-28, and 1,636-kW (2,194-shp) Klimov TV3-117VMA engines. The production Mi-35M will feature reduced empty weight as a result of a new titanium main rotor head, composite rotor blades, shortened stub wings and non-retractable landing gear. A twin-barrelled 23-mm (0.9-in) gun is fitted in the nose turret. Missile options include up to 16 Shturms, or more modern 9M120s, with 9A-220 Ataka AAMs for self-defence. A Night Operation Capable Avionics System (NOCAS) produced by Sextant Avionique/Thomson Optronic provides night vision for target acquisition and identification, missile guidance and gun aiming.

OH-58D
Kiowa Warrior

The most advanced development of the OH-58 family, the Kiowa Warrior is the backbone of US Army Aviation's Cavalry units. Officially an interim aircraft, pending the arrival of the Comanche, the OH-58D will hold a front-line place for many years.

When US Army Aviation began fielding the AH-64A Apache in numbers during the late 1980s, the type's technology immediately outclassed that of all other helicopters in army service. Possessing long range and a TADS/PNVS sensor system, the AH-64A had unrivalled eyes over the battlefield, by day or night.

Apaches replaced AH-1 Cobras, which had traditionally worked as part of a 'scout/gun' team with the OH-58C Kiowa. In its role as an unsophisticated scout, the OH-58C could only provide 'Mk 1 eyeball' surveillance and had limited communications – but it was still a valuable asset to the Cobra crews. However, with the arrival of the Apache in Europe, the OH-58C began to look increasingly antique.

To remedy this, the US Army launched the AHIP (Army Helicopter Improvement Program). The aim of AHIP was to give existing scout helicopters – either the OH-58 or the Hughes OH-6 – a step-up in basic performance and sensor fit. The aircraft would be made more manoeuvrable to undertake low-level, nap-of-the-earth (NoE) flying and thus improve survivability. It would also be fitted with a new long-range target acquisition and designation system to give it the same sensor reach as the AH-64A. The improved AHIP battlefield scout was intended to work not just with Apache units, but also (and perhaps more importantly) to provide accurate target-finding and designation capability for artillery units, in addition to scouting for advancing armoured units.

Bell won the AHIP competition in September 1981 with its Model 406 design. The name Aeroscout was initially applied to the AHIP, but this was later abandoned when the armed role evolved and the Kiowa Warrior title was introduced. The 'new' AHIP was designated OH-58D.

The first flight of the OH-58D prototype took place on 6 October 1983 and deliveries began in December 1985. The first operational aircraft were based with US Army Europe, from June 1987 onwards. The OH-58D acquisition plan has suffered many changes over the years. The original US Army total of 592 was cut back to 477 and then to 207, before Congress stepped in and re-instated

Mast-mounted sight

Fitted above the rotor hub is the ball-shaped mast-mounted sight (MMS), which is at the heart of the Bell OH-58D's operational capability. The MMS (right) integrates a daytime TV camera with x12 magnification and a night/adverse weather infra-red system (known as the 'tis', or thermal imaging sensor) – all with automatic tracking and boresighting functions. The MMS has a laser rangefinder/designator, allowing it to mark targets for

weapons such as the Apache's AGM-114 Hellfire anti-tank missile (ATM) and the US Army's Copperhead laser-guided artillery shell. The mast-mounted sight can rotate through 360° and can look up or down to an angle of +/-30°. The OH-58D Kiowa Warrior also has an automatic target hand-off system (ATHS) that allows it to transmit very precise (eight-digit grid) target positions to artillery batteries 'in the field'.

Mission-tasking and weapons

In the early 1990s a decision was made to transfer most of the OH-58D(I) force to Army Aviation Cavalry units for use as armed scouts. Cavalry units fight as the vanguard of heavy armoured units, conducting operations including reconnaissance and security, flank protection, advanced scouting and movement-to-contact missions. The Kiowa Warrior has been armed with the Hellfire (below left), Hydra 70 rockets (below right), and Stinger

(right, flanking Hellfires and 7.62-mm/0.3-in gun pods) – becoming the only US Army helicopter with a dedicated air-to-air capability. The combination of firepower and advanced MMS sensor systems – a generation ahead of those fitted to US Apaches – makes the Kiowa Warrior the most flexible and effective combat helicopter in US Army service.

funding to push the numbers back up to 424 by 1998. All of the aircraft involved are existing OH-58s, which have been rebuilt and allocated a new serial on completion to OH-58D standard.

Prime Chance

Just as the OH-58D was entering army service, it was called upon to adopt an unexpected role. By 1987, international shipping in the Persian Gulf was coming under attack from Iranian gunboats, which were harassing oil tankers, particularly around the Straits of Hormuz. In a clandestine US Army programme named Prime Chance, 15 helicopters were modified with weapons pylons, becoming the OH-58D (Armed). These aircraft served as part of the Army's Task Force 118 aboard US Navy ships, and conducted night-time operations, together with other US Army special operations

forces and USN SH-60Bs. Prime Chance OH-58Ds were armed with Hydra rockets, 7.62-mm (0.3-in) Miniguns, 12.7-mm (0.5-in) machine-guns and Hellfires. The OH-58Ds were able to use their MMS systems to locate and engage the small, fast-moving gunboats and proved a success during their highly-classified service, in which they flew over 8,000 hours of mission time. The Prime Chance experience paved the way for a full production-standard weapons fit for the OH-58D. In 1989 the army gave the go-ahead to refit its OH-58Ds to the same standard as the OH-58D (Armed) aircraft, under the designation OH-58D(I) Kiowa Warrior. In 1991, halfway through the ongoing conversion process, the OH-58D line switched to producing the OH-58D(I), while the existing OH-58Ds were retrofitted to Kiowa Warrior standard.

Saudi Arabia operates a Model 406 derivative, the 406CS Combat Scout, and the Royal Saudi Land Forces ordered 15 Combat Scouts in 1988.

SPECIFICATION	
Bell OH-58D Warrior **Type:** Text **Powerplant:** one 485-kW (650-shp) Allison (now Rolls-Royce) 250-C30R turboshaft **Performance:** maximum speed 237 km/h (147 mph) 'clean at 1220 m (4,002 ft); maximum climb rate 469 m (1,539 ft) per minute; range 463 km (288 miles)	**Weights:** empty 1381 kg (3,045 lb); maximum take-off 2041 kg (4500 lb) **Dimensions:** main rotor diameter 10.67 m (35 ft); length 12.85 m (42 ft 2 in); height 3.93 m (12 ft 10 in); rotor disc area 89.37 m² (962 sq ft) **Armament:** 12.7-mm (0.5-in) machine-guns, seven-tube 70-mm (2.75-in) rocket pods, plus provision for Stinger air-to-air missiles and Hellfire anti-armour missiles

OH-58D Kiowa Warrior

This OH-58D wears the markings of the 4th Squadron, 17th Cavalry. The 'Thugs' are a designated seagoing unit, and operate in place of the Prime Chance aircraft.

Main rotor assembly
The most obvious difference between the OH-58D and its predecessors is a new four-bladed rotor, built with elastomeric bearings and composite blades.

Hellfire missile
Up to four AGM-114C Hellfires can be carried; in this instance, a pair has been combined with a single M260 seven-round pod of 70-mm (2.75-in) Hydra 70 rockets.

Powerplant
The OH-58D is powered by a 485-kW (650-shp) Allison (now Rolls-Royce) 250-C30R turboshaft (military designation T703-AD-700). Later versions now feature the FADEC-equipped R/3 engine. Transmission is limited to 410 kW (550 shp). Aft of the engine is the ALQ-144 IRCM turret, providing defence against IR-seeking missiles.

Upgrades
Virtually all of the OH-58Ds in service have now been brought up to OH-58D(I) Kiowa Warrior standard. With their transformation from D to D(I) standard, the aircraft were given new serials yet again, with the result that all of the helicopters involved have now had three separate identities during their time in the US Army.

The primary role of the Royal Navy's Sea Kings was anti-submarine warfare, but some **HAS Mk 5s** were converted to the rescue role as **SAR HAR Mk 5s** by the removal of anti-submarine equipment. Here a crewman is about to make a practice rescue.

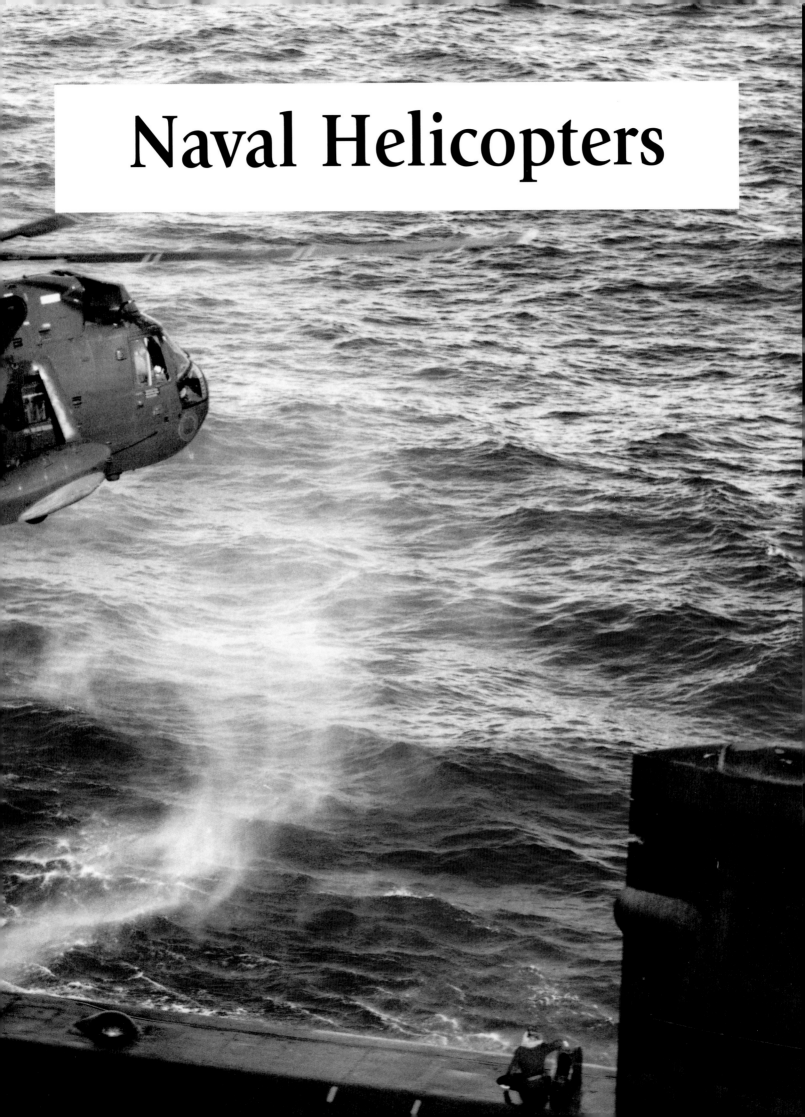

Naval Helicopters

Aérospatiale Dauphin

By adopting a twin-engined layout, Aérospatiale's Dauphin is able to fulfil a greater variety of civil roles and undertake attack missions in its military guise.

While externally similar to earlier members of the Dauphin family, the AS 365N Dauphin 2 differed in that, from this model onwards, the original 'SA' designation (for Sud-Aviation) was changed to 'AS' (for Aérospatiale). It also introduced a large number of changes and had 90 new component parts. Increased use was made of composites, such as Nomex, Kevlar and Rohacell glass fibre, making up about 20 per cent of the structure. Other features included a redesigned and lengthened cabin for 11 passengers, separated from the crew, tapered tips to the main rotor blades, a re-profiled and more pointed nose, new air intakes, re-designed underfloor fuel tanks, and a retractable tricycle landing gear. Power was provided by two 529-kW

(710-shp) Turbomeca Arriel 1C turboshaft engines. The first flight of the prototype (F-WZJD) was made on 31 March 1979. French certification for Visual Flight Rules (VFR) operations was received on 9 April 1981, followed by single-pilot Instrument Flight Rules (IFR) certification on 7 August that same year.

Progressive enhancements for the civil market resulted in several new and upgraded models. Eurocopter, which was formed on 16 January 1992 out of Aérospatiale and Germany's MBB, revealed yet another improvement to the Dauphin family at the Paris Air Show, where the latest model made its first flight on 17 June 1997. Initially known as the AS 365N4, it was quickly re-designated the EC 155. Its lineage is unmistakable. It still looks like a

Dauphin, but has been streamlined with a longer nose, a re-designed and enlarged cabin to give a wide-body look and 40 per cent more volume for 12 passengers and baggage, a five-bladed rotor with composite blades on a Spheriflex rotor head, and a tail boom stabiliser terminating in a shrouded fenestron tail-rotor with 10 unequally-spaced composite blades.

In camouflage

Aérospatiale had always intended to expand the Dauphin's capability into the military market, but it was not until Saudi Arabia placed an order for 24 navalised helicopters for SAR and anti-ship duties on 13 October 1980 that the concept began to take off. An SA 365N was modified to SA 365F prototype configuration with radar and anti-ship missiles, making its first flight on 22 February 1982 with test registration F-WZJD. The first production aircraft, equipped as a SAR helicopter, flew on 2 July that same year. The SA 365F was powered by two 522-kW (700-shp) Arriel 520M turboshaft engines and had the larger 11-blade fenestron to improve hovering performance,

especially in severe conditions. All military models were later named Panther and re-designated in the AS 565 series.

The first such re-designations were the AS 565MA Panther, which was essentially an unarmed naval version of the SA 365F, and the AS 565SA, the armed equivalent for anti-ship and Anti-Submarine Warfare (ASW) missions. Both models were replaced from 1997 by the AS 565MB and AS 565SB respectively, with more powerful 635-kW (851-shp) Arriel 2C engines for improved hot-and-high performance. The ASW version is equipped with Sextant Avionique Magnetic-Anomaly Detection (MAD) or Thomson Sintra sonar and two homing torpedoes, while the anti-ship variant has four side-mounted AS 15TT radar-guided missiles and chin-mounted Agrion 15 radar. Search and Rescue (SAR) versions have the Omera nose-mounted search radar. The first flight of the AS 365M prototype (F-WZJV), aimed at army and air force use, as a light assault and 12-troop utility transport and powered by two 680-kW (913-shp) Turbomeca TM.333-1M turboshafts, took place on 29 February 1984.

Early in the development of the Dauphin, Aérospatiale, along with MBB, developed the Spheriflex rotor head, one of the first all-composite components.

Aérospatiale SA 321 Super Frelon
SAR and transport helo

Delivery of 16 SA 321Ja Super Frelons to the Chinese navy took place between 1975 and 1977 and was expanded with licence-built Changhe Z-8s.

France's SA 321 Super Frelons are retained in service for SAR and heavylift transport, for which their long-range capability proves useful.

To meet a French armed services requirement for a medium transport helicopter, Sud-Aviation flew the prototype **SE.3200 Frelon** (hornet) on 10 June 1959. Powered by three Turmo IIIB turboshafts, the SE.3200 had large external fuel tanks that left the interior clear for a maximum 28 troops, and a swing-tail fuselage to simplify cargo loading. However, development was terminated in favour of a larger and more capable helicopter designed in conjunction with Sikorsky and Fiat. What was to become Western Europe's largest production helicopter emerged with a rotor system of Sikorsky design, and with a watertight hull suitable for amphibious operation. Two military prototypes of the Super Frelon were built, the **SA 3210-01** troop transport, and the **SA 3210-02** maritime version for the Aéronavale on 28 May 1963.

Four pre-production aircraft were built under the new designation **SA 321 Super Frelon**. These were followed in October 1965 by production **SA 321G** ASW helicopters for the Aéronavale. Apart from ship-based ASW missions, the SA 321G also carried out sanitisation patrols in support of 'Rédoutable'-class ballistic missile submarines. Some were modified with nose-mounted targeting radar for Exocet AShMs. Five **SA 321Ga** freighters, originally used in support of the Pacific nuclear test centre, were transferred to assault support duties. In 2003, the surviving Aéronavale Super Frelons are assigned to transport duties including commando transport, VertRep and SAR.

Exports

Six radar-equipped **SA 321GM** helicopters were delivered to Libya in 1980–81. The SA 321G was also modified for air force and army service. Designated **SA 321H**, a total of 16 was delivered from 1977 to the Iraqi air force with radar and Exocets. These aircraft were used in the Iran-Iraq conflict and the 1991 Gulf War.

The **SA 321Ja** was a higher weight version of the commercial **SA 321J**, of which the People's Republic of China navy received 16 aircraft fitted with targeting radar. Non-amphibious military export versions included 12 **SA 321K** transports for Israel, 16 similar **SA 321L** transports for South Africa and eight **SA 321M** SAR/transports for Libya.

When French production ended in 1983 a total of 99 Super Frelons had been built, but production continued in China under licence as the **Changhe Z-8**. Eight Israeli aircraft were re-engined and sold to Argentina.

SPECIFICATION	
Aérospatiale SA 321G Super Frelon **Type:** medium SAR and transport helicopter **Powerplant:** three Turboméca Turmo IIIC7 turboshafts each rated at 1201 kW (1,610 shp) **Performance:** maximum cruising speed at sea level 248 km/h (154 mph); maximum rate of climb at sea level 300 m (984 ft) per minute; service ceiling 3100 m (10,170 ft); hovering ceiling 1950 m (6,400 ft) in ground effect; range	1020 km (633 miles) with a 3500-kg (7,716-lb) payload **Weights:** empty 6863 kg (15,130 lb); maximum take-off 13000 kg (28,660 lb) **Dimensions:** main rotor diameter 18.9 m (62 ft); length overall, rotors turning 23.03 m (75 ft 6½ in); height overall 6.76 m (22 ft 2¼ in); main rotor disc area 12.57 m² (135.27 sq ft) **Payload:** maximum payload 5000 kg (11,023 lb)

Agusta-Bell
AB 212ASV/ASW
ASV and ASW helicopter

Three Italian navy squadrons operate the Agusta-Bell AB 212ASW, which first entered service in 1968. Of the 68 ordered, about 49 remained in use into 2003.

Production of the Bell Model 212 in Italy followed quickly upon the development in the USA of this twin-engined derivative of the Bell 205, undertaken in the first instance to meet USAF and Canadian Forces requirements. In essence, the Bell 212 (and essentially similar **Agusta-Bell AB 212**) comprised the airframe of the Model 205 combined with the Pratt & Whitney Canada PT6T-3 Turbo Twin-Pac powerplant. The latter comprised paired PT6 turboshaft engines offering far greater operational reliability as either of the engines could sustain the helicopter in level flight. In its accommodation and equipment options, the AB 212 closely resembled the AB 205A-1 but offers enhanced performance as well as greater reliability. Deliveries of the Italian-built version started in late autumn 1971.

The standard AB 212 carries a pilot and up to 14 passengers, but the cabin is easily adaptable for other roles, including VIP transport. Optional equipment includes a rescue hoist, external cargo hook, auxiliary fuel tanks, and float and snow landing gear, according to customer's requirements. The cabin can also be converted into an ambulance and has space for six stretchers and two medical attendants.

Naval variant

Following the precedent set with the AB 204AS, Agusta alone developed an anti-surface vessel/ anti-submarine warfare version of the AB 212 as the **AB 212ASV/ASW**. Designed to

The Turkish navy operates around nine AB 212ASW helicopters.

Right: Unlike Italy, which will replace its naval AB 212s with NH90s, Turkey has ordered S-70 Seahawks to replace its aircraft.

Below: Greater versatility is bestowed upon the basic AB 212ASV/ASW by the provision of a rescue hoist mounted above the starboard cabin door.

the AB 212ASW can also be used as a passive guidance post for ship-launched surface-to-surface stand-off missiles.

To provide a search-and-rescue capability, a hydraulically-operated external hoist is fitted. The normal crew comprises three or four including the two-person tactical crew and two pilots, with provision for up to seven passengers, or four litters plus an attendant.

For other tasks, the AB 212ASW can be fitted with either a 2270-kg (5,000-lb) capacity external cargo hook, a 270-kg (595-lb) rescue hoist, inflatable emergency pontoons, and internal and external auxiliary fuel tanks.

Production

Agusta began work on the AB 212ASW in 1971, and the Italian navy successfully evaluated the prototype in 1973. Production examples of the AB 212ASV/ASW entered service in 1976 and the company built more than 100 examples for seven operators, of which the largest is the Italian navy, with more than 60 delivered.

operate from small shipboard platforms, the type features local strengthening, the addition of deck mooring points and increased airframe protection against salt-water corrosion.

The most notable external change is the addition of a dorsal radome for the antenna of the search radar (with options for several types including Ferranti Seaspray). The main changes are internal and

concern the outfitting of the cabin as a tactical centre manned by two operators, with all-weather flight instrumentation and, perhaps most importantly, the introduction of an automatic flight-control system.

This last system combines inputs from the automatic stabilisation system, radar altimeter, Doppler navigation system and other sensors to

provide automatic transition from cruise to sonar hover under all weather conditions by day and night. The automatic navigation system also locates the helicopter's position on the radar's tactical display screen, which additionally shows target data provided by the Bendix AQS-18B/F variable-depth dunking sonar equipment.

With its search radar and target data transmission system

The Turkish navy has an operational fleet of about nine AB 212ASWs. The aircraft are flown by 351 Filo.

Agusta-Bell AB 212ASV/ASW
Type: medium anti-ship and anti-submarine helicopter with secondary utility capability
Powerplant: one Pratt & Whitney Canada PT6T-6 Turbo Twin Pac coupled turboshaft engine rated at 1398 kW (1,875 shp), derated to 962 kW (1,290 shp)
Performance: maximum speed 196 km/h (122 mph) at sea level; cruising speed 185 km/h (115 mph) at optimum altitude with armament; initial climb rate 396 m (1,300 ft) per minute; hovering ceiling 3200 m (10,500 ft) in ground effect and 396 m (1,300 ft) out of ground effect; range 667 km (414 miles) with auxiliary fuel and 615 km (382 miles) on an ASV mission with AS12 missiles; average

search endurance with Mk 46 torpedoes 3 hours 12 minutes; maximum endurance with auxiliary tanks 5 hours
Weights: empty 3420 kg (7,540 lb); maximum take-off 5070 kg (11,177 lb) for the ASW mission with two Mk 46 torpedoes, or 4973 kg (10,961 lb) for the ASV mission with AS12 missiles, or 4937 kg (10,883 lb) for the SAR mission
Dimensions: main rotor diameter 14.63 m (48 ft); length overall 17.4 m (57 ft 1 in) with rotors turning and fuselage 12.92 m (42 ft 4¾ in); height 4.53 m (14 ft 10¼ in); main rotor disc area 168.1 m² (1,808.52 sq ft)
Armament: up to 490 kg (1,080 lb) of stores (see main text)

Of these, the first 12 had MEL ARI.5955 radar and the remainder APS-705 radar matched to the AS12 light air-to-surface missile for the ASV mission. As the Italian navy's standard shipboard helicopter aboard its destroyers and frigates, the AB 212ASV/ASW carries a pair of Mk 44, Mk 46 or MQ44 homing torpedoes in the anti-submarine role, or AS12 ASMs in the anti-ship role, although the helicopters surviving in Italian service were later upgraded with the Marte Mk II system (including SMA MM/APS-706 radar) for air-launched Sea Killer Mk 2 anti-ship missiles.

Greece received 14 AB 212ASV/ASW helicopters including three for ECM use and the others for deployment on two 'Elli'-class frigates, while the Peruvian navy's air arm has around six of the type for reconnaissance. Spain's 10 AB 212ASV/ASW machines are armed with AS12s and machine-guns, and are used by Tercera Escuadrilla (Eslla 003) from the assault transport *Galicia* for close-support duties. The Turkish navy bought an initial 12 and then an additional four helicopters of this type with Seaspray radar and Sea Skua ASMs, and these operated at first from the service's 'Yavuz'-class frigates. Venezuela has about eight OTO-Melara Sea

Killer-equipped AB 212ASV/ASW helicopters with its Esc Aero Antisubmarino 3, based at Puerto Cabello, to operate from the service's 'Sucre'-class frigates.

A 1983 contract covered the sale of 10 helicopters to Iraq,

Right: Greek navy AB 212ASWs usually embark on the navy's five ex-Dutch navy 'Elli'-class frigates and three ex-US Navy 'Epirus'-class frigates.

Below: Among the features fitted to the AB 212 for naval operations are deck mooring points and, optionally, skid-mounted flotation gear.

but this contract was placed under embargo and discussions for their release were finally ended by the Iraqi invasion of Kuwait. Approximately 20 were ordered for the Iranian navy early in 1974, with provision for AS12 wire-guided missiles, and these light ASMs were used for attacks on shipping in the

Both Turkey and Greece have taken special EW variants of the AB 212ASV/ASW.

Persian Gulf during 1985–86. The Iranians have received few spare parts, so the helicopters suffer from poor serviceability and are probably now non-operational.

Boeing Vertol H-46 Sea Knight
Assault and transport helo

Photographed in June 2003, this US Navy CH-46D is seen replenishing USS Sacramento from USS Carl Vinson in the Philippine Sea. The CH-46 is now long overdue for replacement.

Shortly after the formation of the Vertol Aircraft Corporation in March 1956, the company initiated a design study for a twin-turbine commercial transport helicopter and in the event, the US armed forces showed an interest in the type's procurement.

Early Army interest

Allocated the designation **Vertol Model 107**, a prototype was flown for the first time on 22 April 1958. The first of the armed forces wishing to evaluate the new helicopter was the US Army which, in July 1958, ordered 10 slightly modified aircraft under the designation **YHC-1A**. The first of these flew for the first time on 27 August 1959. By that time the US Army had come to favour a larger and more powerful helicopter, which Vertol had developed from the Model 107, and reduced its order to only three YCH-1A (later **YCH-46C**) machines. The company subsequently equipped the third of these with 783-kW (1,050-shp) T58-GE-6 turboshafts and rotors of increased diameter, and, with a commercial interior, this aircraft first flew as the **Model 107-II** on 25 October 1960. By that time Vertol had become a division of the Boeing company.

When the USMC showed an interest in this helicopter, one was modified as the **Model 107M** with two T58-GE-8s and this was successful in winning a contract for the **HRB-1** (changed to **CH-46A** in 1962) production model, which was named **Sea**

Knight. Since then, Sea Knights have been used extensively by the USMC and the USN. The former uses them for troop transport, the latter mainly in the vertical replenishment role.

Production variants

The first of 160 CH-46As entered full USMC service early in 1965. Since then, a number of versions has been built, these including 266 examples of the **CH-46D** for the USMC to a standard generally similar to that of the CH-46A except for its 1044-kW (1,400-shp) T58-GE-10 engines; 174 examples of the **CH-46F** for the USMC to a standard generally similar to that of the CH-46D but with additional avionics; 14 examples of the **UH-46A**, similar to the CH-46A, for the USN; and 10 examples of the **UH-46D** for the USN to a standard virtually identical to that of the CH-46D. The USMC updated 273 of its

older Sea Knights to the **CH-46E** standard.

Foreign service

Six utility helicopters, almost identical to the CH-46A, were delivered to the RCAF in 1963 under the designation **CH-113 Labrador**, and 12 similar aircraft were built for the Canadian Army during 1964–65, these being designated **CH-113A Voyageur**. Boeing of Canada was later contracted to modify

six CH-113s and five CH-13As to an improved SAR standard by mid-1984. In 1962–63 Boeing Vertol supplied Model 107-II helicopters to the Swedish the air force for SAR, and to the Swedish navy for ASW and minesweeping duties; both of these versions received the local designation **Hkp 4A**.

In 1965 Kawasaki in Japan acquired the worldwide sales rights for the Model 107-II, and built the type up to about 1990.

SPECIFICATION

Boeing Vertol CH-46A Sea Knight
Type: two/three-crew twin-rotor transport helicopter
Powerplant: two General Electric T58-GE-8B turboshaft engines each rated at 932 kW (1,250 shp)
Performance: maximum speed 249 km/h (155 mph) at sea level; cruising speed 243 km/h (151 mph) at 1525 m (5,000 ft); initial climb rate 439 m (1,440 ft) per minute; service ceiling 4265 m (14,000 ft); hovering ceiling 2765 m (9,070 ft) in ground effect and 1707 m (5,600 ft) out of ground

effect; range 426 km (265 miles) with maximum internal payload
Weights: empty 5627 kg (12,406 lb); maximum take-off 9707 kg (21,400 lb)
Dimensions: rotor diameter, each 15.24 m (50 ft); length overall, rotors turning 25.4 m (83 ft 4 in); height 5.09 m (16 ft 8¼ in); rotor disc area, total 364.82 m² (3,926.99 sq ft)
Payload: up to 25 troops, or 1814 kg (4,000 lb) of freight carried internally or 2871 kg (6,330 lb) of freight carried externally

EH Industries
EH 101/Merlin
ASW helicopter

This pre-production Merlin HM.Mk 1 was initially used for trials with the Type 23 frigate HMS Norfolk. It then moved onto sonobuoy drop trials and was fitted with full Merlin avionics.

The **EH 101** has its roots in the Westland WG.34 design that was adopted in late 1978 to meet the UK's Naval Staff Requirement 6646 for a replacement for the Westland Sea King. Work on the WG.34 was cancelled before a prototype had been completed, however, opening the way for revision of the design to meet Italian navy as well as Royal Navy requirements. European Helicopter Industries Ltd was given a formal go-ahead to develop the new aircraft in 1984.

The EH 101 is a three-engined helicopter with a five-bladed main rotor. Much use is made of composites throughout, although the fuselage itself is mainly of aluminium alloy. Systems and equipment vary with role and customer. For the Royal Navy, which calls its initial

Merlin HM.Mk 1 equipment includes GEC Ferranti Blue Kestrel 360° search radar, GEC Avionics AQS-903 processing and display system, Racal Orange Reaper ESM and Ferranti/Thomson-CSF dipping sonar.

variant of the EH 101 the **Merlin HM.Mk 1**, IBM is the prime contractor in association with Westland and provides equipment as well as overall management and integration. Armament on the Merlin comprises four Marconi Sting Ray torpedoes, and there are also two sonobuoy dispensers.

Merlin HM.Mk 1

The initial Royal Navy requirement for 50 Merlins to operate from Type 23-class frigates, 'Invincible'-class aircraft carriers, ships of the Royal Fleet Auxiliary and other ships or land bases has been reduced to 44, with delivery starting late in 1998 rather than in 1996, as hoped. These British helicopters are each powered by RTM 322 turboshafts, whereas the Italian helicopters (16 on order, out of a requirement for 36) each have the alternative powerplant of three 1278-kW (1,714-shp) General Electric T700-GE-T6A turboshafts, assembled in Italy. Earlier CT7 commercial variants of the General Electric engine were used to power the

prototypes, the first of which was a Westland-built machine that achieved its maiden flight on 9 October 1987. A similar Agusta-built basic model flew in Italy on 26 November 1987. Next to fly in Italy, on 26 April 1989, was a prototype of the Italian ASW version, followed in the UK by a basic ASW version on 15 June and then the definitive Merlin prototype on 24 October of that year.

The second prototype was lost in an accident on 21 January 1993, resulting in a suspension of all flight-testing until 24 June that year. The RTM 322 engines were first flown in the fourth prototype during July 1993, and subsequently fitted to the fifth prototype.

Canada ordered 35 of the naval version as the **CH-148 Petrel**, to meet its New Shipborne Aircraft requirement for a Sea King replacement. Assembled and fitted out by IMP Group Ltd in Canada, these EH 101s were to have been powered by 1432-kW (1,920-shp) CT7-6A1 turboshaft engines. The deal was hard-

Merlin HM.Mk 1 options include the Exocet, Harpoon, Sea Eagle and Marte Mk 2 AShMs, as well as the Stingray torpedo (as here).

fought, subject to constant scrutiny and not unimportant to the chances of the EH 101's long-term success. Deliveries were scheduled to begin early in 1998, although an increasingly bitter argument over the costs versus acquisition of less complex aircraft saw the EH 101 become a campaign issue in the Canadian elections of 1993. The pro-EH 101 Conservative government was ousted in favour of a Liberal administration

which, true to its election pledge, cancelled the entire programme. Then, in January 1998, the Canadian government placed a new order for 15 examples of the revised AW320 Cormorant version for the SAR role, for delivery between 2000 and 2003. Further development of the EH 101 resulted in variants, including an airborne early warning version of the type, for both the Italian navy and the Royal Navy.

SPECIFICATION	
EH Industries Merlin HM.Mk 1 **Type:** one/two-crew shipborne and land-based anti-submarine and utility helicopter **Powerplant:** three Rolls-Royce/Turbomeca RTM 322-01 turboshaft engines each rated at 1724 kW (2,312 shp) **Performance:** cruising speed 278 km (173 mph) at optimum altitude; hovering ceiling 3810 m (12,500 ft) in ground effect; range 1056 km (656 miles) **Weights:** empty 10500 kg (23,149 lb); maximum take-off 14600 kg (32,188 lb)	**Dimensions:** main rotor diameter 18.59 m (61 ft); length 22.81 m (74 ft 10 in) with the rotors turning; height 6.65 m (21 ft 10 in) with the rotors turning; main rotor disc area 271.51 m² (2,922.60 sq ft) **Armament:** up to 960 kg (2,116 lb) of disposable stores carried on the lower sides of the fuselage, and generally comprising four homing torpedoes **Payload:** up to 45 troops, or up to 16 litters plus a medical team, or up to 3660 kg (12,000 lb) of freight carried internally or as a slung load

Crew accommodation

The SH-2F was fitted with full dual controls, and the occupant of the left-hand seat acted as the navigator, tactical co-ordinator and co-pilot. The handling pilot, who usually acted as the aircraft commander, sat in the right-hand seat. The sensor operator, who was responsible for operating and interpreting the radar, sonics, ESM and MAD, sat in the front of the cabin, behind the Tactical Control Officer. One passenger or stretcher case could be carried in the cabin, even with full LAMPS equipment installed. With the sonobuoy launcher removed, four passengers or two stretcher cases could be accommodated.

Kaman
SH-2F Seasprite

Search radar

A Canadian Marconi LN-66HP surveillance radar was fited to the Seasprite to give the over the horizon targetting capability required by the Light Airborne Multi-Purpose System (LAMPS) Mk I programme. The Sea Skua anti-ship missile compatible APS-128 radar was offered as an option on export models of the Seasprite.

HSL-35 'Magicians' was established on 15 January 1974. Based at NAS North Island, California, the unit provided SH-2F LAMPS Mk I detachments to Pacific Fleet warships. The US Navy SH-2F fleet was formerly divided between the Atlantic Fleet Naval Air Force, with Seasprites based at NAS Norfolk, Virginia, and the Pacific Fleet Naval Air Force, with operations centred at North Island. HSL-35's 'sister' units with the Pacific Fleet during the mid-1980s comprised HSL-31 'Archangels', HSL-33 'Sea Snakes' and HSL-37 'Easy Riders'; the latter unit was based at NAS Barbers Point in Hawaii. SH-2F BuNo. 149780 was originally built as a single-engined HU2K-1 (UH-2A), and was rebuilt as a twin-turbine UH-2C before joining the SH-2F programme.

Powerplant

Initial Seasprite variants were single-engined, but the design became a twin with the UH-2C, which introduced a second General Electric T58-GE-8B turboshaft engine. The SH-2F was powered by a pair of T58-GE-8Fs rated at 1007 kW (1,350 shp); in the SH-2G these were replaced by a pair of 1260-kW (1,690-shp) General Electric T700-GE-401s of the type installed in the Sikorsky SH-60 Sea Hawk. The SH-2G may therefore be identified by the prominent gearbox housing protruding from the air intake at the front of the SH-2G's engine nacelle.

Rotor and rotor blades

The SH-2F was fitted with a Kaman 101 four-bladed main rotor, with a titanium hub and retention straps. The 13.4-m (44-ft) rotor rotated at 298 rpm. Each manually-folding main rotor blade was of conventional aluminium and glassfibre construction, with an aluminium D-section leading-edge spar, a honeycomb trailing-edge pocket and glassfibre skin. Composite blades were fitted to new aircraft delivered in 1987 and were retrofitted to existing machines. Charles H. Kaman invented a revolutionary new helicopter flight control system in which the blade incidence is controlled not by torque at the blade root, but by aerodynamic forces imparted by aileron-like servo flaps on the outer trailing edge of each main rotor blade.

Magic Lantern

Magic Lantern was developed by Kaman as a follow-on to an earlier system, dubbed ML30, which earned prominence in hunting mines during the Gulf War. Magic Lantern uses pulses of laser light to detect and provide images of sea mines located in the 'upper water column' (keel depth) using a process known as LIDAR (light detection and ranging). Although advanced naval mines are now found at greater depths, most damage caused by mines is attributed to those near the surface, which are vulnerable to this system. Given the low priority assigned to mine warfare 'between wars', Magic Lantern (which has no military designation) was slow to enter service and was unique to the SH-2G, eventually equipping just one unit – HSL-94 in late 1996. Kaman has been developing LIDARs for detecting naval mines since 1987, following the effective use of moored sea mines to disrupt tanker traffic in the Persian Gulf during the 1980–88 Iran-Iraq war. This effort was intensified following the devastating damage caused to the USS *Samuel B. Roberts* (FFG-58) on 14 April 1988. In that incident, a primitive $1,500 Iranian M08 mine caused damage to the ship that cost $96 million to repair. Kaman field tested a prototype mine-detection LIDAR during 1989 and 1990, and in 1991 this system, now called ML30, was activated by the Navy for deployment to the Persian Gulf during Operation Desert Storm. Operating from an SH-2F aboard the frigate USS *Vreeland* (FF-1058), the ML30 flew more than 80 sorties in the northern Persian Gulf between mid-February and mid-April 1991, detecting a large number of mines in areas otherwise thought to be clear. Despite the fact that the ML30 system was a brassboard never intended for deployment and was subjected to dust, salt spray and heavy smoke from the Kuwaiti oil well fires, the system maintained a 90 per cent availability rating.

Weapons pylon

The Seasprite's weapons pylons are usually used for the carriage of an external 378-litre (100-US gal) fuel tank and MAD winch to starboard and a single Mk 46 torpedo to port. SH-2 Early variants could carry the AIM-7 Sparrow for ship defence, and export versions of the aircraft have been offered with BAe Sea Skua and Kongsberg Penguin and Hughes AGM-65 Maverick anti-ship missile capability.

▶

SH-2 Seasprite
Briefing

HSL-84 'Thunderbolts', based at NAS North Island, was the last Seasprite unit on the US west coast and disestablished in FY2001.

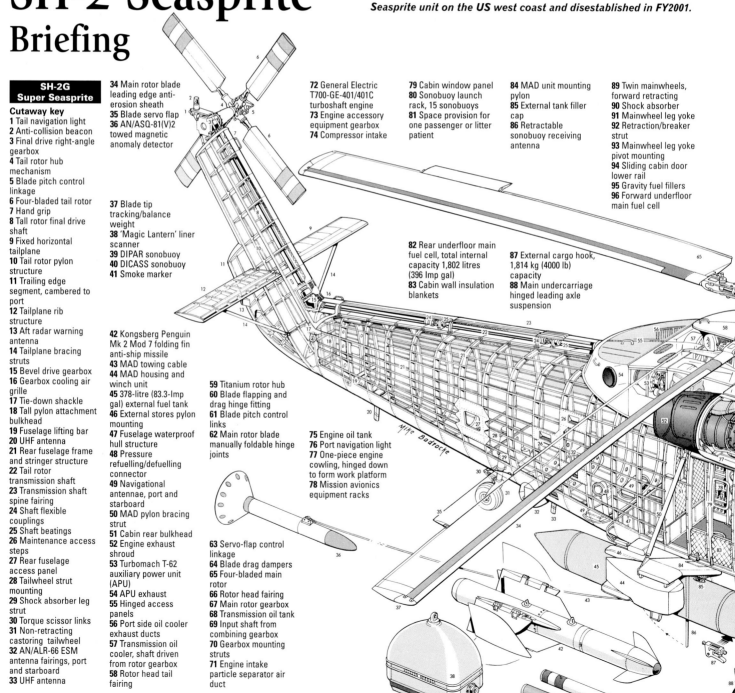

SH-2G Super Seasprite

Cutaway key

1 Tail navigation light
2 Anti-collision beacon
3 Final drive right-angle gearbox
4 Tail rotor hub mechanism
5 Blade pitch control linkage
6 Four-bladed tail rotor
7 Hand grip
8 Tall rotor final drive shaft
9 Fixed horizontal tailplane
10 Tail rotor pylon structure
11 Trailing edge segment, cambered to port
12 Tailplane rib structure
13 Aft radar warning antenna
14 Tailplane bracing struts
15 Bevel drive gearbox
16 Gearbox cooling air grille
17 Tie-down shackle
18 Tall pylon attachment bulkhead
19 Fuselage lifting bar
20 UHF antenna
21 Rear fuselage frame and stringer structure
22 Tail rotor transmission shaft
23 Transmission shaft spine fairing
24 Shaft flexible couplings
25 Shaft beatings
26 Maintenance access steps
27 Rear fuselage access panel
28 Tailwheel strut mounting
29 Shock absorber leg strut
30 Torque scissor links
31 Non-retracting castoring tailwheel
32 AN/ALR-66 ESM antenna fairings, port and starboard
33 UHF antenna

34 Main rotor blade leading edge anti-erosion sheath
35 Blade servo flap
36 AN/ASQ-81(V)2 towed magnetic anomaly detector
37 Blade tip tracking/balance weight
38 'Magic Lantern' liner scanner
39 DIPAR sonobuoy
40 DICASS sonobuoy
41 Smoke marker
42 Kongsberg Penguin Mk 2 Mod 7 folding fin anti-ship missile
43 MAD towing cable
44 MAD housing and winch unit
45 378-litre (83.3-Imp gal) external fuel tank
46 External stores pylon mounting
47 Fuselage waterproof hull structure
48 Pressure refuelling/defuelling connector
49 Navigational antennae, port and starboard
50 MAD pylon bracing strut
51 Cabin rear bulkhead
52 Engine exhaust shroud
53 Turbomach T-62 auxiliary power unit (APU)
54 APU exhaust
55 Hinged access panels
56 Port side oil cooler exhaust ducts
57 Transmission oil cooler, shaft driven from rotor gearbox
58 Rotor head tail fairing

59 Titanium rotor hub
60 Blade flapping and drag hinge fitting
61 Blade pitch control links
62 Main rotor blade manually foldable hinge joints
63 Servo-flap control linkage
64 Blade drag dampers
65 Four-bladed main rotor
66 Rotor head fairing
67 Main rotor gearbox
68 Transmission oil tank
69 Input shaft from combining gearbox
70 Gearbox mounting struts
71 Engine intake particle separator air duct

72 General Electric T700-GE-401/401C turboshaft engine
73 Engine accessory equipment gearbox
74 Compressor intake
75 Engine oil tank
76 Port navigation light
77 One-piece engine cowling, hinged down to form work platform
78 Mission avionics equipment racks

79 Cabin window panel
80 Sonobuoy launch rack, 15 sonobuoys
81 Space provision for one passenger or litter patient
82 Rear underfloor main fuel cell, total internal capacity 1,802 litres (396 Imp gal)
83 Cabin wall insulation blankets
84 MAD unit mounting pylon
85 External tank filler cap
86 Retractable sonobuoy receiving antenna
87 External cargo hook, 1,814 kg (4000 lb) capacity
88 Main undercarriage hinged leading axle suspension

89 Twin mainwheels, forward retracting
90 Shock absorber
91 Mainwheel leg yoke
92 Retraction/breaker strut
93 Mainwheel leg yoke pivot mounting
94 Sliding cabin door lower rail
95 Gravity fuel fillers
96 Forward underfloor main fuel cell

This YSH-3E (converted from an HH-3D, originally built as a UH-2A) was operated by the Naval Air Development Center as a testbed for radar and others systems intended for LAMPS II (later superceded by LAMPS III).

SPECIFICATION

SH-2G Super Seasprite

Dimensions

Main rotor diameter: 13.51 m (44 ft 4 in)
Tail rotor diameter: 2.46 m (8 ft 1 in)
Main rotor disc area: 143.41 m² (1,543.66 sq ft)
Tail rotor disc area: 1.32 m² (14.19 sq ft)
Length overall, rotors turning: 16.08 m (52 ft 9 in)
Fuselage length, excluding tail rotor: 16.08 m (52 ft 9 in)
Fuselage length, with nose and blades folded: 11.68 m (38 ft 4 in)
Wheel track: 3.30 m (10 ft 10 in)

Powerplant

Two General Electric T700-GE-401/401C each rated at 1285 kW (1,723 shp)

Weights

Empty: 3483 kg (7,680 lb)
Maximum take-off weight: 6123 kg (13,500 lb)

Fuel and load

Internal fuel: 1045 litres (276 US gal)
External fuel: up to two 379-litre (100-US gal) auxiliary tanks
Maximum payload: 1814 kg (4,000 lb)

Performance

Maximum level speed 'clean' at sea level: 256 km/h (159 mph)
Normal cruising speed: 222 km/h (138 mph)
Maximum range: 885 km (500 miles) with two auxiliary tanks
Operational radius: 65 km (40 miles) for a patrol of 2 hours 10 minutes with one torpedo or of 1 hour 30 minutes with two torpedoes
Endurance: 5 hours with two auxiliary tanks

Maximum rate of climb at sea level: 762 m (2,500 ft) per minute
Service ceiling: 7285 m (23,900 ft)
Hovering ceiling: 6340 m (20,800 ft) in ground effect and 5485 m (18,000 ft) out of ground effect

SH-2F Seasprite

(generally similar to the SH-2G except in the following particulars)

Dimensions

Main rotor diameter: 13.41 m (44 ft)
Tail rotor diameter: 2.49 m (8 ft 2 in)
Main rotor disc area: 141.26 m² (1,520.53 sq ft)
Tail rotor disc area: 4.87 m² (52.38 sq ft)
Length overall, rotors turning: 16.03 m (52 ft 7 in)
Wheel track: 5.11 m (16 ft 9 in)

Powerplant

Two General Electric T58-GE-8F each rated at 1007 kW (1,350 shp)

Weights

Empty: 3193 kg (7,040 lb)
Maximum normal take-off: 5805 kg (12,800 lb)

Fuel and load

External fuel: up to two 227-litre (60-US gal) auxiliary tanks
Maximum ordnance: 544 kg (1,200 lb)

Performance

Maximum level speed 'clean' at sea level: 265 km/h (165 mph)
Normal cruising speed: 241 km/h (150 mph)
Maximum range: 679 km (422 miles)
Maximum rate of climb at sea level: 774 m (2,440 ft) per minute
Service ceiling: 6860 m (22,500 ft)
Hovering ceiling: 5670 m (18,600 ft) in ground effect and 4695 m (15,400 ft) out of ground effect

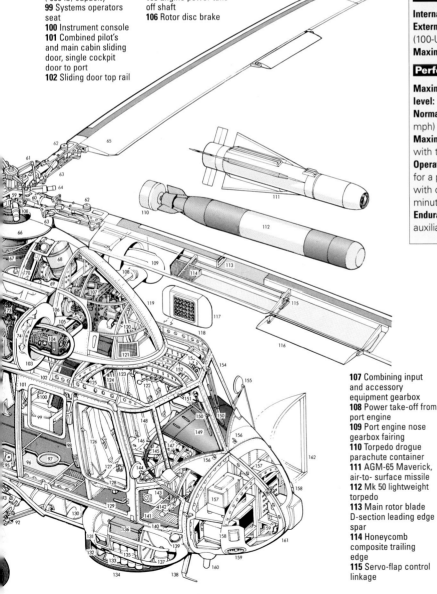

97 Tank access panel
98 Rescue hoist/winch, stowed position, 272 kg (600 lb) capacity
99 Systems operators seat
100 Instrument console
101 Combined pilot's and main cabin sliding door, single cockpit door to port
102 Sliding door top rail
103 Engine air intake
104 Right-angle nose gearbox
105 Engine power take-off shaft
106 Rotor disc brake

107 Combining input and accessory equipment gearbox
108 Power take-off from port engine
109 Port engine nose gearbox fairing
110 Torpedo drogue parachute container
111 AGM-65 Maverick, air-to- surface missile
112 Mk 50 lightweight torpedo
113 Main rotor blade D-section leading edge spar
114 Honeycomb composite trailing edge
115 Servo-flap control linkage
116 Servo-flap
117 AN/ALQ-144 flare launcher, two on port fuselage
118 Cockpit roof glazing
119 Hinged gearbox front cowling
120 Dual generators
121 Electrical equipment cooling air intake
122 Rotor brake handle
123 Sloping bulkhead
124 Control runs
125 Cabin dome light
126 Pilot's seat
127 Safety harness
128 Bulged cockpit door observation windows
129 Door latch
130 Main undercarriage wheel bay
131 Boarding step
132 Canadian Marconi LN-66HP surveillance radar
133 Ground power socket
134 Ventral radome
135 Marine markers
136 Marker stowage/launch unit
137 Ventral floodlight, lower anti-collision light to port
138 Position of pitot head on port side
139 Windscreen de-icing fluid reservoir filler cap
140 Downward vision window
141 Foot boards
142 Yaw control rudder pedals
143 Cyclic pitch control column, full dual controls
144 Pilot's rear view mirror
145 Collective pitch lever
146 Centre control console
147 Instrument panel
148 Co-pilot/Tactical Control Officer's seat
149 Instrument panel shroud
150 Windscreen wipers
151 Stand-by compass
152 Overhead switch panel
153 Sonobuoy launch control unit
154 Optically flat windscreen panels
155 Co-pilot's rear view mirror
156 Windscreen de-icing fluid spray nozzles
157 Nose compartment avionics equipment racks
158 Forward radar warning antennae
159 Retractable landing light, port and starboard
160 IFF antenna, port and starboard
161 Split hinged nose fairing/access panels
162 Nose fairing folded position, access and hanger stowage

Left: In this view of a US Navy SH-2G in the hover the fairings protruding from the front of the T700 engine nacelles – unique to the SH-2G – are apparent.

Above: Lt Cdrs Mike Branco (left) and Steve Ude are seen aboard an HSL-84 SH-2G over the Pacific Ocean. The original SH-2G cockpit is quite conventional in layout; the SH-2G(A)s for Australia feature a 'glass' cockpit, four large MFDs replacing conventional dials and gauges. The RAN machines will also have only two crew, with the tactical operator in the left-hand seat.

Below: The SH-2F and G carry a Texas Instruments AN/ASQ-81(V)2 towed MAD 'bird' on the starboard pylon: the same equipment employed by the SH-60B. This is used in conjunction with the Marconi LN-66HP surface-search radar, a tactical navigation/ communications system and active sonobouys and torpedoes with which to detect and engage sub-surface threats.

Above: The ability of the Seasprite to operate from the decks of small warships – which are now proliferating – gave the SH-2 a new lease of life. Operating at weights some 10,000 lb (4536 kg) lighter than the Seahawk (LAMPS III), the SH-2G has few rivals.

Seasprites in the Gulf

Assigned to numerous USN vessels on patrol in the Persian Gulf and Red Sea, the SH-2F saw service largely in SAR and communications roles, though they had a limited offensive capability. Six squadrons are known to have operated detachments aboard ships in the region, namely HSLs-32, -33, -34, -35, -36 and -37. Here an SH-2F of HSL-36 undergoes maintenance at Bahrain after hostilities had ceased (April 1991). For service in the Gulf many new-build SH-2Fs and some earlier ships were converted to MEEF (Middle East Expeditionary Force) standard, with AN/ALQ-66A(V)1 RWRs and AN/ALE-39 chaff/flare dispensers fitted. From 1987, 16 SH-2Fs received a package of modifications to allow them to operate in the Persian Gulf. The package included the provision of AN/AAQ-16 FLIR under the nose, AN/ALQ-144 IR jammer, AN/AAR-47 and AN/DLQ-3 missile warning and jamming equipment, new radios and cabin-mounted M60 machine-guns.

SH-2G exports

Though now in the twilight of its US Navy career, the Seasprite has found some export success in recent years, with the proliferation of small warships in the world's navies. Kaman has notched up SH-2G Super Seasprite sales in Egypt, Australia and New Zealand.

For operation by joint RNZAF/RNZN crews from ANZAC-class frigates, No. 3 Sqn, RNZAF received four refurbished SH-2Fs (pictured) in 1998, pending the delivery of five SH-2G(NZ)s during 2001-03.

Egypt was the first customer for the Super Seasprite, ordering 10 examples (rebuilt from ex-US Navy SH-2Fs) in 1995. These SH-2G(E)s were delivered during 1997/98 and feature and AlliedSignal AQS-18A dipping sonar equipment. In the market for a new helicopter to equip

their new 'ANZAC'-class frigates, the navies of both Australia and New Zealand opted for the SH-2G in the face of stiff competition from, in particular, the Westland Super Lynx. Australia ordered 11 SH-2G(A)s, rebuilt from ex-USN SH-2Fs, the first of which was delivered in early 2001. These aircraft will be

armed with Penguin Mk 2 Mod 7 anti-ship missiles, the first such weapon to service with the RAN Fleet Air Arm.

Later in the year New Zealand received the first two SH-2G(NZ)s of five ordered; these machines are able to employ AGM-65D Maverick ASMs and replace four refurbished SH-2Fs

acquired in the late 1990s as much needed temporary replacements for obsolete Westland Wasps.

In 2000 Kaman was in negotiation with the Thai navy for the sale of 10 SH-2Fs rebuilt to -2G standard; the type was also on offer to Malaysia, Canada and Singapore.

USN SH-2F/G operators

As earlier examples were brought up to SH-2F standard and new-build aircraft delivered, the F-model became the most important Seasprite variant.

Between 1973 and 1982, the US Navy took delivery of 104 SH-2F LAMPS I aircraft, 88 of which were converted from earlier models (using up most of the surviving airframes in the Navy inventory) and a further 16 from SH-2Ds. The first examples equipped light ASW helicopter squadron HSL-30 and -31 (formerly HC-4

and HC-5), established as the Atlantic and Pacific fleet readiness (training) units, respectively. Later aircraft equipped six operational squadrons – HSL-32 to HSL-37 – three per fleet. These provided one- or two-aircraft detachments for deployment aboard a range of USN carriers, destroyers and frigates.

After an upgraded version of the Seasprite was rejected for LAMPS III in favour of the Sikorsky SH-60B, the type was retained for service aboard US Navy 'Knox'- and 'Kidd'-class frigates, the 'Truxton'-class cruisers and the first two 'Ticonderoga'-class cruisers. All but the first 'Belknap'-class cruisers carried SH-2Fs, as did the first and the third through to the 25th 'Oliver Hazard Perry'-class ASW frigates. The aircraft was re-instated in production during 1981, when the US Navy placed an order for the first batch of an eventual 60 new-build SH-2Fs, the last six being delivered as upgraded SH-2Gs.

In 1992 the SH-2F was operated by eight front-line and three Reserve HSL squadrons (HSL-74, -84 and -94), but by the end of April 1994 post-Cold War defence cuts had reduced the force to two Reserve units, the last fleet squadron having been HSL-33. These units (HSL-84 'Thunderbolts' at NAS North Island, California and HSL-94 'Titans' at NAS Willow Grove, Pennsylvania) transitioned to SH-2Gs during 1994, with eight aircraft assigned to each.

Ten SeaSprite airframes have been delivered to Thailand, and are being upgraded to SH-2G standard in an ongoing programme.

Kamov Ka-25 'Hormone'

This Ka-25BSh 'Hormone-A' (displaying the flag of the Soviet navy) is bereft of flotation gear, fuel tanks and all the usual ASW equipment. In this configuration, the Ka-25 could carry a useful load of freight or 12 passengers, enabling it to perform an important secondary ship-to-shore transport role.

Naval helicopter family

Designed to meet a 1957 Soviet navy requirement for a new shipborne ASW helicopter, the first member of the Ka-20/25 family was the **Ka-20 'Harp'**, which initially flew during 1960. The production **Ka-25BSh 'Hormone-A'** was of near identical size and appearance, but was fitted with operational equipment and uprated GTD-3F turboshaft engines (from 1973 these were replaced by GTD-3BMs). It entered service in 1967.

Although the lower part of the fuselage is sealed and watertight, the Ka-25 is not intended for amphibious operations, and flotation bags are often fitted to the undercarriage for use in the event of an emergency landing on the water. The cabin is adequate for the job, but is not tall enough to allow the crew to stand upright. Progressive additions of new equipment have made the interior more cluttered.

Primary sensors for the ASW mission are the I/J-band radar (ASCC/NATO 'Big Bulge'), OKA-2 dipping sonar, a downward-looking 'Tie Rod' electro-optical sensor in the tailboom and a MAD sensor, either in a recess in the rear part of the cabin or in a fairing sometimes fitted below the central of the three tailfins. A box-like sonobuoy launcher can also be scabbed on to the starboard side of the rear fuselage. Dye-markers or smoke floats can also be carried externally. Comprehensive avionics, defensive and navigation systems are also fitted as standard.

Armament is not normally carried, although the helicopter can be fitted with a long 'coffin-like' weapons bay which runs along the belly from the radome back to the tailboom, and small bombs or depth charges can be carried on tiny pylons just aft of the nosewheels. The underfuselage bay can carry a variety of weapons, including nuclear depth charges. When wire-guided torpedoes are carried, a wire reel is mounted on the port side of the forward fuselage.

It has been estimated that some 260 of the 450 or so Ka-25s produced were 'Hormone-As', but only a handful remains in Russian and Ukrainian service, mostly fulfiling secondary roles. Small numbers of Ka-25BShs were exported to India, Syria, Vietnam and former Yugoslavia, and most of these aircraft remained in use in mid-2003.

'Hormone' variants

The second Ka-25 variant identified in the West was given the NATO reporting name **'Hormone-B'**, and is designated **Ka-25K**. This variant is externally identifiable by its bulbous undernose radome and small datalink radome under the rear fuselage. Ka-25K was used for acquiring targets and providing mid-course missile guidance, for ship- and submarine-launched missiles. The final version of the military Ka-25 is the **Ka-25PS 'Hormone-C'**, a dedicated SAR and transport helicopter.

SPECIFICATION

Kamov Ka-25BSh 'Hormone-A'
Type: ASW helicopter
Powerplant: two OMKB 'Mars' (Glushenkov) GTD-3F turboshafts each rated at 671 kW (898 shp) in early helicopters, or two GTD-3BM turboshafts each rated at 738 kW (900 shp) in late helicopters
Performance: maximum level speed 'clean' at optimum altitude 209 km/h (130 mph); normal cruising speed at optimum altitude 193 km/h (120 mph); service ceiling service ceiling 3350 m (10,990 ft);

range 400 km (249 miles) with standard fuel
Weights: empty 4765 kg (10,505 lb); maximum take-off 7500 kg (16,534 lb)
Dimensions: rotor diameter, each 15.74 m (52 ft 7¾ in); fuselage length 9.75 m (32 ft); overall 5.37 m (17 ft 7½ in); main rotor disc area 389.15 m² (4,188.93 sq ft)
Armament: provision for torpedoes, conventional or nuclear depth charges and other stores up to a maximum of 1900 kg (4,190 lb)

Kamov Ka-27, Ka-29, and Ka-31 'Helix'

Naval helicopter family

Work on the **Ka-27** family began in 1969. The Ka-27 retains Kamov's well-proven contra-rotating co-axial rotor configuration, and has dimensions similar to those of the Ka-25. With more than double the power of the Ka-25, the Ka-27 is a considerably heavier helicopter with a larger fuselage, but nevertheless offers increased performance with much-improved avionics and a more modern flight-control system.

The first production variant was the **Ka-27PL 'Helix-A'** basic ASW version, which entered service in 1982. The Ka-27PL's fuselage is sealed over its lower portions for buoyancy, while extra flotation equipment can be fitted in boxes on the lower part of the centre fuselage. Ka-27 is extremely stable and easy to fly, and automatic height hold,

automatic transition to and from the hover and autohover are possible in all weather conditions. Ka-27PL has all the usual ASW and ESM equipment, including dipping sonar and sonobuoys as well as Osminog (octopus) search radar.

Variants

The main SAR and planeguard Ka-27 variant is the radar-equipped **Ka-27PS 'Helix-D'**. This usually carries external fuel tanks and flotation gear, and has a hydraulically-operated, 300-kg (661-lb) capacity rescue winch.

Ka-28 'Helix-A' is the export version of the Ka-27PL ordered by China, India, Vietnam and Yugoslavia and with a revised avionics suite.

The **Ka-29TB** (**Transportno Boyevoya**) is a dedicated assault transport derivative of the Ka-27/32 family, intended especially for the support of

Russian navy amphibious operations and featuring a substantially changed airframe. The first example was seen by Western eyes on the assault ship *Ivan Rogov* in 1987, the type having entered service in 1985, and the **Ka-29TB** was initially assumed to be the Ka-27B, resulting in the allocation of the NATO reporting designation **'Helix-B'**. The Ka-29TB features an entirely new, much widened forward

fuselage, with a flight deck seating three members of the crew side-by-side. The Ka-29TB also served as the basis for the **Ka-31**, which was originally known as the **Ka-29RLD**. This AEW type first flew in 1988, and was first seen during carrier trials aboard *Kuznetsov*. All four landing gear units are retractable, making space for the movement of the E-801E Oko (eye) surveillance radar's antenna.

Ka-29TB is a formidable assault and attack helicopter. It mounts a sizeable weapons load on braced fuselage outriggers.

SPECIFICATION	
Kamov Ka-27PL 'Helix-A'	(27,778 lb)

Kamov Ka-27PL 'Helix-A'
Type: three-crew shipborne anti-submarine and utility helicopter
Powerplant: two Klimov (Isotov) TV3-117V turboshaft engines each rated at 1633 kW (2,190 shp)
Performance: maximum speed 250 km/h (155 mph) at optimum altitude; cruising speed 230 km/h (143 mph) at optimum altitude; service ceiling 5000 m (16,404 ft); hovering ceiling 3500 m (11,483 ft) out of ground effect; range 800 km (497 miles) with auxiliary fuel
Weights: empty 6100 kg (13,448 lb); maximum take-off 12600 kg

(27,778 lb)
Dimensions: rotor diameter, each 15.9 m (52 ft 2 in); length, excluding rotors 11.27 m (37 ft 11¾ in); height to top of rotor head 5.45 m (17 ft 10½ in); rotor disc area, each 198.5 m² (2,136.6 sq ft)
Armament: up to 200 kg (441 lb) of disposable stores, generally comprising four APR-2E homing torpedoes or four groups of S3V guided anti-submarine bombs
Payload: up to 5000 kg (11,023 lb) of freight

Mil Mi-14 'Haze'
Naval helicopter family

In order to produce a replacement for the large numbers of Mi-4 'Hounds' in Soviet naval service, a version of the Mi-8 'Hip' with a boat-like hull was developed as the **Mi-14 'Haze'**. The prototype of the series, designated **V-14**, flew for the first time in 1973, to be followed by the initial production **Mi-14PL 'Haze-A'** ASW helicopter.

Improvements incorporated during production included more powerful engines and the switching of the tail rotor from the starboard to the port side for increased controllability.

New variants

The latest 'Haze-A' aircraft have revised equipment which includes a repositioned MAD system and are designated **Mi-14PLM**.

Above: Illustrated as it appeared in Soviet service during the 1980s, this Mi-14PL shows the type's standard configuration. Early PLs had undercarriage doors, but these were soon deleted. Note the search radar radome beneath the fuselage.

From 1983, trials were carried out with the **Mi-14BT 'Haze-B'** minesweeper. The helicopter has various airframe changes for its role and as primary equipment uses a towed mine sled. Although Mi-14BTs have been used on international mine-clearing operations, few were built. Russian forces prefer to use surface minesweepers, while some of the six BTs delivered to East Germany passed to the Luftwaffe as SAR helicopters, before emerging as civilian water bombers.

Above: The Mi-14BT lacks a towed MAD 'bird', the aft fuselage instead housing mine countermeasures towing equipment. Only 25-30 examples were built, including a pair for Bulgaria's Naval Air Arm (illustrated).

The final production 'Haze' variant was the **Mi-14PS 'Haze-C'** SAR helicopter. Built primarily for the AV-MF, 'Haze-C' was also exported to Poland.

A few non-standard Mi-14 versions and designations have also appeared. **Mi-14PL 'Strike'** was a variant proposed for attack missions with AS-7 'Kerry' ASMS. **Mi-14PW** is the Polish designation for the Mi-14PL, while the **Mi-14PX** is one Polish Mi-14PL stripped of its ASW gear and used for SAR training.

The boat hull of the 'Haze' allows operations in Sea States 3-4, or for planing at up to 60 km/h (37 mph). Note the sponson-mounted flotation bags and tail float of this Russian navy Mi-14PS.

SPECIFICATION

Mil Mi-14PL 'Haze-A'
Type: ASW helicopter
Powerplant: two Klimov (Isotov) TV3-117A turboshafts each rated at 1268 kW (1,700 shp) in early helicopters; or two TV3-117MT turboshafts each rated at 1434 kW (1,923 shp) in late helicopters
Performance: maximum level speed 'clean' at optimum altitude 230 km/h (143 mph); maximum cruising speed at optimum altitude 215 km/h (133 mph); initial rate of climb 468 m (1,535 ft) per minute; service ceiling 4000 m (13,123 ft);

range 925 km (575 miles) with standard fuel
Weights: empty 8902 kg (19,625 lb); maximum take-off 14000 kg (30,864 lb)
Dimensions: rotor diameter, each 21.29 m (69 ft 10¼ in); length overall, rotors turning 25.32 m (83 ft 1 in); height 6.93 m (22 ft 9 in); main rotor disc area 356 m² (3,832.08 sq ft)
Armament: one AT-1 or APR-2 torpedo, or one 'Skat' nuclear depth bomb, or eight depth charges

Sikorsky **S-61/H-3** Sea King
ASW and multi-role helicopter

One of the most important helicopter families yet developed, the **Sikorsky SH-3 Sea King** series began life as the **HSS-2** anti-submarine helicopter for the US Navy. The prototype of this helicopter first flew on 11 March 1959, and the aircraft, which has the company designation **Sikorsky S-61**, was the first which could carry all the sensors and weapons needed for ASW missions without external help (though the US Navy policy developed to regard the aircraft as an extension of the ASW surface vessel from which it operates, so that helicopter-carried sensors detect the hostile submarine before the warship is called in for the kill).

Sea King features

New features included an amphibious boat hull with retractable tailwheel landing gear, twin turboshaft engines (for power, lightness, reliability and single-engine flight capability) above the cabin and an unobstructed tactical compartment for two sonar operators whose sensors included a dipping sonobuoy lowered through a keel hatch. Above the extensive avionic systems was an attitude-hold autopilot and a sonar coupler which maintained exact height and station in conjunction with a radar altimeter and Doppler radar. Over 1,100 **H-3** type helicopters were built, the ASW models being SH-3s in four basic models.

The US Navy produced its 150-strong SH-3H (illustrated) fleet by converting earlier SH-3A, SH-3D and SH-3G aircraft. Even a pair of ex-USAF CH-53Bs was consumed.

ASW variants

The **SH-3A** was the original model with 933-kW (1,260-shp) T58-GE-8B turboshafts, the **SH-3D** is the upgraded version; the **SH-3G** is the utility version; and the **SH-3H** is the multi-role model fitted with dipping sonar and MAD gear for ASW and search radar for the detection of incoming anti-ship missiles. Single examples of the SH-3D and SH-3G, plus 50 SH-3Hs remained in US Navy service in mid-2003.

Licence-production

Agusta has built the Sea King under licence in Italy as the **AS-61/ASH-3**, some variants being equipped with Marte anti-ship missiles. Mitsubishi built 55 Sea Kings in three versions, all retaining the original HSS-2 designation, for the JMSDF. By far the most important overseas manufacturer, however, has been Westland in the UK. Westland-built aircraft are powered by Rolls-Royce H.1400 Gnome-series engines and have much UK-sourced equipment. The initial **Sea King HAS.Mk 1** made its first flight on 7 May 1969 and was little more than a re-engined SH-3D. Subsequent ASW variants for the Royal Navy have included the **HAS.Mk 2**, **HAS.Mk 5** and **HAS.Mk 6**. To fill an AEW gap, the **Sea King AEW.Mk 2A** was produced by conversion from HAS.Mk 2 standard. Later, HAS.Mk 5 aircraft were converted to **AEW.Mk 5** and **AEW.Mk 7** standard. **Sea King HAR.Mk 3** and **Mk 3A** SAR helicopters have been built for the RAF.

US Navy squadron HC-2 remained a Sea King operator in 2003. Its UH-3H utility helicopters were produced by conversion from SH-3H standard.

SPECIFICATION	
Sikorsky SH-3D Sea King	**Dimensions:** main rotor diameter 18.9 m (62 ft); fuselage length 16.69 m (54 ft 9 in); height 5.13 m (16 ft 10 in); main rotor disc area 280.5 m² (3,019.10 sq ft)
Type: ASW helicopter	
Powerplant: two 1044-kW (1,400-shp) General Electric T58-10 turboshafts	
Performance: maximum speed 267 km/h (166 mph); range with maximum fuel and 10 per cent reserves 1005 km (625 miles)	**Armament:** external hardpoints for a total of 381 kg (840 lb) of weapons, normally comprising two Mk 46 torpedoes
Weights: empty 5382 kg (11,865 lb); max. take-off 9752 kg (21,500 lb)	

Sikorsky S-80/MH-53 Sea Dragon
Mine-sweeping helicopter

Though the original Sikorsky S-65 production models have only two engines, the **S-80**/H-53E has three engines each of 3266 kW (4,380 shp) and is the most powerful helicopter ever built outside Russia. Of the early versions, the CH-53A and more powerful CH-53D were transports for the US Marines Corps. All CH-53As were delivered with provisions deploying for towed mine-sweeping equipment, but the US Navy decided that a dedicated mine counter-measures version would need more power and additional modifications. Accordingly, 15 CH-53As were transferred to the US Navy as **RH-53A** mine-sweeping machines fitted with equipment for towing the EDO Mk 105 hydrofoil anti-mine sled.

Still more power

The RH-53As were used to explore the possibilities of these new mine-sweeping techniques, which had previously been tried only with machines of inadequate power, pending the arrival of 30 **RH-53D Sea Dragon** purpose-built machines. Equipped with drop tanks and, later, inflight-refuelling probes, the RH-53Ds were soon re-engined with 3266-kW (4,380-shp) T64-GE-415 turboshafts. The aircraft were delivered to the US Navy from the summer of 1973 and about 19 remained in US Navy service in early 2003, but were being replaced by MH-53Es. Six RH-53Ds were delivered to the Imperial Iranian Navy.

The CH-53E was developed to meet a 1973 demand for an upgraded heavy-lift transport for the US Navy and US Marine Corps. From it was developed the **MH-53E Sea Dragon**. This definitive MCM (mine countermeasures) version has enormously enlarged side sponsons for an extra 3785 litres (833 Imp gal) of fuel,

An MH-53E from HM-14 'Vanguards' prepares for take-off. The aircraft was deployed to Bahrain in support of Operation Enduring Freedom.

for extended sweeping missions with the engines at sustained high power. The first prototype MH-53E made its initial flight on 23 December 1981 and around 44 remained in service in 2003.

The **MH-53J** has been sold to the JMSDF.

SPECIFICATION	
Sikorsky MH-53E Sea Dragon **Type:** shipboard minesweeping helicopter **Powerplant:** three 3266-kW (4,380-shp) General Electric T64-GE-416 turboshafts **Performance:** maximum speed 315 km/h (196 mph); cruising speed at sea level 278 km/h (173 mph); maximum self-ferry range 2074 km (1,289 miles) **Weights:** empty 16482 kg (36,336 lb); maximum take-off with	internal payload 31640 kg (69,750 lb); maximum take-off with external payload 33340 kg (73,500 lb) **Dimensions:** main rotor diameter 24.08 m (79 ft); length overall, rotors turning 30.19 m (99 ft ½ in); height to top of main rotor head 5.32 m (17 ft 5½ in); main rotor disc area 455.38 m² (4,901.7 sq ft) **Armament:** provision for window-mounted 12.7-mm (0.5-in) or 7.62-mm (0.3-in) guns

Sikorsky **S-70/H-60** Seahawk
ASW and multi-role helicopter

Mitsubishi has built SH-60Js (illustrated) and UH-60Js for the JMSDF.

Mitsubishi has built SH-60Js (illustrated) and UH-60Js for the JMSDF.

A derivative of the US Army's UH-60 Black Hawk, the **Sikorsky SH-60B Seahawk** (originally produced under the company designation **S-70L**, later **S-70B**) won the US Navy's LAMPS (Light Airborne Multi-Purpose System) III competition in September 1977. A complex and extremely expensive machine, the SH-60B was designed for two main missions: ASW and ASST (anti-ship surveillance and targeting). The ASST mission involved the aerial detection of incoming sea- skimming AShMs, and the provision of radar-derived data for similar weapons launched from US warships. Secondary missions included SAR, medevac and vertrep (vertical replenishment). The basic airframe differs from that of the UH-60 in being marinised, with a sealed tailboom, having its tailwheel moved and inflatable bags for emergency buoyancy fitted, and having an electrically-folding main rotor and pneumatically-folding tail (including upward-hinged tailplanes). Other modifications are greater fuel capacity and the removal of cockpit armour for the pilot and co-pilot. The type is also fitted with haul-down equipment to facilitate recovery onto small platforms on pitching and rolling ships in heavy seas. Under the nose is the large APS-124 radar and on the left side of the fuselage is a large vertical panel with tubes for launching sonobuoys.

On the right of the rear fuselage is a pylon for a towed MAD 'bird'. The first prototype flew on 12 December 1979 and a total of 181 was built for the USN.

Subsequent variants for US Navy service have included the **SH-60F Ocean Hawk**, equipped with dipping sonar for inner-zone ASW cover around aircraft-carriers; the **HH-60H Rescue Hawk** for ship-borne SAR, plane guard and special forces missions and the **MH-60R** multi-mission helicopter. The latter were to be produced by conversion from SH-60B/F/HH-60H helicopters, but 243 new-build helicopters were bought for delivery from 2005. They joined 237 **MH-60S** utility aircraft, which combine much of the UH-60's airframe with SH-60 systems and began replacing CH-46 Sea Knights in 2002.

SPECIFICATION	
Sikorsky SH-60B Seahawk **Type:** multi-role shipboard helicopter **Powerplant:** (aircraft delivered from 1988) two 1417-kW (1,900-shp) General Electric T700-GE-401C turboshafts **Performance:** dash speed at 1525 m (5,000 ft) 234 km/h (145 mph); operational radius 92.5 km (57.5 miles) for a 3-hour loiter	**Weights:** (for the ASW mission) empty 6191 kg (13,648 lb); mission take-off 9182 kg (20,244 lb) **Dimensions:** main rotor diameter 16.36 m (53 ft 8 in); fuselage length 15.26 m (50 ft ¾ in); height overall, rotors turning 5.18 m (17 ft); main rotor disc area 210.05 m² (2,262.03 sq ft) **Armament:** normally two Mk 46 torpedoes, or Penguin AShMs

The many roles now tackled by the SH-60 family are shown here by an HH-60H taking off for a plane guard sortie.

Easily identified by the two windows in its portside cabin door, this HH-60H is shown performing a vertrep mission.

Westland Lynx

Multi-role helicopter

Under the design leadership of Westland, the Lynx emerged as an effective medium-lift helicopter which, in dedicated army and navy variants, effectively fulfils the disparate anti-tank and battlefield reconnaissance roles, as well as flying anti-surface vessel and ASW missions.

The Lynx is a compact helicopter design suited to ASW and other naval roles, as well as to multi-role armed and unarmed land missions. Of conventional, mainly light alloy, construction, the Lynx nevertheless introduced glass-fibre access panels, doors and fairings, and also made use of composites in the four main rotor blades. The later production Super Lynx and Battlefield Lynx introduced more advanced composite blades with swept tips developed under the British Experimental Rotor Programme (BERP), offering improved speed and reduced vibration.

The pilot and co-pilot or observer are seated side-by-side. Maximum high-density seating is provided for one pilot

and 10 armed troops on lightweight bench seats. The Super Lynx has a chin-mounted Sea Spray or AlliedSignal RDR 1500 360° scan radar. For armed escort and anti-tank missions, the army version can be equipped with 20-mm (0.79-in) cannon, rocket pods or up to eight HOT, Hellfire or TOW air-to-surface missiles. For the ASW role, armament typically includes two Sting Ray homing torpedoes, or up to four Sea Skua or two Penguin AShMs. More than 400 have been built for the UK and several export customers, and the type remains in production.

Development
After the end of World War II, Westland decided to branch out into the new rotary-wing field.

Above: In August 1978, the Lynx AH.Mk 1 became operational with the BAOR. This aircraft was photographed just after launching a TOW missile from its starboard-side launch tubes.

Most of the Lynx airframe is of conventional aluminium alloy, but the aircraft did introduce a number of innovations. Not least of these was its rotor system, with its main rotor hub and inboard flexible arm portions being built as a titanium monobloc forging.

Westland built a single Lynx 3 demonstrator as a heavier and more powerfully-armed version of the aircraft. It featured a WG.30 tailcone, revised engines and intakes, and BERP rotor blades.

Initially building heavily-modified Sikorsky models under licence, the company began designing its own machines when it was left as the only manufacturer, following a rationalisation of the British helicopter industry in 1959/60. Westland began work on a series of proposals for future military helicopters. One of these was the W.3, to be powered by the Pratt & Whitney PT6A turboshaft engine and targeted at Naval/Air Staff Requirement 358 for a medium helicopter for the RAF and RN. Several variants, re-designated W.13, were projected before the Army's General Staff Operational Requirement 3335 was issued in October 1964. This called for a multi-role helicopter capable of carrying a crew of two and seven fully-armed troops at a speed of 274 km/h (170 mph).

A requirement issued in June 1966 added yet another twist, this time detailing a specific need for a helicopter capable of operating from frigates and destroyers in high-sea states.

French involvement

France had a parallel requirement for this and other types, and the W.13, together with the SA 330 Puma and the SA 341 Gazelle, formed part of the Anglo-French agreement signed on 22 February 1967. Westland was given W.13 design leadership and proceeded with the development of a medium helicopter to fulfil Britain's requirements, as well as French demands for an armed reconnaissance and ASW helicopter.

The official go-ahead was given in July 1967 and work was stepped up. The task was made easier with the development by Rolls-Royce of the 670-kW (900-shp) RS.360 turboshaft, which had begun life at Bristol Siddeley as the BS.360. However, Rolls-Royce had difficulties in achieving the required thrust, and the first flight of the Lynx, as it was now known, was delayed by some eight months. The first of 13 prototypes finally lifted off on 21 March 1971, flown by Ron Gellatly, followed by the third on 28 September, and the fourth and second on 8 and 24 March 1972, respectively. Once the engines, named Gem from 1971, had delivered the maximum rated power, the Lynx quickly demonstrated its capabilities, setting two world records with a maximum speed of 321.74 km/h (199.92 mph).

The first British Army Lynx AH.Mk 1 became airborne on 12 April that same year, while the Royal Navy HAS.Mk 2 first flew on 25 May, but was lost in an accident on 21 November 1972. The naval version differed in having a lengthened nose to accommodate a radar scanner and a wheeled undercarriage. The second HAS.Mk 2 made the first at-sea landing on 29 June 1973. Eight more aircraft were used on the military development programme and the first production Lynx AH.Mk 1 for the AAC with Gem 2 engines, flew on 11 February 1977.

More power, more speed

Second-phase development produced the naval Super Lynx and army Battlefield Lynx, to which standards later UK Mk 8 and 9 models were built, alongside those for export customers. Both the Super Lynx and Battlefield Lynx, as well as having the BERP main rotor and reversed direction tail rotor for improved control, also have increased take-off weight, all-weather day/night capability and extended payload range. Current versions are the Super Lynx 100, an upgraded naval Lynx powered by Gem 42-1 turboshafts, and the Super Lynx 200 with more powerful LHTEC CTS800 engines with dual-channel FADEC and some LCD flat panel displays.

With 45 new airframes on order in mid-1999, the Super Lynx production line is at its busiest for many years. In addition to seven new aircraft being built for the German navy, 13 new Super Lynxes are in production for the Korean navy, and GKN Westland is also upgrading the 17 existing German navy Sea Lynxes and eight Lynxes in service with the Danish navy to Super Lynx standard. The upgrade programmes for the latter two are the first life-extension programmes to include the supply of new airframes into which the existing engines, flying controls, hydraulic systems, avionics and electrical systems are transferred.

In parallel with work on the existing contracts, rapid progress is also being made on the first Super Lynx 300. This latest version also incorporates LHTEC CTS800 engines, but differs from the Series 200 in introducing a full night-vision goggle compatible 'glass' cockpit. The Super Lynx 300 first flew in January 1999 with Gem 42 engines and will begin flight tests with the CTS800 later in 1999. It has been selected by South Africa to meet its shipborne helicopter requirement, and six have also been supplied to Malaysia. ▶

SPECIFICATION	
Westland Lynx HAS.Mk 2 **Type:** twin-engined naval helicopter **Powerplant:** two Rolls-Royce Gem 42-1 turboshafts each rated at 846 kW (1,135 shp) **Performance:** maximum continuous cruising speed at optimum altitude 232 km/h (144 mph); maximum rate of climb at sea level 661 m (2,170 ft) per minute; combat radius 178 km (111 miles) on a SAR mission with 11 survivors **Weights:** empty 2740 kg (6,040 lb); maximum take-off 4763 kg (10,500 lb)	**Dimensions:** main rotor diameter 12.8m (42 ft); fuselage length 11.92 m (39 ft 1 1/4 in); height 3.48 m (11 ft 5 in); main rotor disc area 128.71 m² (1,385.44 sq ft) **Armament:** pylons for two Mk 44, Mk 46 or Sting Ray torpedoes, two Mk 11 depth charges or four Sea Skua AShMs, plus one FN HMP 0.5-in (12.7-mm) machine-gun for self protection. An ALQ-167 ECM pod can also be carried

UK naval variants

As a small ship's helicopter the Lynx is without peer. Thanks to its small size, manoeuvrability, harpoon recovery gear and negative-force rotor, it can operate in much higher sea states than its rivals.

Lynx HAS.Mk 2

The Lynx HAS.Mk 2 was the baseline Royal Navy Lynx, a dedicated ASW platform optimised for 'small ship' operation. Basically similar to the original Army AH.Mk 1, the HAS.Mk 2 had a fixed wheeled tricycle undercarriage in place of skids, and naval features including a 'deck-lock' harpoon, a two-bag flotation system and a folding tailboom. The basic Lynx's rotor system was also well-suited to small ship operation, providing quick response to control inputs and high control power, both useful for precise positioning over a rolling flight deck, and for ensuring an accurate and firm touch down. The new naval version also had hardpoints to allow the carriage of weapons, including two Mk 44 or Mk 46 torpedoes, or two Mk 11 depth charges, or up to four Sea Skua anti-ship missiles. Its bulged nose housed radar in the form of a Seaspray Mk 1, though the prime purpose of the set was to provide illumination for the semi-active radar homing Sea Skua missile, and to improve all-weather capability. The naval version entered service before the AH.Mk 1. HAS.Mk 2 production for the Royal Navy totalled 60 new-build aircraft. Fifty-three HAS.Mk 2s were subsequently converted to HAS.Mk 3 standards. The Lynx HAS.Mk 2 entered service with No. 700L Squadron when it formed on September 1976. This functioned as a joint Royal Navy/Royal Netherlands Navy Intensive Flying Trials Unit, and at full strength operated six RN HAS.Mk 2s and two Dutch Lynx Mk 25s. One of the unit's aircraft deployed aboard

WG.13 prototype batch

The first example of a naval Lynx was XX469 (below, foreground) which differed from earlier test aircraft by having a more bulbous nose representative of the Seaspray radar installation. The naval aircraft also had conventional tricycle undercarriage rather than the skids of the Army variants. XX469 was lost in 1972 and XX510 took over its trials duties. Testing by the MoD and Aéronavale continued until the late 1970s and the emergence of the HAS.Mk 2.

HMS *Sirius* in 1977. The unit disbanded on 16 December 1977, and formed the nucleus of the Lynx training squadron, No. 702, which formed on 3 January 1978. No. 702 Squadron also functioned as the HQ Squadron for Lynx-equipped Ships Flights until 1 January 1981, when No. 815 Squadron took over as the HQ unit. The first operational deployment of the Lynx took place from 8 February 1978, aboard the 'Leander'-class frigate *Phoebe*. The aircraft was subsequently deployed aboard, 'Tribal'-, 'Leander'- and Type 21 frigates, Type 42 destroyers, and later aboard Type 22 and Type 23 frigates. As the maritime threat to the Royal Navy evolved and intensified, the Lynx HAS.Mk 2s were modified to fulfil new roles, including the ASV (Anti-Surface Vessel) mission, autonomous ASW, and the Electronic Counter Surveillance Measures task. Sea Skua ASMs, a towed MAD 'bird' and ESM were all retrofitted to most HAS.Mk 2s after delivery, to allow them to assume their new duties.

Naval Lynx 3

The Naval Lynx 3 (not to be confused with the HAS.Mk 3) was developed in parallel with the Army Lynx 3. A mock-up was revealed in September 1985, with 360° radar in an undernose radome, an overnose PID, a WG.30-style tail rotor and pylon, and a lowered tailplane. The version was soon abandoned in favour of advanced derivatives of the HAS.Mk 3.

Lynx HAS.Mk 3

The Lynx HAS.Mk 3 (above) was a modestly improved derivative of the Royal Navy HAS.Mk 2, with transmission, dynamic system and powerplant improvements. The new variant's improved performance and payload capabilities were accompanied by some new items of operational equipment, including Racal Decca MIR-2 Orange Crop ESM. The aircraft was fitted with a new four-bag flotation system, and was fitted with new towed MAD (Magnetic Anomoly Detector), ESM and the Sea Skua ASM. New-build aircraft were delivered between March 1982 and April 1985. They were augmented by the conversion of all surviving HAS.Mk 2s to 3 or 3S standards. The Lynx HAS.Mk 3 serves only with No. 702 (training) and No. 815 Squadrons, No. 829 having disbanded in March 1993. Since entering service, the HAS.Mk 3 fleet has been subject to a series of modifications, as detailed below.

Lynx HAS.Mk 3GM (above right): There were three standards of 'Gulf Modification' among the 14 aircraft deployed during Operation Granby, of 18 or 19 aircraft originally 'Granby Modified' and all re-designated as HAS.Mk 3GMs. All aircraft are understood to have been fitted with MIR-2 ESM. LORAL Challenger IR jammers were fitted above the cockpit doors, but these were removed in-theatre to save weight, because the naval Lynxes were not felt to face a credible threat from shoulder-launched SAMs. Royal Navy Lynxes operating in Desert Storm scored 17 direct hits with their Sea Skua missiles and sank 12 Iraqi vessels.

Lynx HAS.Mk 3S: The Lynx HAS.Mk 3 was re-designated with the addition of an 'S' for 'secure' suffix after the addition of dual GEC-Marconi AD3400 UHF secure speech radios. It has been reported that the third batch of new-build HAS.Mk 3s was delivered to this standard.

Lynx HAS.Mk 3ICE (right): When the Lynx replaced the Wasp in the 'small ships' ASW role, it was inevitable that it would also replace the Wasps used aboard the Antarctic survey/ice patrol ship HMS *Endurance*.

The Royal Navy has thus equipped a number of Lynxes for service in the Antarctic. The most obvious modification is the application of high-visibility International Orange patches on the nose and cabin doors, though the aircraft also carry a range of specialised equipment. This includes a vertical (survey) camera pod, and a cabin-mounted periscope for sighting, while Sea Skua equipment is removed to comply with the prohibition against armed aircraft in Antarctica.

Lynx HAS.Mk 3SICE: When equipped with AD3400 UHF Secure Speech radios, the *Endurance* Flight Lynx HAS.Mk 3ICEs are designated as HAS.Mk 3SICEs. During a seven-month voyage by HMS *Endurance* into the heart of the Antarctic in early 1999, two Lynxes became the first helicopters to operate below 73° S, exploring the Carroll Inlet, taking aerial photographs and gathering scientific data.

Lynx HAS.Mk 3S/GM: When equipped with, or when given provision for the various Granby modifications, Secure Speech-capable HAS.Mk 3Ss are officially known as HAS.Mk 3S/GMs.

Lynx HAS.Mk 3CTS: The HAS.Mk 3CTS was never intended as a front-line variant in its own right, but only as a tool for the development and evaluation (including operational evaluation) of the CTS, which also forms the heart of the ultimate Royal Navy Lynx, the HMA.Mk 8.

Lynx HMA.Mk 8

The latest Navy Lynx variant is the HMA.Mk 8, which represents a real modernisation of the Navy Lynx design, and which parallels the Army's AH.Mk 7 upgrade. Designated HAS.Mk 8 until late 1995, the aircraft then became the HMA.Mk 8. If the HAS.Mk 3 modernised the Navy Lynx for the needs of the 1980s, the HMA.Mk 8 transformed the type into a state-of-the-art maritime helicopter for the new millenium. The new variant introduced 686-kW (920-shp) Gem 42 Series 200 engines, and an improved rotor system with the better tail rotor of the AH.Mk 7. The aircraft gained a number of new systems which enhance its surveillance and ASV capabilities, and which give a higher degree of autonomy. The HMA.Mk 8 will introduce digital radar processing for the old 180° Seaspray, this upgrade resulting in a change of designation to HMA.Mk 8 DSP (Digital Signal Processing) or HMA.Mk 8(DP). The Royal Navy's HMA.Mk 8s are now able to use the FN Herstal 12.7-mm (0.5-in) heavy machine-gun pod (HMP), regularly used by HAS.Mk 3GMs, though it is unclear whether such a weapon has received a formal release to service. Three former HAS.Mk 3CTS aircraft were used for HAS.Mk 8 development. XZ236 was used for CTS development and integration, ZD266 served as an avionics development aircraft, and ZD267 flight-trialled the new undernose radome and nose-mounted PID. Westland received a contract for the conversion of the first seven (of a planned 44 conversions) in May 1992, and subsequently received a follow-on contract for four more, as well as a contract to bring the development aircraft ZD267 to full Mk 8 standards. The first of these was delivered in July 1994 to an OEU formed within No. 815 Squadron. All seven of the initial batch were delivered by mid-1995. The first HMA.Mk 8s went to No. 702 Squadron (the Lynx training unit) from February 1996, and the type made its first sea deployment (aboard HMS *Montrose*) in late 1995. MoD plans originally called for the conversion of all surviving Lynx HAS.Mk 3s to the new standard.

▶

Foreign operators

Naval Lynx variants have sold well abroad, Westland tailoring the aircraft to the individual needs of customers, with revised engines/transmissions and operational equipment.

Brazil – Lynx Mk 21, Super Lynx Mk 21A

Brazil's ASW/ASV-roled Mk 21 was closely based on the baseline RN HAS.Mk 2, though they are armed with Sea Skua ASMs, Mk 9 depth charges or Mk 46 torpedoes. The first made its maiden flight on 30 September 1977; nine were built, the last flying on 14 April 1978. They were locally referred to as SAH-11s, and equipped Esquadrão de Helicopteros de Esclarecimento e Ataque 1 (HA-1) at São Pedro da Aldeia from 1978. The Lynxes are most commonly seen aboard the 'Niteroi'-class (Vosper-Thorneycroft Mk 10) frigates.

Brazil took delivery of 14 Super Lynxes, nine newly-built and five produced by the conversion of Mk 21s, in a £150 million deal signed in 1993. Broadly equivalent to the Portuguese Mk 95, the Brazilian Lynxes were equipped with the 360° SeaSpray 3000 radar and have provision for FLIR, recce pods or a 'dunking' sonar. The aircraft are powered by the 836-kW (1,120-shp) Gem 42-1, with composite main rotor blades and the reverse direction tail rotor. The first airframe for conversion made its first flight in its new configuration on 23 March 1996. The first new-build Mk 21A (N4001) made its maiden flight on 12 June 1996.

France – Lynx Mk 2(FN), Mk 4(FN)

Based on the RN HAS.Mk 2, but with the higher (4763 kg/10,500 lb) all up weight normally associated with the Gem 4-engined Dutch Lynx Mk 27, the Aéronavale Mk 2 (pictured) also had an ASV capability from the start, the latter being added to the RN variant only by retrofit. The French OMERA-Segid ORB31W radar replaced the usual Seaspray, while armament in the ASV role comprised Aérospatiale AS 12 ASMs. Twenty-six were built; the first flying on 24 October 1979.

The Aéronavale's Lynx Mk 4 was the French equivalent to the British HAS.Mk 3, though the dynamics, transmission and powerplant changes were not accompanied by any major improvement. Fourteen Mk 4s were produced. The French Lynxes have been improved and modernised in service, and now have BERP main rotor blades.

Argentina – Lynx Mk 23

Acquired for use in the ASW role aboard Argentina's two ex-RN Type 42 destroyers (*Hercules* and *Santisima Trinidad*), Argentina's two Lynx Mk 23s first flew on 17 May and 23 June 1978, and were similar to the baseline RN HAS.Mk 2, and to the Brazilian Mk 21. Both deployed to Port Stanley in the wake of the Argentine invasion of the Falklands, but played little part in the war that followed. One (0735/ 3-H-42, above) was lost in an accident on 2 May 1982, and the other was grounded then or soon afterwards. It was sold to Denmark in November 1987 (together with the Navy's entire Lynx spares holding).

Denmark – Lynx Mk 80, Mk 90, Super Lynx Mk 90B

Denmark acquired 10 Lynxes (eight Mk 80s and two Mk 90s) for fishery protection duties with the Sovaernets Flyvetjeneste (Naval Flying Service). Twin-engined safety and the ability to refuel in flight while hovering above a vessel (HIFR – Helicopter In Flight Refuelling) were crucial capabilities for the Danes. All of the Danish Lynxes were based on the HAS.Mk 3, with Seaspray radar. The first batch of eight of these new helicopters was newly-built as Lynx Mk 80s, the first aircraft making its maiden flight on 3 February 1980. Two more aircraft were acquired in 1987/1988 to replace two of the original aircraft (which had crashed in 1985 and 1987), these being designated as Mk 90s.

In service, the surviving Danish aircraft have been upgraded and further upgrades are planned under a recently announced MLU. When modified, the aircraft will be designated Lynx Mk 90B.

Netherlands – Lynx Mk 25, Mk 27, Mk 81, STAMOL Lynx

The first six Dutch Lynxes were broadly equivalent to the HAS.Mk 2, and were procured for use in the SAR role. They made their maiden flights between 23 August 1976 and 16 September 1977. The UH-14As were also used for training, utility transport and for support of the Royal Netherlands Marine Corps' BBE anti-terrorist unit.

The Netherlands Navy's Mk.27 was based on the basic Lynx HAS.Mk 2, although it was powered by 1,120-shp (836-kW) Gem 4 Mk 1010 engines. Optimised for the ASW role, the 10 Mk 27s were intended to operate from 'Tromp'-, 'Kortenaar'-and 'Van Speijk'-class frigates. The first made its maiden flight on 6 October 1978. The new version was fitted with Alcatel (now Thomson-CSF) DUAV-4A dipping sonar, and was armed with one or two Mk 46 torpedoes.

The third batch of Dutch Lynxes were HAS.Mk 3-based ASW aircraft, and were locally designated SH-14C. The first SH-14C made its first flight on 9 July 1980. The SH-14Cs initially lacked dipping sonar, but were instead fitted with a Texas Instruments AN/ASQ-81(V)2 magnetic anomaly detector. This was found to be less effective than sonar and was removed, and the SH-14Cs were relegated to training and utility duties.

Under the STAMOL (SH-14D) programme 22 surviving Dutch Lynxes were upgraded to a common standard, essentially that of the dipping sonar-equipped SH-14B. Other changes included an upgraded engine, new rotor blades and advanced avionics. A new radar was also planned, but later abandoned for budgetary reasons, though a FLIR was installed.

Malaysia – Super Lynx Mk ?

In September 1999 Westland announced the sale of six Super Lynxes to the Royal Malaysian Navy, to replace elderly Westland Wasps. At the time no specific version or equipment fit was announced.

Norway – Mk 86

The Norwegian air force (Luftforsvaret) ordered six Lynxes for use by the civil Kystvakt (Coast Guard) for SAR, fishery patrol and environmental control duties. The first made its first flight on 23 January 1981. Assigned to the air force's No. 337 Skvadron at Bardufoss, the aircraft operate mainly from three Coastguard 'Nordkap'-class patrol vessels in the North Atlantic (north of 65° N).

With the same Gem 4 Mk 1010 engines and increased AUW as the Dutch Mk 27, the six Norwegian Lynx Mk 86s were only semi-navalised, lacking the normal folding tailboom of the navy Lynx. They are equipped with Seaspray radar and, in addition to the usual UHF, HF and VHF/AM radios, have a police/emergency service VHF/FM radio. The TANS is connected to the Agiflite camera, which allows navigational data to be imprinted on photos of border/territorial water violations. A rescue hoist is used for SAR and for winching inspectors down to vessels being examined. It is also used to lift a fuel line to allow HIFR. The aircraft have been used intensively, and a requirement for a replacement will soon be formally issued.

Portugal – Super Lynx Mk 95

Portugal selected the Super Lynx to meet its requirement for a shipborne ASW helicopter. Always the preferred choice of the Portuguese Navy, five Super Lynxes were ordered on 2 November 1990. Although designated as a 'Super Lynx' by Westland, and though nominally 'based on the HMA.Mk 8', the Portuguese Navy Lynx Mk 95s lacks the distinctive overnose Passive Identification Device (PID) associated with third-generation Royal Navy Lynxes, or the overnose FLIR associated with the Mk 88A. The aircraft does have a Racal RNS252 GPS-aided INS, together with a Bendix AN/AQS-18(v) 'dunking' sonar and Bendix RDR 1500 radar in an undernose radome, and was the first Super Lynx variant with these

features. Five Mk 95s were produced for service on Portugal's 'Vasco da Gama'-class (MEKO 200) frigates, and are shore-based at Montijo, near Lisbon. Three of the Portuguese Super Lynxes are new-build, but the first two were produced through conversion of ex-Royal Navy HAS.Mk 3s. The first converted Mk 95 made its maiden flight on 27 March 1992. The first new-build aircraft flew for the first time on 9 July 1993.

South Korea – Super Lynx Mk 99

South Korea ordered Super Lynxes in 1988, making it the first export customer for the type, despite their aircraft's late numerical designation. This was reportedly allocated at Korea's request, the number 9 reportedly having connotations of good fortune in Korea! Although labelled as a Super Lynx, the Korean Mk 99 lacked the later reverse direction composite tail rotor and the composite BERP main rotor blades. The aircraft did have the new undernose radome, however, housing Seaspray 3 radar. Purchased for service aboard the Korean Navy's 'Sumner'- and 'Gearing'-class destroyers, the 12 new-build Lynx Mk 99s are shore-based at Chinhae with No. 627 Squadron. As well as the 360° Seaspray Mk 3 radar, they may be armed with Mk 44 torpedoes or Sea Skua ASMs. The first Mk 99 made its maiden flight on 16 November 1989, and deliveries were made between July 1990 and May 1991. The serial No. 90-0704 was omitted for reasons of superstition, '4' being considered 'unlucky'.

South Africa – Super Lynx Mk 64

In September 1999 Westland announced the sale of six Super Lynxes to the Royal Malaysian Navy, to replace elderly Wasps. At the time no specific version or equipment fit was announced.

Nigeria – Lynx Mk 89

The last HAS.Mk 3-based Lynx variant was Nigeria's Mk 89, which was broadly similar to the Mk 88 used by the Kriegsmarine, albeit without the Bendix sonar, and with folding tailboom. The Nigerian Lynxes have 847-kW (1,135-shp) Gem 43-1 Mk 1020 engines with improved hot and high performance. Three aircraft were supplied for use by No. 101 Sqn, the first making its maiden flight on 29 September 1983.

Pakistan – Lynx HAS.Mk 3 (Pakistan)

Pakistan signed an agreement for the purchase of three second-hand Royal Navy basic standard Lynx HAS.Mk 3s in June 1994, with an option to purchase three more. They were acquired for service aboard three of the six ex-Royal Navy Type 21 frigates also purchased by Pakistan. The aircraft were refurbished to 'half-life' standards prior to delivery, but have Sea Skua HIE (Helicopter Installed Equipment) removed.

Qatar – Lynx Mk 28

The Qatar Police became the only export customer to actually receive the Army/Battlefield Lynx when it purchased three Lynx HC.Mk 28s. These were the first helicopters actually delivered under the AOI deal, and were broadly similar to the original Lynx AH.Mk 1 used by the Army Air Corps, albeit with sand filters over the engine intakes. The first Mk 28 first flew on 2 December 1977, and the trio was delivered in 1978. The Qatari Lynxes had a relatively short career however, and were sold back to BAe, and then to the UK MoD, in 1991.

(West) Germany – Lynx Mk 88, Super Lynx Mk 88A

The German Navy's Lynx Mk 88 was based on the RN HAS.Mk 3. Like the Danish and Norwegian aircraft, the Mk 88s lacked tail rotor folding, although they were always intended to deploy aboard small ships. Optimised for ASW duties, the aircraft were fitted with Bendix AN/AQS-18(v) 'dunking' sonar. Nineteen were built for service with Marinefliegergeschwader 3 at Nordholz, in three batches of 12, two and five aircraft. The first of these made its maiden flight on 26 May 1981. The 17 survivors are being converted to Super Lynx standards as Mk 88As, which involves 're-airframing' the aircraft, together with the incorporation of various new systems.

Seven new-build Mk 88A aircraft (pictured) were also ordered in a £100 million contract signed in September 1996, the first of these flying on 1 May 1999. Mk 88A 83+21 is pictured. The Mk 88A is similar to the Brazilian Mk 21A, and includes a 360° GEC-Marconi Seaspray 3000 radar and an overnose FLIR turret containing a GEC Sensors MST FLIR, in a turret installation.

Westland **Sea King**

A mid-1960s agreement with US helicopter manufacturer Sikorsky for licence production of the S-61 resulted in four US-built examples being shipped to Westland to serve as pattern aircraft.

In the hands of Westland's Chief Test Pilot Slim Sears, the first of four Sikorsky-supplied SH-3Ds lifts off from Avonmouth Docks for its flight to Yeovil in October 1966. It would be three more years before a Westland-built Sea King HAS.Mk 1 would make its maiden flight.

The first British Sea King was an SH-3D (allocated the serial G-ATYU/ XV370), which was flown from Avonmouth docks on 11 October 1966. Three more (XV371-373) were used for British ASW systems trials as part of Sea King HAS.Mk 1 (Spec. HAS.Mk 261) development for the Royal Navy.

The first of 56 production Westland Sea King HAS.Mk 1s (XV642-677/XV695-714) began flying on 7 May 1969, followed by 13 HAS.Mk 2s (with uprated Rolls-Royce Gnome H.1400 turboshafts and six-bladed tail

rotors) from mid-1976, and the first 15 HAR.Mk 3s for RAF SAR roles from September 1977. Eight more HAS.Mk 2s from early 1979 included a prototype HAS.Mk 5 ASW upgrade conversion, many of the earlier RN Sea Kings also being converted to HAS.Mk 5/6 or

HAR.Mk 5 standards. New-build HAS.Mk 5s and 6s followed from mid-1980, eventually increasing overall RN ASW Sea King deliveries to 113. The HAS.Mk 5 introduced Thorn-EMI Sea Searcher radar in a large, flat-topped radome, Racal MIR-2 Orange Crop ESM, new

sonobuoy dropping equipment and a GEC-Marconi AQS902 LAPADS acoustic processing system. The cabin was enlarged to make room for the new equipment. The HAS.Mk 6 has a further enhanced ASW suite and reduced equipment weight, resulting in a 30-minute

The first Westland Sea King (G-ATYU/XV370) was merely a navalised Sikorsky SH-3D. The next three aircraft (XV371-373) were used in trials for Royal Navy specified anti-submarine systems, and delivery of the production-standard HAS.Mk 1s to the Royal Navy began in May 1969.

Externally similar to RN HAS.Mk 1s, Germany's Sea King Mk 41s were equipped with an increased rear cabin area, with room for up to 21 passengers. The first examples entered service with Marineflieger MFG 5 at Kiel-Holtenau on 6 March 1972.

extension to endurance. Among other improvements, the Orange Crop ESM system is raised to Orange Reaper standard, and the dunking depth of the sonar is increased from 75 m (245 ft) to 213 m (700 ft).

The acquisition of three more HAR.Mk 3 SAR versions in 1985 brought RAF procurement to 19. This included one which had been acquired, in 1980, for the ETPS at Boscombe Down which was transferred to No. 202 and, later, No. 22 SAR Squadron. Another early-1992 RAF order added six upgraded HAR.Mk 3As, recommencing production of the Sea King and providing further Wessex replacements.

Assault variant

Development of a non-amphibious Sea King (without

floats) as the Commando assault, tactical and general transport began in mid-1971. The first customer deliveries were made to the Egyptian air force in early 1974. These were followed by successive RN orders, from 1979, for 41 similar HC.Mk 4 Commando helicopters. Two Mk 4X Sea Kings (ZB506/7) were built by Westland as DRA avionics, rotor and systems test aircraft for EH101 development, bringing the overall UK service procurement of all variants to 175.

Westland has supplied 147 Sea Kings (and the related Commando) to overseas customers. German Sea Kings were converted from SAR to anti-ship roles from 1986 with Ferranti Seaspray Mk 3 radar and BAeD Sea Skua AShMs (anti-ship missiles). These also arm Indian navy Mk 42Bs, while some Pakistani and Qatari Sea Kings/Commandos are equipped to launch Aérospatiale AM39 Exocet AShMs. Indian navy Mk 42Bs are Advanced Sea Kings, with 1092-kW (1,465-shp) Gnome H.1400-1T turboshafts, composite main and tail rotors and improved avionics.

The RN's lack of airborne early-warning capability resulted

in two HAS Sea Kings (XV650 and 704) being modified to AEW.Mk 2A standard with Thorn-EMI Searchwater radar and associated equipment, including anti-Exocet I-band jammers and Racal MIR-2 Orange Crop ECM. This involved fitting a large radome suspended to the starboard of the cabin and swinging back through 90° for ground stowage. Both AEW.Mk 2A development aircraft began flying in July 1982 with No. 824 Sqn. Eight other Sea Kings were modified as AEW.Mk 2As and equipped No. 849 Sqn, the FAA's historic AEW unit (shore-based at RNAS Culdrose) and RN V/STOL carrier flights from 1 November 1984.

The result of an urgent requirement for a shipboard AEW platform, the Sea King AEW.Mk 2 has proved itself to be highly effective, able to detect hostile aircraft and missiles at distances well beyond the range of the fleet.

A rarely-seen Sea King variant is the Mk 47 operated by the Egyptian air force. Comparable in equipment and role to the RN's HAS.Mk 2, it serves alongside assault variants.

Today, the Sea King remains an important type to the UK, not only for the Royal Navy, but also in financial terms, with Westland continuing to offer modifications and upgrades to operators. With the Royal Navy still taking delivery of the Sea King HAS.Mk 6 for service with its five ASW squadrons, and the RAF operating two squadron-strength SAR units as well as one flight from No. 78 Squadron in the Falkland Islands, the Sea King's future is secure. However, Westland is not planning further airframe development due to the imminent introduction of the Anglo-Italian EH101.

Below: Broadly similar to the RAF's HAR.Mk 3, Belgian Mk 48s combined the rescue-type airframe of the German and Norwegian aircraft with the engines and tail rotor of the HAS.Mk 2. In 1983 Westland undertook an upgrade which saw the introduction of an improved navigational suite and a FLIR turret.

Westland variants

Westland's Sea King is a much improved version of the Sikorsky SH-3. The versatile UK development is a successful ASW aircraft and has also given rise to capable, dedicated AEW, ASV and SAR derivatives.

Westland Sea King HAS.Mk 2

The Sea King HAS.Mk 2 came about as a direct result of improvements designed for the Australian Mk 50, whose prototype flew on 30 June 1974. The Royal Navy's HAS.Mk 2 used the same uprated 1200-kW (1,600-shp) Gnome H1400-1 engines that gave better 'hot-and-high' performance. The new variant also had the new six-bladed tail rotor which improved yaw authority at high all-up weights, plus a prominent 'barn door' intake guard. Only 21 Sea King HAS.Mk 2s were built by Westland, the rest being produced by conversion of HAS.Mk 1s. The first HAS.Mk 2 (XZ570) made its maiden flight on 18 June 1976 and No. 706 Squadron re-equipped with the new version in December 1976. The avionics fit of the HAS.Mk 2 included Plessey Type 2069 Sonar, Racal Decca 71 Doppler, TANS. Several avionics upgrades and modifications were applied during the service career of the HAS.Mk 2 and most were fleet-wide.

Westland Sea King Mk 42/42A, Mk 43 and Mk 50/50A

Mk 41: The first export customer for the Sea King was the West German Marineflieger, which ordered 22 Mk 41s for search and rescue. The Sea King Mk 41 was closely based on the Royal Navy's HAS.Mk 1 but lacked sonar and ASW role equipment. It introduced a lengthened cabin, achieved by moving the rear bulkhead 1.7 m (5 ft 8 in) further aft and the extra pair of bubble observation windows. Deliveries took place in 1973–74. Twenty surviving Mk 41s were extensively modernised and updated by MBB to give an anti-surface vessel capability in a programme which ended in 1988. They gained a Ferranti Seaspray Mk 3 radar for over-the-horizon targeting of the BAe Sea Skua ASMs, and the provision of a Ferranti Link II datalink.

Mk 42/42A: The Indian navy received batches of twelve Sea King Mk 42s in 1971 (six) and 1973-74 (six). Basically equivalent to the HAS.Mk 1, these equipped INAS 330 and INAS 336 shore-based at INS Garuda (Cochin), but frequently deployed aboard INS *Vikrant*. The first six aircraft operated from shore bases during the 1971 war with Pakistan. At least five Sea King Mk 42s have been written off, and the survivors, together with three Sea King Mk 42As (delivered in 1980) are now concentrated within INAS 330. The Mk 42As are broadly equivalent to the Royal Navy HAS.Mk 2.

Mk 50/50A: The Royal Australian Navy received ten Mk 50s in 1975-76. These essentially acted as prototype for the second generation of Sea Kings although they were fitted with the US Bendix Oceanics AN/ASQ-13A dipping sonar and a winch-operated refuelling system that permitted refuelling from ships while in flight, without having to alight. Two Mk 50As were delivered in 1983 as attrition replacements. Upon replacement by the Sikorsky S-70B-2 Seahawk, the Mk 50/50As were withdrawn from the ASW role during 1990. At about the same time, they received composite main rotor blades. The seven surviving Sea Kings serve in the utility role; their tasks include military and civilian SAR, VertRep, transport and SAS support.

Sea King HAS.Mk 1

The Royal Navy placed a production order for 56 production Sea Kings in 1966. The first prototype, XV642, made its maiden flight on 7 May 1969 and the type entered service shortly after. Serialled between XV642 and XV677, and XV695 and XV714, the 56 HAS.Mk 1s were fitted with Ecko AW391 search radar (also known as the MEL ARI.5955 or MEL lightweight) with a prominent dorsal thimble radome. Most of the avionics were housed in the bottom of the nose. The aircraft also had a Marconi AD580 Doppler, a Plessey 195 dunking sonar, electronic automatic flight control

system (AFCS) and a comprehensive communications fit. These made even the baseline Westland Sea King a significant improvement over the original US-built SH-3D from which it was derived. Armament consisted of four Mk 44 homing torpedoes, four Mk 11 depth charges, or a single WE177 nuclear depth bomb. Even with the sonar equipment left in place, the Sea King HAS.Mk 1 could carry 11 fully equipped troops, the number rising to 20 without sonar and 27 with the cabin stripped out. A 272-kg (600-lb) capacity variable-speed rescue hoist could be installed above the cabin door, and up to 2720 kg (6,000 lb) could be carried underslung. Most surviving HAS.Mk 1s were converted to HAS.Mk 2 standards. All HAS.Mk 1s had disappeared from RN service by the end of 1980.

Westland Sea King. AEW Mk 2A, AEW.Mk 5 and AEW.Mk 7

The Royal Navy's lack of organic airborne early warning cover for its carriers was highlighted by the loss of HMS *Sheffield* (acting as a radar picket) on 4 May 1982 during the Falklands war. A crash programme was instituted to provide the fleet with its own AEW platform resulting in flying hardware within only 11 weeks. The AEW Sea King was produced by conversion of Sea King HAS.Mk 1s and HAS.Mk 2s, with an I-band Thorn EMI ARI 5980/3 Searchwater maritime surveillance radar forming the heart of the programme. The pulse-compression, frequency-agile search unit is the same as used in the RAF's maritime reconnaissance Nimrods. It had a proven ability to detect low-flying targets in any sea state, and with severe weather clutter, although it had been optimised for the detection of surface targets (such as submarine periscopes) and not fast-moving airborne targets. At 3048 m (10,000 ft) the radar has a range of about 200 km (125 miles) against a fighter-sized target. The antenna for the search radar is pitch and roll stabilised and offers a full 360° scan. It is housed in an unusual inflatable domed 'kettle drum' radome made of impregnated Kevlar fabric. It can be swung down to the vertical position in flight to project below the aircraft, and can swing back to the horizontal to give sufficient ground/deck clearance to allow the aircraft to land. The radar antenna is bulky, and does cause some drag, and cruising speed with the radar deployed is limited to 166 km/h (103 mph). The original radar was retained for tactical and navigation purposes, but sonar was removed. The AEW.Mk 2A also featured Racal MIR-2 'Orange Crop' ESM, but was otherwise similarly equipped to the ASW HAS.Mk 2. Nine AEW.Mk 2As were produced by conversion, the first of these flying on 23 July 1982.

Westland Sea King HAR.Mk 3/3A and HAR.Mk 5

HAR.Mk 3: In 1975 the RAF placed an order for 15 Sea King HAR.Mk 3s to replace elderly Wessex and Whirlwind aircraft in the search and rescue (SAR) role. The HAR.Mk 3 featured lengthened cabins, long-reach winches, extra fuel tankage and extra bubble observation windows, as well as H.1400-1 engines and a six-bladed tail rotor. The aircraft's avionics were generally similar to those of the HAS.Mk 2, but also had a VHF radio for communications with the police, mountain rescue teams, etc. The initial batch of HAR.Mk 3s entered service in 1978 and was followed by a further four aircraft. Six aircraft were specially modified for service with No. 78 Sqn on the Falklands Islands. These have NVG-compatible cockpits, Navstar GPS and Racal RNS252 SuperTANS, as well as ARI 18228 radar warning receivers and provision for chaff/flare dispensers.

HAR.Mk 3A: The HAR.Mk 3A is the RAF's second-generation SAR Sea King and features a digital colour search radar, an upgraded flight control system and improved communications equipment. The first of six aircraft ordered entered service in 1993.

HAR.Mk 5: The Royal Navy's dedicated SAR Sea King is essentially a HAS.Mk 5 stripped of much of its ASW mission equipment. Uniquely among rescue Sea Kings presently in service, the four known HAR.Mk 5 conversions have MEL Sea Searcher radar.

Westland Sea King Mk 42B/42C, Mk 45/45A and Mk 47

Mk 42B/Mk 42C: India became the first customer for the Advanced Sea King when it received 20 Mk 42Bs in batches of 12 and eight. These feature 'hot-and-high' Gnome H1400-1T engines, composite main rotor blades and a new five-bladed tail rotor. Other new equipment includes launch beams for two Sea Eagle missiles, MEL Super Searcher radar, AQS-902 sonobuoy processor, HS-12 dipping sonar and Hermes ESM. The Indian Mk 42Bs serve with INAS 336, shore-based at Cochin, but are regularly deployed aboard the carriers *Viraat* and *Vikrant*, and the indigenous 'Godavri'-class frigates. The Sea King Mk 42C is a dedicated utility transport and SAR version of the Advanced Sea King. Its avionics are similar to those of the RAF's Sea King HAR.Mk 3s, but with a nose-mounted Bendix radar. Delivery of six aircraft took place between 1987 and 1988.

Mk 45/Mk 45A: The Mk 45 designation applies to six ASW Sea Kings ordered by Pakistan and delivered between 1975 and 1977. These were broadly equivalent to the Royal Navy HAS.Mk 1. Five were modified for a secondary

ASV role with provision for AM39 Exocet ASMs. The aircraft equip No. 111 Squadron (the 'Sharks') shore-based at Sharea Faisal. A single Mk 45A (ex-Royal Navy HAS.Mk 5) was acquired as an attrition replacement.

Mk 47: Saudi Arabia ordered six ASW Sea Kings on behalf of Egypt in 1974. The Sea King Mk 47 was basically similar to the Royal Navy HAS.Mk 2 and the Australian Mk 50, with virtually the same avionics and equipment fit but with the original Plessey Type 195M sonar as fitted to the HAS.Mk 1. Deliveries began in 1976. The six aircraft are based at Alexandria for ASW duties. The Egyptian Mk 47s are all winch-equipped and can perform SAR missions.

Westland Sea King HAS.Mk 5 and HAS.Mk 6

HAS.Mk 5: Main features of HAS.Mk 5 upgrade were an all-digital MEL Sea Searcher X-band radar, Plessey Type 2069 dipping sonar and AQS902 LAPADS acoustic processing and display system. Thanks to LAPADS the Sea King HAS.Mk 5 could monitor signals from passive or active sonobuoys. Some HAS.Mk 5s were equipped with the USN SH-3H's AN/AQS-81 towed MAD birds purchased from Sikorsky. The majority of HAS.Mk 5s (55) were produced by conversion of existing airframes (comprising one HAS.Mk 1, 19 HAS.Mk 2s and 35 HAS.Mk 2As); these were augmented by 30 new-build aircraft. Royal Navy Sea Kings were deployed to the Gulf for mine countermeasures and ASV duties. Two were fitted with GPS, AN/ALQ-157 IRCM jammers, M-130 chaff/flare dispensers, RWRs, secure speech radios and a door-mounted 7.62-mm (0.3-in) GPMG. Role equipment included Sandpiper FLIR, Menagerie ECM, hand-held thermal imaging equipment and Demon, a video-based mine-hunting system. Crews were expanded to include a diving supervisor and three divers. They successfully provided a rapid-reaction mine detection and destruction unit.

HAS.Mk 6: The HAS.Mk 6 is primarily an update of existing HAS.Mk 5 airframes. It offers a dramatic improvement in ASW capability pending the service entry of the EH101 Merlin. It features composite main rotor blades and a new fully integrated tactical mission system that includes a digital AQS-902G-DS enhanced sonar system integrating data from the sonobuoys and a new Digital Type 2069 dipping sonar with a much improved deep water capability. Other new equipment includes an internal AIMS (Advanced Integrated MAD System), improved IFF, ESM upgraded to Orange Reaper configuration, and a pair of VHF/UHF secure speech radios. The HAS.Mk 6 is 227–363 kg (500–800 lb) lighter than the HAS.Mk 5, this approximating to 30 minutes of extra fuel. The first converted HAS.Mk 6 flew in 1987 and was followed by 72 further conversions plus five new-build aircraft.

Sea King Mk 43 and Mk 48

Mk 43: Between 1972-73, Norway received 10 Sea Kings to provide military and civilian SAR cover. The resulting Sea King Mk 43 was broadly equivalent to the German Mk 41, and was thus based on the RN's HAS.Mk 1 airframe and engine. The aircraft equip 330 Skvadron headquartered at Bodø with operational flights at Bodø, Banak, Ørland and Sola. The nine surviving Sea Kings have been upgraded to Mk 43B standard, and have been joined by three new-build aircraft. The Mk 43B is a unique hybrid and features MEL Sea Searcher, plus a nose-mounted Bendix/King weather radar, upgraded navigation avionics and a FLIR 2000 turret.

Mk 48: Belgium received five Sea Kings for SAR duties in 1976. These were broadly similar to the RAF's HAR.Mk 3. The Sea Kings were delivered to Escadrille 40 (40 Smaldeel) at Koksijde by 1976. The aircraft have secondary VIP, troop transport, parachute jumping, underslung load, medevac, organ delivery and paramilitary and police duties. They were retrofitted with composite main rotor blades during the 1980s, and also received a major navigation systems update. All five aircraft have been upgraded with a Bendix RDR1500B radar, a FLIR Systems FLIR 2000F and an improved navigation suite.

Westland Wasp
Multi-role naval helicopter

Though its development can be traced back to the **Saro P.531**, first flown in 1958, the **Westland Wasp HAS.Mk 1** emerged in October 1962 as a highly specialised machine for flying missions from small ships, such as frigates and destroyers with limited deck pad area. The missions were ASW and general utility, but the Wasp was not sufficiently powerful to carry a full kit of ASW sensors as well as weapons, and thus in this role relied on the sensors of its parent vessel and other friendly naval forces. In the ASV role the Wasp was autonomous, and though it had no radar, it could

steer the AS12 wire-guided missile under visual conditions over ranges up to 8 km (5 miles). Other duties included SAR, liaison, VIP ferrying, casevac, ice reconnaissance and photography/ survey. The stalky quadricycle landing gear had wheels that castored so that, while the machine could be rotated on deck, it could not roll in any direction even in a rough sea. Sprag (locking) brakes were fitted to arrest all movement. Provision was made for various hauldown systems.

Wasp service

Deliveries to the Royal Navy began in 1963, and a few

were flown in Operation Corporate in the South Atlantic right at the end of their active lives when most had been replaced in RN service by the Lynx. Wasp HAS.Mk 1s operated from eight ships in that campaign, all assigned to No. 829 Squadron, FAA. Most were used in reconnaissance and utility missions, though several operated in the casevac role. Three, two from HMS *Endurance* and one from

the frigate HMS *Plymouth*, engaged the Argentine submarine *Santa Fe* and holed its conning tower with AS12s which passed clean through before exploding. Other Wasp helicopters served with the Australian, Brazilian, New Zealand and South African navies. In 2006 the Wasp remained a first-line aircraft with Indonesia, Malaysia having retired its Wasps in 2002 in favour of the Eurocopter Fennec.

SPECIFICATION

Westland Wasp HAS.Mk 1
Type: light multi-role ship-based helicopter
Powerplant: one 529-kW (710-shp) Rolls-Royce Nimbus 503 turboshaft
Performance: maximum speed with weapons 193 km/h (120 mph); cruising speed 177 km/h (110 mph); range 435 km (270 miles)

Weights: empty 1566 kg (3,452 lb); maximum take-off 2495 kg (5,500 lb)
Dimensions: main rotor diameter 9.83 m (32 ft 3 in); length overall 12.29 m (40 ft 4 in); height 3.56 m (11 ft 8 in); main rotor disc area 75.90 m² (816.86 sq ft)
Armament: two Mk 44 AS torpedoes or two AS12 AShMs

The Westland Wasp took a long time to see action. In service with the Royal Navy for nearly 20 years, Wasps were very active during the Falklands War, just in the twilight of their careers.

In 1996 the police in Toyama, Japan, took delivery of an Agusta 109K2 which was named 'Tsurugi' after Mount Tsurugi in Toyama Prefecture. The helicopter, as seen here, is optimised for mountain rescue.

Utility & Multi-Purpose Helicopters

Aérospatiale Alouette II and Lama

The Lama is used widely by Pakistan for high-altitude mountain work. The type features raised skids for better ground clearance on rough terrain.

From the outset, the Alouette II was a winner. Finding favour with military and civil operators worldwide, it was not long before it was joined by an advanced variant, the Lama.

The Alouette (lark) family of general-purpose helicopters originated with the three-seat SE.3120, which first flew on 31 July 1952. A complete redesign to utilise the 269-kW (360-shp) Turbomeca Artouste I turboshaft resulted in the SE.3130 Alouette II, flown on 12 March 1955. Further evolution of the basic helicopter produced the SE.3140 with a 298-kW (400-shp) Turbomeca Turmo II turboshaft, no

production of which ensued, and then the SA.3180 with an Astazou IIA, flown on 31 January 1961. As the Alouette II Astazou, this was certificated in France in February 1964, production aircraft taking the designation SA.318C and deliveries commencing in 1965.

Large-scale production

The Alouette II achieved unprecedented levels of production for a European

rotary-wing aircraft. Its 'bug-eye' glazed cabin seated up to five. A skid-type landing gear was standard, with retractable wheels for ground manoeuvring, and high skids, wheels or floats as options. A rescue hoist was available, with 120-kg (265-lb) capacity, and listed roles included those of flying crane, liaison, observation, training, agricultural work, photographic survey, and ambulance. In the military role, rockets, guns or air-to-surface missiles could be carried. Production ended

in 1975, with a total of 1,305 built.

Lama

Following an Indian armed forces requirement, design of the Aérospatiale Lama was begun in late 1968. Externally resembling the Alouette II, the Lama is in effect a 'hot-and-high' variant of the SE.313B. The required performance is derived by combining features of the Alouette II and III; the Lama has the Alouette II's airframe (with some reinforcement) and dynamic components of the SA.316 Alouette III, including the rotor system and powerplant.

The SA.315B prototype flew on 17 March 1969 and production was launched simultaneously in France (where the name Lama was adopted) and India (with the name Cheetah). In Brazil, Helibras assembled the Lama, using French components, as the HB 315B Gavião. This version was operated by the Bolivian air force and the Brazilian navy.

French production of the SA.315B had ended by 1991, with a total of 407 delivered.

The Alouette II is becoming quite rare in French army (ALAT) service, but a number is retained for regional defence work and for training.

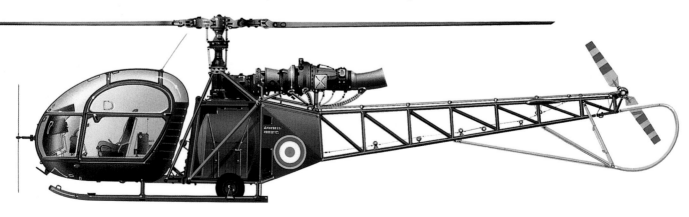

Aérospatiale **Alouette III**

Right: The performance of the SA.316B was demonstrated in 1960 when an Alouette III carrying seven people performed landings and take-offs at an altitude of 4810 m (15,780 ft) on Mont Blanc. Five months later, the same Alouette, with two crew and a 250-kg (551-lb) payload, made landings and take-offs at an altitude of 6004 m (19,698 ft) in the Himalayas, both hitherto unprecedented achievements for a helicopter. This aircraft carries Bophuthatswanan markings.

Left: The Pakistani air force shares about 30 Alouette IIIs with the army. In service since 1967, the air force machines are used for general utility, liaison, casevac and SAR duties. Pakistan's navy also operates the type in the general utility role.

Below: The Fuerza Aérea Ecuatoriana (Ecuadorian air force) obtained five SA.316Bs (right) and three SAR-configured Lamas, while the Servicio Aéreo del Ejército Ecuatoriana (army) inventory includes two Lamas. One of the Army Lamas is regularly loaned out to the Instituto Geográfico Militar for survey purposes.

Aérospatiale
Alouette family
Alouette III

Developed from the successful Alouette II, the Alouette III sold well around the world. Military operators were particularly attracted by the aircraft's versatility, allowing it to fulfil a host of different roles.

The Alouette (lark) story began with the Sud-Est SE 3101, the first all-French helicopter designed and built after World War II. This piston-engined design was refined successively through the two-seat SE 3110 and three-seat SE 3120 Alouette to the first major production version, the turboshaft-powered SE 3130 Alouette II, which set a number of world records. The Alouette II was a major success, with over 1,300 being produced, and many remaining in service today.

The Alouette III, originally designated the SE 3160, was a natural development of the Alouette II, but featured an extensively-glazed and widened cabin to accommodate seven. The dynamic components were derived from those of the Alouette II, but the more powerful 410-kW (550-shp) Artouste III turboshaft was introduced, with an extended-diameter main rotor and three-bladed tail rotor. The centre section and tail boom were covered, and tricycle landing gear was fitted.

The prototype made its first flight on 28 February 1959, and in June 1960 the new aircraft reached 4810 m (15,781 ft) in the Mont Blanc region. It immediately aroused the interest of the French military, which needed a fast, well-armed machine for the war in Algeria. Military trials were carried out with various weapons fits, including wire-guided missiles and pivot-mounted guns.

Able to fly at about 113 kt (210 km/h; 130 mph), the Alouette III was well suited to the armed forces' requirements, but the Algerian conflict ended before the type entered service. Initial deliveries were mainly to overseas customers, starting with three examples for the Burmese air force in 1961. This was followed by others to the South African Air Force and the Rhodesian Air Force. The French ALAT and Aéronavale took only 11 such helicopters between them from the initial production batch, and other early military customers included Peru and the Danish navy.

South Africa was one of the first operators of the Alouette III, which still serves with three squadrons and the Helicopter Flying School. The type took the brunt of the fighting during airborne assaults in South West Africa (Namibia) and Angola, and played a crucial part in every big cross-border operation, fulfilling a host of roles including target-spotting, airborne control, SAR and fire support.

New turboshaft

At the end of 1970 the SA 316B version with strengthened

Above: Alouette IIIs of the 3rd Air Region of the Portuguese air force were used extensively during the civil war in Mozambique between 1962 and 1975. Here, two armed crewman prepare to depart on a casualty evacuation flight in the war torn region of Cabo Delgado.

Below: The Alouette III has seen combat in a number of African countries including Mozambique, Angola, Namibia, Zaire, Portuguese Guinea and Rhodesia. South African examples were often fitted with door-mounted machine-guns.

transmission was introduced and, two years later, the SA 316C went into production with the new 649-kW (870-shp) Artouste IIID turboshaft derated to 447 kW (600 shp). Another variant, which adopted an Astazou XIV turboshaft of the same power rating, was designated the SA 319B. This last version had much greater capability, with a 25 per cent reduction in fuel consumption. A navalised version of the Alouette III was developed to deal with small surface craft such as fast torpedo-boats. It can be equipped with an autostabilisation system, ORB 31 surveillance radar, APX-Bezu 260 gyro-stabilised sight and two AS12 wire-guided missiles. For the ASW role, it can carry two Mk 44 homing torpedoes beneath the fuselage, or one torpedo and MAD gear in a streamlined container which is towed behind the helicopter on a 50-m (164-ft) cable. For air-sea rescue, a hoist is mounted on the port side of the fuselage.

French production of the Alouette III ended in 1983, by which time Aérospatiale had delivered 1,455 such helicopters to 74 countries, of which some 60 or more operated the type in military service. Production has also been extended to India and Romania under licence. HAL of India named the aircraft 'Chetak', and has built nearly 300 for home military and

government orders, and production continues. A few have been exported to a small number of countries, including the USSR.

The SA 316B version was produced in Romania by Intreprinderea de Constructii Aeronautice (ICA) as the IAR-316B, and more than 200 were built, including a number exported via Aérospatiale to Pakistan, Algeria and Angola.

Romanian development

During the early 1980s, ICA of Romania also began development of its own light attack and liaison helicopter and the result employed much of the IAR-316B's dynamic system and other components of the locally produced Alouette III. The IAR-317 Airfox was a low-cost ground-attack helicopter, and featured a slimmed-down tandem-seat cockpit, with an elevated pilot position behind the weapons operator. The IAR-316B's main landing gear, rear fuselage, tail unit and Artouste IIIB powerplant were retained, and the armament fits included podded machine-guns, unguided rockets or six anti-tank

South African Air Force Alouette IIIs are fitted with large box-type dust filters to prevent engine damage, and infra-red diffusion boxes, making them less susceptible to ground-launched heat-seeking missiles.

missiles. In addition, two 7.62-mm (0.3-in) machine-guns were built in, one on each side of the front cockpit. The prototype Airfox first flew at the ICA Brasov factory in April 1984, but development was cancelled by President Ceausescu before he was toppled from power.

South African Air Force pilots long cried out for their own attack helicopter, but the strict international arms embargo put an end to South Africa buying any such machines on the open market. So the South Africans set about building their own, again based on the Alouette III. The Alpha XH1 light attack helicopter was developed by the Atlas Aircraft Corporation in direct response to the arms restrictions.

Design of the XH1 began in March 1981 to fulfil a requirement for the SAAF. Atlas took the locally manufactured rotor and transmission system of the SA 316B, together with a Turbomeca powerplant, and married these components to a

new fuselage. The tail boom was based closely on that of the Alouette III. The cockpit was in the traditional gunship style, with the weapons operator seated in front of and below the pilot, with side entry doors and extensive glazing. Below the front fuselage was a turret-mounted 20-mm (0.79-in) GA.1 cannon, slaved to the weapons operator's helmet sight. Alternative weapons could be carried on stub pylons. The prototype first flew on 3 February 1985, under conditions of great secrecy, and its existence was not publicly announced until March 1986. Although the Alpha project never went any further, lessons learned were applied to the Puma-derived Rooivalk which followed.

The Alouette III has acquitted itself extremely well for many years in numerous countries around the world, and is appreciated where reliability and ease of maintenance are key factors.

▶

Civil use

The Alouette III was not strictly aimed at the military user and its usefulness for civilian operators was heavily promoted. It was capable of several different roles, including passenger transport, air ambulance, rescue, cargo-carrying, surveillance and aerial photography. While in the civil market its export success has never rivalled that of its military counterpart, the SA.316B has been adopted by a number of logging companies and by police forces. The French Formations Aériennes de la Gendarmerie uses its examples for rescue operations in the Alps.

Crew

The Alouette III is flown from the right-hand seat of the three forward seats, the second pilot sitting in the middle of the airframe. The flight technician (tech) or crew chief is responsible for the basic maintenance of the helicopter, acts as crewman and would man any armament fitted (in some cases, a door-mounted machine-gun). Both he and the pilots wear body armour in the otherwise unarmoured helicopter. For operational area flying, the crew chief typically sits facing aft.

Accommodation

Normal accommodation is for a pilot and six crewmen or passengers, with three seats in front and a four-person folding seat at the rear of the cabin. Two baggage holds are located in the centre-section, one on each side of the welded structure, and enclosed by the centre-section fairings. There is also provision for carrying two stretchers at the rear of the cabin, along with capacity for two medics. Alternatively, all seats can be removed to enable the aircraft to be used for freight-carrying purposes. An external sling can be fitted for loads of up to 750 kg (1,650 lb).

Naval Alouettes

The Alouette can fulfil a variety of shipborne roles, and features common naval equipment such as a quick-mooring harpoon to ensure instant and automatic mooring on landing and before take-off, a nosewheel locking device, and folding main rotor blades. For detecting and destroying small surface craft such as torpedo-boats, it can be equipped with an APX-Bézu 20 gyro-stabilised sight and two AS12 wire-guided missiles. For the ASW role, the aircraft can carry two Mk 44 homing torpedoes beneath the fuselage, or one torpedo and MAD (magnetic anomaly detection) gear in a streamlined container which is towed behind the helicopter on a 50-m (150-ft) cable. The aircraft can be used for air/sea rescue, the cabin door being protected by an anti-corrosion covering so as to prevent seawater from reaching vital components. A rescue hoist, with the capacity to lift 225 kg (500 lb), can be mounted on the port side of the fuselage.

Army and Air Force operational equipment

In the assault role, the Alouette III can be equipped with a wide range of weapons. This includes a 7.62-mm (0.3-in) machine-gun mounted athwartships on a tripod behind the pilot's seat and firing to port either through a small window in the sliding door, or through the open door. The rear seat is removed to accommodate the gun's installation. In this configuration, accommodation is reduced to pilot, co-pilot, gunner and one passenger, although one pilot and gunner is the more typical crew. Alternatively, a 20-mm (0.79-in) cannon on an open turret-type mounting can be fitted on the port-side cabin. For this installation, all seats except those of the pilots are removed, the crew consisting of just the pilot and the gunner. In the anti-armour role, the AS11 or HOT missile can be carried, while rocket pods can be fitted for the close support mission.

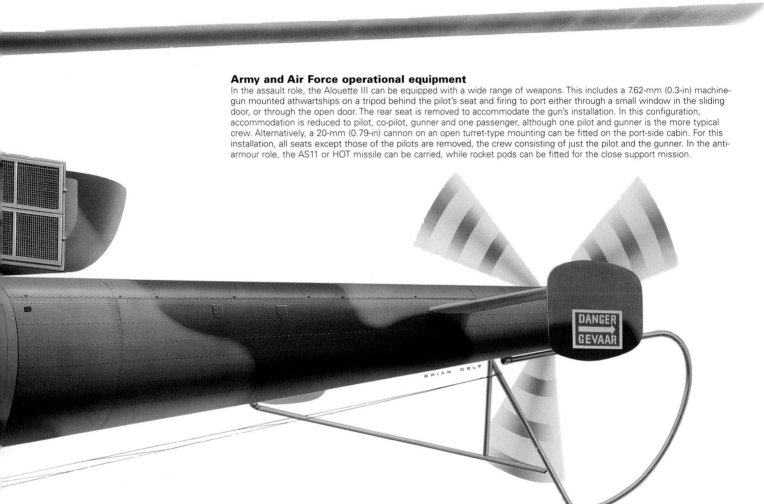

SA.316B Alouette III

Alouette IIIs played a major part in the clashes between the old, white-dominated South Africa and its neighbours from the late 1960s through to the 1990s. South African Air Force (SAAF) Nos 16, 17 and 31 Squadrons operated up to a total of 60 SA.316Bs in the transport, counter insurgency, liaison and SAR roles. Portuguese Angola became a major rival of South Africa and allowed SWAPO (South-West Africa People's Organisation) and its military arm, the People's Liberation Army of Namibia (PLAN), to secure bases on its lands. The SAAF responded with a series of assaults – one in 1976 saw eight Alouette IIIs destroy a vital waterworks system that had helped to irrigate vast swathes of farmland. Throughout the troubles, Alouette IIIs regularly transported paramilitary forces across the region or acted in support of South African ground forces. The Angolans also operated a number of Alouettes.

▶

Alouette briefing

*Aérospatiale's SA.316B has been exported to 190 operators in 72 countries. A further 400 examples have been built by **HAL** in India and by **ICA-Brasov** in Romania. This example (escorted by a Puma) is from the South African Air Force.*

SA.316B
Alouette III

Cutaway key
1 FM homing antennas, port and starboard
2 Pitot head
3 Instrument access panel
4 Cockpit ventilating air intake
5 Antenna mounting
6 Downward-view windows
7 Curved windscreen panels
8 Standby compass
9 Instrument panel shroud
10 Pilot's instrument console
11 Weapons system control panel
12 Centre control pedestal
13 Yaw control rudder pedals
14 Landing lamp
15 Floor beam construction

16 Levered suspension nose landing gear leg strut
17 Non-retracting castoring nosewheel
18 Port navigation light
19 Door jettison linkage
20 Cyclic pitch control column
21 Central power and engine condition levers
22 Collective pitch control lever
23 Control column handgrip
24 Missile hand-controller
25 Safety harness
26 Starboard jettisonable cockpit door
27 Outside air temperature gauge
28 Starboard sliding cabin door
29 Cabin roof glazing

30 APX-Bezu 260 gyro-stabilised sight
31 Retractable sight controller and binocular viewer
32 Pilot's seat
33 Co-pilot/weapons officer's seat
34 Sliding side window panel
35 Port jettisonable cockpit door
36 Collective pitch-control lever
37 Seat mounting rails (three-abreast front seat row)
38 Boarding step
39 Lower fuselage 'raft' section skin panelling
40 Port sliding cabin door

41 Passenger/cargo loading
42 Door hatches/stretcher handle apertures
43 Door latches
44 Troop-carrying folding seats (four)
45 Fixed backrest
46 Control rod linkages
47 Sliding doortop rail
48 Cabin rear-sloping bulkhead
49 Trim/insulating panelling
50 First-aid kit

51 Anti-collision light
52 VHF aerial
53 Cabin roof skin panelling
54 Rotor head control rods
55 Main transmission gearbox
56 Swash plate mechanism
57 Blade pitch angle control rods
58 Torque scissor links
59 Rotor head hinge fitting
60 Lifting fitting
61 Hydraulic drag hinge dampers
62 Bracing cables
63 Three-bladed main

rotor
64 Blade root attachment joints
65 Blade pitch angle control horn
66 Engine inlet filter screen
67 Starboard engine inlet
68 Accessory equipment gearbox
69 Generator
70 Engine transmission shaft
71 Rotor brake
72 Transmission oil cooler
73 Oil tank

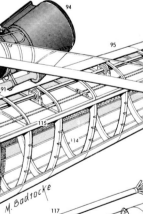

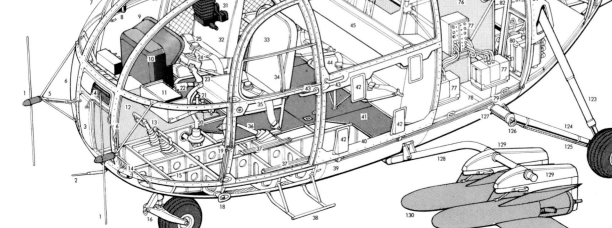

M. Badtocke

France still retains a significant Alouette capability and the Aéronavale is the major operator. These ageing aircraft remain in service due to the delays over the entry into service of the NH 90. About 70 examples of the Alouette II and the Alouette III are operated by 20, 22 and 23 Escadrille de Servitude, performing in the general utility and training roles.

74 Oil cooler airduct
75 Gearbox mounting deck
76 Fuel tank, capacity 126.5 Imp gal (575 litres)
77 Electrical system

bellmouth air inlet
90 Rear engine mounting strut
91 Tailpipe negative pressure cooling air duct
92 Engine combustion section

SPECIFICATION

SA.319 Alouette III Astazou

Dimensions

Fuselage length: 10.03 m (32 ft 10¾ in)
Length with rotors turning: 12.84 m (42 ft 1½ in)
Height: 3 m (9 ft 10 in)
Wheeltrack: 2.60 m (8 ft 6¼ in)
Main rotor diameter: 11.02 m (36 ft 1¾ in)
Tail rotor diameter: 1.90 m (6 ft 3¼ in)
Main rotor disk area: 95.38 m² (1,026.68 sq ft)
Tail rotor disk area: 2.87 m² (30.84 sq ft)

Powerplant

One 649 kW (870-shp) Turbomeca Astazou XIV derated to 447 kW (600 shp)

Weights

Empty: 1140 kg (2,513 lb)
Maximum take-off: 2250 kg (4,960 lb)

Fuel and load

Internal fuel: 575 litres (126.5 Imp gal)
External fuel: None
Maximum payload: 750 kg (1,653 lb)

Performance

Maximum level speed 'clean' at sea level: 118 kt (220 km/h; 136 mph)
Maximum cruising speed at sea level: 106 kt (220 km/h; 136 mph)
Maximum rate of climb at sea level: 270 m (885 ft) per minute
Hovering ceiling: 3100 m (10,170 ft)
Range: 326 nm (605 km/375 miles)

Armament

A wide range of light weaponry can be carried by the Alouette when it is engaged in combat duties. A 7.62-mm (0.3-in) machine-gun can be fired through the port door, while a 20-mm cannon in a fixed axial fairing can be mounted on the port side of the cabin. One or two MATRA 155H rocket pods firing 68-mm (2.67 in) unguided rockets are useful against soft or dispersed targets. For anti-armour missions, the Euromissile HOT, the AS11 or the FN ETNA TMP-5-twin 7.62-mm (0.3-in) machine gun pod is used. Naval Alouettes carry a pair of Mk 44 torpedoes or a MAD bird and single torpedo or search radar.

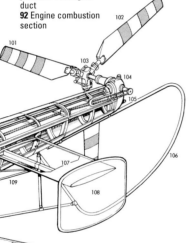

equipment
78 Equipment loading deck
79 Sliding cabin door bottom rail
80 Missile system avionics equipment
81 Position of fuel filter on starboard side
82 Welded steel tube centre fuselage framework
83 Gearbox mounting struts
84 Non-structural skin panelling
85 Fireproof engine mounting deck
86 Angled tail rotor transmission shaft
87 Engine reduction gearbox
88 Ignition control unit
89 Port engine

93 Turboméca Artouste IIIB turboshaft engine
94 Engine exhaust duct
95 Tailboom top decking/access panel
96 Tail rotor transmission shaft
97 Transmission shaft bearings
98 Tail rotor control cables
99 Starboard fixed tailplane
100 Endplate tailfin
101 Three-bladed tail rotor
102 All-metal tail rotor blades
103 Blade pitch control mechanism
104 Right-angle final drive gearbox
105 Tail navigation light

106 Steel tube tailskid/rotor protector
107 Port fixed tailplane
108 Port endplate tailfin
109 Tailplane bracing struts
110 Main rotor blade balance weights
111 Aluminium alloy blade spar
112 Moltoprene foam trailing-edge filler
113 Bonded aluminium alloy rotor blade skin panels
114 Tailboom frame and stringer construction
115 Upper longeron
116 Tailboom attachment joints
117 68-mm folding fin aircraft rocket (FFAR)
118 MATRA rocket launcher pack

119 Missile pylon adaptor
120 Missile launch rail
121 AS12 wire-guided air-to-surface missiles (two)
122 Port mainwheel
123 Shock absorber leg strut
124 Trailing axle beam
125 Hydraulic brake pipe
126 Tie-down point
127 Axle beam pivot fixing
128 Weapons pylon mount
129 Detachable missile pylons
130 AS11 wire guided air-to-surface missiles (four)

Still remaining in service with several Alouette III operators, the AS12 air-to-surface missile entered service in 1960. Four of these missiles can be carried by the SA.316B and are generally used in the anti-tank role. The AS12 has three different warhead fits: semi-armour piercing, shaped charge and fragmentation. Detonation of the missile is delayed until the missile has passed through 20 mm (¾ in) of armour; it will then explode 2 m (6½ ft) beyond the entry point. The most famous use of the AS12 was by British Wasp helicopters, which used the weapon to damage the Argentine submarine, Santa Fé. Most Alouette III operators now use the HOT missile rather than the AS12.

Military & police operators

The Squirrel (Ecureuil) has proved to be a versatile military helicopter. Quite apart from basic transport and training aircraft, Eurocopter has developed a number of armed variants and even seagoing anti-submarine versions. The Squirrel family has also been adopted by police forces as a capable and efficient law-enforcement helicopter.

Australia

Development of a dedicated military version of the AS 350 did not come until several years after the basic aircraft had been introduced. The AS 350B formed the basis of the militarised AS 350L, which first flew in March 1985. Powered by an Arriel 1D turboshaft, this aircraft was fitted with taller landing gear, sliding cabin doors and provision for armoured seats and weapons pylons. The AS 350L later became the AS 350L1, when powered by the 546-kW (732-shp) Arriel 1D1 turboshaft engine.

Several customers ordered civilian-standard AS 350Bs before the AS 350L/L1 came on the market. Australia acquired a total of 24 AS 350Bs, which have since been upgraded to AS 350BA standard. Six of these aircraft serve in a shipboard role with a single squadron of the Royal Australian Navy (illustrated), while 18 are attached to the Army-run Australian Defence Force Helicopter School, which provides basic training for all service helicopter pilots.

Other developments and operators

As the Squirrel was intended to be an Alouette II and III replacement, it was inevitable that it would soon find its way into military service. The Ecureuil has been acquired in respectable numbers by the French air force, but it has also been widely exported and even built under licence in Brazil and China.

The basic AS 350B was first bought by Australia, but Singapore also uses the AS 350B as a basic transport and training aircraft. An initial batch of six AS 350Bs was reinforced with 20 later-model AS 550 aircraft, which are now split between two squadrons of the Republic of Singapore Air Force.

In January 1990 Aérospatiale dropped the original name and designations of the Ecureuil family in favour of a new distinct military identity, the single-engined AS 550 Fennec and twin-engined AS 555 Fennec. A series of sub-types was introduced for each model. For the AS 550 family these included the AS 550U2 utility transport; AS 550A2 cannon-armed combat version; AS 550C2 missile-armed combat version; AS 550C2 unarmed naval utility version; and AS 550C2 armed naval version. In 1990 the Danish army acquired 12 combat-capable AS 550C2s, armed with the ESCO HeliTOW system. This comprises a roof-mounted sight and four TOW missiles in twin pods on each pylon. A similar system is in service in Singapore. The AS 555 family has its own sub-divisions, including the: AS 555UN utility transport; AS 555AN cannon-armed combat version; AS 555MN naval utility version; and AS 555SN armed naval version.

The naval version of the AS 555 is intended for operation from vessels as small as 600 tons. It can be fitted with an AlliedSignal (formerly Bendix King) RDR-1500 360° search radar in a radome under the nose and can carry a Sextant Avionique Mk 3 MAD (Magnetic Anomaly Detector) under the tailboom. A comprehensive Sextant Nadir Mk 10 Doppler navigation fit was added, as was an SFIM three-axis autopilot. The AS 555 can carry an offensive load of two NATO-standard Mk 44 or Mk 46 torpedoes or two French-built Murène weapons.

Defence Helicopter Flying School, UK

A specialist training version of the civil-standard AS 350B2, the AS 350BB, was developed by Eurocopter for the UK MoD to serve with Britain's tri-service Defence Helicopter Flying School (DHFS), based at RAF Shawbury. The School operates two versions of the aircraft – 26 Squirrel HT.Mk 1s (pictured) and 12 NVG-capable Squirrel HT.Mk 2s. The latter are based at Middle Wallop and are operated by No. 670 Sqn Army Air Corps.

Colombia

The Colombian navy has acquired an indeterminate number of AS 555 Fennecs. The aircraft are equipped with search radar in a large undernose radome and are presumably used in the anti-surface vessel, anti-submarine warfare and search and rescue roles. ARC 203, illustrated below, was the third Fennec delivered and was photographed aboard the Colombian warship ARC *Almirante Padilla* at NS Roosevelt Roads, Puerto Rico in July 1999. It was taking part in the multi-national Unitas '99 exercise.

Royal Air Force, UK

In 1996 two AS 355F1s, leased from a civil contractor, entered service with the RAF's No. 32 (The Royal) Squadron, replacing the Wessex in the VVIP transport role. A further machine (illustrated) was subsequently leased by the same unit.

Brazil

Brazil has become an important Squirrel operator and Helibrás (now a Eurocopter subsidiary) has built over 300 aircraft under licence. Approximately 150 civil HB 350BAs, HB 350B2s and HB 355F2s have been produced

as the Esquilo and delivered to state police forces, government agencies, aeromedical services and offshore support operators. A wide range of variants has been developed for the military. The air force has acquired 16 CH-50 Esquilo transports (HB 550U2), 20 TH-50 trainers (below, right) with a secondary fire-fighting role (HB 550U2), 11 armed CH-55s (HB 555U2) and two VIP-dedicated VH-55s (HB 355F2). The Brazilian navy operates 16 UH-12s (HB 550BA) and nine UH-12Bs (HB 355F2) (above). The army flies a mix of 36 HA-1s (HB 550A2) (below, left), 16 devoted to transport tasks and 20 for basic training/firefighting.

Paraguay

The Paraguayan air force has taken delivery of two HB 350B Esquilos (illustrated), while the navy has acquired another two HB 350Bs.

Police aviation

Together with McAlpine Helicopters in the UK, Aérospatiale/Eurocopter has developed a version of the AS 355N, known as the Police Twin Squirrel. This helicopter is capable of carrying a GEC thermal-imaging camera (FLIR) under the nose, with an operator's station in the rear cabin. A 30-million candlepower NiteSun searchlight is mounted in an articulated pod aft of the cabin and two Skyshout loudhailers can be carried on the undercarriage legs. The Police Squirrel has military-style sliding cabin doors and extended skids to accommodate all the new underfuselage equipment. In the UK, Staverton-based Police Aviation Services currently acts as a service provider for most Police Air Support Units (ASUs) around Britain. It has a fleet of 10 Police Squirrels, each of which is attached to a different force (or emergency medical service).

France

The more powerful AS 355 Twin Squirrel (Ecureuil 2) was a more attractive choice to some military operators, and a dedicated military version, the AS 355M, was developed in 1988/89. France became the primary customer for this version, with an initial order for 50 placed by the Armée de l'Air. France eventually acquired 52 Ecureuil 2s, the first eight of which were powered by Allison 250-C20F turboshafts. The other 44 (delivered from January 1990 onwards) were fitted with Turboméca TM 319 Arrius-1M engines. An

export version was dubbed AS 355M2. Development of the AS 555 was driven by the French requirement for an armed patrol and escort version. Aérospatiale qualified several rocket systems for the AS 555 and the aircraft is also notionally HOT- or

TOW-capable. In French service the AS 355AN has been solely gun-armed, usually with the GIAT M621 20-mm (0.79-in) cannon, though MATRA or FN machine-gun pods are also available. The AS 555ANs (top) are attached to transport helicopter units around the country, but perhaps the best-known are those operated by EHOM 00/068 in French Guyana, which provide perimeter security for the Ariane rocket launch site. The French army originally expressed a need for 100 Ecureuils but has acquired just 18 AS 555UNs for IFR training tasks. The Formations Aériennes de la Gendarmerie has a fleet of 30 single-engined Ecureuils (above).

Argentina

1ª Escuadrilla Aeronaval de Helicópteros, of the Argentine navy's Fuerza Aeronaval No. 2, flies the AS 555MN alongside SA 316B Alouette IIIs. The Fennecs are unarmed, but operate with undernose radar. Flotation equipment is fitted to the skids, in case of a ditching at sea, since the aircraft regularly operate from Argentine navy warships.

Special equipment 1989
At this time the helicopter was used primarily as an observation platform to assist units on the ground. It could, however, be used as a means of detecting speeding motorists on London's motorways by means of a small hand-held computer, stopwatch and pre-surveyed points on the road such as bridges or painted road markings.

Special equipment 1999
A typical police fit in 1999 would include thermal imaging and video cameras, searchlights, loudspeakers, a microwave downlink and even a Direct Voice Command system. In some cases, ground units are able to see exactly what is being viewed from the helicopter by means of real-time transmissions.

Colour schemes
This aircraft has a replacement door, taken from an aircraft of another ASU, hence the discontinuity and incorrect badge. The machine is finished in what was considered a high-conspicuity scheme, but new research has led to the majority of forces adopting overall black and yellow colours for high conspicuity in a wide range of light conditions.

AS 355 Ecureuil 2

G-BOSK is illustrated as it appeared in 1989 with the Metropolitan Police Force Air Support Unit (ASU). The aircraft has a very basic equipment fit by the standards of the late 1990s, but marked a great improvement over previous types in police use. The safety benefits of the AS 355's twin engines are appreciated when flying over urban areas.

Agusta A 109
Utility helicopter

Deliveries of the A 109 to Italy's military police force began in 1979. A total of 17 A 109As and 12 A 109A Mk IIs was originally received, but a joint total of just 25 remained in service in the late 1990s.

The A 109 was designed primarily for the civil market, but it has also been bought, to a lesser extent, by military operators. The A 109 features retractable landing gear, a fully articulated, four-bladed main rotor using blades of bonded aluminium alloy construction over a Nomex core and a swept vertical tail surface with a two-bladed tail rotor to port.

The initial A 109 was powered by a single Turbomeca Astazou XII turboshaft rated at 515 kW (690 shp), but was revised in 1967 to the uprated and considerably more reliable twin-engined powerplant of two Allison 250-C14s, each rated at 276 kW (370 shp). The A 109B was planned as a utility model for military use, but was abandoned in 1969. Deliveries of the production version of the helicopter began in 1976. By then redesignated as the A 109A, this model soon proved a commercial success.

Several air arms procured the type in small numbers for liaison and utility transport. Of four

The US Coast Guard's MH-68A Stingrays are operated by the Helicopter Interdiction Tactical Squadron, based at Jacksonville, Florida, on armed patrol duties.

bought by Argentina, two were captured by British forces during the Falklands War of 1982 and pressed into service with No. 7 Regiment, Army Air Corps, at Netheravon and later augmented by two more.

The Italian job
In 1989, a 'wide-body' A 109C version with uprate transmission was introduced, featuring a more roomy and comfortable cabin. One example was delivered to 31° Stormo of the AMI for use as a presidential transport.

By this time, it had been fully appreciated that as a result of its very good performance, the A 109 offered greater military potential than originally

No. 8 Flight is normally based at Hereford and operates four Agusta A 109As and two Gazelles in support of the SAS. Two of the A 109As were captured from Argentina by CBAS (Commando Brigade Air Squadron) personnel during the Falklands War. They were then transported back to Britain and handed over to the AAC, where they remained in storage for some years before being returned to military use.

envisaged, and the type was therefore developed to fill a variety of military roles including the scout, casevac and attack tasks. The Italian army's Aviazione Leggera dell'Esercito procured 24 examples of the **A 109EOA** (Elicottero d'Osservazione Avanzata, or advanced observation helicopter) with the uprated powerplant of two Allison 250-C20Rs, each rated at 335.5 kW (450 shp). These were all delivered during 1988 to a standard that included sliding rather than hinged cabin doors for rapid access, a roof-mounted SFIM M334-25 daylight sight with boresighted CILAS laser rangefinder and a variety of armament options – the latter was carried on two outrigger pylons installed one on each side of the main cabin. Further militarisation resulted in fixed landing gear, ECM equipment and a crashworthy fuel system being fitted.

Agusta then offered as its principal military model the **A 109CM**, which was based on the A 109EOA but with a wider range of options including different sights. The Belgian army was the only customer, with 46 such **A 109BA** machines comprising 18 configured as scouts and the remaining 28 configured for the anti-armour role, with the local designations **A 109HO** and **A**

109HA, respectively. The scouts feature a Saab Helios roof-mounted observation sight, while the anti-tank helicopters have a Saab/ESCO HeliTOW 2 sight and provision for eight TOW 2A anti-armour missiles. The A 109BA helicopters were assembled in Belgium by SABCA and feature cable-cutters for enhanced low-level flight safety in a northern European operational environment littered with potentially lethal power and telephone cables.

'Hot and high' model

Looking to African and Middle Eastern markets, more recent development concentrated on the multi-role **A 109K** for 'hot and high' applications, with a new powerplant driving an uprated transmission, a lengthened nose to accommodate a more comprehensive array of avionics and a number of detail improvements. Dedicated military versions are the **A 109KM** land-based version, with fixed landing gear and sliding cabin doors, and the similar **A 109KN** naval version, which added shipborne capability and maritime weapons.

Military A 109s can be armed with 7.62- or 12.7-mm (0.3- or 0.5-in) trainable machine-guns pintle-mounted in the cabin

doorways. They also have four hardpoints extended from the sides of the lower fuselage on pylons for the carriage of stores, including 7.62- or 12.7-mm machine-gun pods, 70- or 80-mm (2.75- or 3.15-in) rocket launchers, up to eight TOW anti-tank missiles or Stinger short-range air-to-air missiles. The A 109 can also carry light UAVs (unmanned aerial vehicles), and in the maritime role can launch anti-ship missiles.

Further developments in the A 109 series have been the **A 109G** coastal patrol and law enforcement variant powered by a pair of Allison 250-C20Rs. An armed derivative of the civilian A 109 Power, eight **MH-68A Stingray** helicopters are leased by Agusta Westland to the US Coast Guard for use on drug interdiction and homeland security missions. The USCG's

Helicopter Interdiction Tactical Squadron was commissioned in May 2003 and is the first US airborne law enforcement unit authorised to use airborne force. The MH-68A features Pratt & Whitney 206C engines and advanced FLIR equipment.

Customers for the latest **A 109LUH** (Light Utility Helicopter) and **A 109LOH** (Light Observation Helicopter) models include Malaysia (11 LOH for army aviation), South Africa (30 LUH for the SAAF, of which 25 are to be assembled locally by Denel) and Sweden (20 LUH for air force training duties, under the local designation **Hkp 15**, and with airframes manufactured by Denel). The Swedish machines will also be used for utility, ASW, SAR and medevac, with a number being equipped for ship-based operations.

Both the LOH and LUH are powered by two Turboméca Arrius 2K2 or Pratt & Whitney 207C turboshafts. The LOH version is intended to undertake observation, recon, tactical transport and area suppression roles. Slovenia, meanwhile, acquired a single civilian A 109 Power helicopter for use in the border patrol, civil protection, SAR and medevac roles.

SPECIFICATION
Agusta A 109KM

Type: eight-seat light utility helicopter
Powerplant: two Turbomeca Arriel IK turboshaft engines, each rated at 522 kW (700 shp) for take-off and 436 kW (585 shp) for continuous running
Performance: never-exceed speed 281 km/h (174 mph); maximum cruising speed 264 km/h (164 mph) 'clean' at sea level; initial climb rate 530 m (1,740 ft) per minute; service ceiling 6095 m (20,000 ft); hovering ceiling 5640 m (18,500 ft)

in ground effect and 3350 m (11,000 ft) out of ground effect; range 537 km (333 miles)
Weights: empty 1595 kg (3,517 lb); maximum take-off 2850 kg (6,283 lb)
Dimensions: main rotor diameter 11 m (36 ft 1 in); length overall 13.04 m (42 ft 9½ in) with rotors turning and fuselage 11.11 m (36 ft 5½ in); height 3.3 m (10 ft 10 in) to top of fin; main rotor disc area 95.03 m² (1,022.96 sq ft)
Armament: see main text

Agusta A 119 Koala
Utility/training helicopter

First flown early in 1995, the **Agusta A 119 Koala** is a light utility helicopter derived from the A 109 helicopter, although it differs most obviously in the use of fixed twin-skid landing gear in place of the earlier type's retractable tricycle landing gear. The dynamic system is of the classic light helicopter type, with the single turboshaft engine located above the rear part of the pod-and-boom fuselage's pod section and immediately to the rear of the gearbox that translates the power to the rotor system. The latter comprises a four-bladed main rotor (with fully articulated composite blades attached to a titanium alloy hub) and a two-bladed tail rotor on its port side.

The prototype was built with a Turbomeca Arriel I turboshaft, rated at 596.5 kW (800 shp), but the engine selected for the production version, after consideration of Allison and Pratt & Whitney Canada units, was the latter's PT6B-37/1. It is claimed that the Koala offers 30 per cent more cabin volume than any comparable single-engined light helicopter. The incorporation of a large sliding door on each side of the cabin certainly provides easy access for up to six passengers (or two litters when the helicopter is used in the medical evacuation role). A seventh passenger can also be carried alongside the pilot if required.

Seen here in the colours of a civilian operator, the A 119 is operated on police duties in both the United States and China and can be equipped with specialised communications and surveillance equipment.

SPECIFICATION
Agusta A 119 Koala

Type: eight-seat light utility helicopter

Powerplant: one Pratt & Whitney Canada PT6B-37/1 turboshaft engine rated at 746 kW (1,000 shp)

Performance: maximum speed 278 km/h (173 mph) at optimum altitude; cruising speed 259 km/h (161 mph) at optimum altitude; service ceiling 5455 m (17,900 ft); hovering ceiling 3320 m (10,900 ft) in ground effect and 2450 m (8,030 ft) out of ground effect; range 655 km (407 miles)

Weights: maximum take-off 2850 kg (6,283 lb) with an external load

Dimensions: main rotor diameter 11 m (36 ft 1 in); length overall 13.1 m (42 ft 11¾ in) with rotors turning and fuselage 11.06 m (36 ft 3¼ in); overall height 3.3 m (10 ft 10 in); main rotor disc area 95.03 m² (1,022.96 sq ft)

Eurocopter/CATIC/ST Aero
EC 120B Colibri
Light utility/training helicopter

The **EC 120B Colibri** is a five-seat light helicopter designed, developed and produced as a collaborative venture between Eurocopter France (overall leadership with 61 per cent as well as the dynamic system, seats, final assembly, flight test and certification), the China National Aero-Technology Import and Export Corporation (24 per cent in the form of the Harbin Aircraft Manufacturing Corporation for the cabin, landing gear and fuel system) and Singapore Aerospace Technologies (15 per cent for the boom, fins, doors and instrument pedestal). The type was initially planned as the **P120L** from February 1990, but was then extensively revised to trim 500 kg (1,102 lb)

from the maximum take-off weight. The development contract was signed in October 1992, the helicopter was redesignated in January 1993, and the first prototype recorded its maiden flight on 9 June of the same year.

The influence of Eurocopter is very evident in the overall concept of this light helicopter, which combines light alloy and composite material in a pod-and-boom fuselage and other elements of the airframe, which include twin-skid alighting gear, a three-bladed main rotor (titanium alloy Spheriflex head and composite blades of wide chord) and a tail unit (horizontal surface ahead of the large vertical surface incorporating the eight-blade advanced 'fenestron'

shrouded tail rotor). The EC 120B Colibri received its European and American certifications in July 1997 and January 1998 respectively, and delivery of production helicopters began in January 1998. The first military customers for the Colibri are

Eurocopter estimates a market for 1,600–2,000 Colibris (hummingbirds) in the period up to 2010.

Spain and Indonesia. The Spanish air force ordered 15 examples in late 1999 for use for training, based at Granada.

SPECIFICATION

Eurocopter France/CATIC/ST Aero EC 120B Colibri

Type: one-crew light utility helicopter

Powerplant: one Turboméca TM319 Arrius 2F turboshaft engine rated at 376 kW (504 shp)

Performance: maximum cruising speed 228 km/h (142 mph) at optimum altitude; initial climb rate 404 m (1,325 ft) per minute; service ceiling 5365 m (17,600 ft); hovering ceiling 3050 m (10,000 ft) in ground effect and 2530 m (8,300

ft) out of ground effect; range 731 km (454 miles)

Weights: empty 950 kg (2,094 lb); maximum take-off 1770 kg (3,902 lb)

Dimensions: rotor diameter 10 m (32 ft 9¾ in); length 11.52 m (37 ft 9½ in) with the rotor turning; height 3.4 m (11 ft 1¾ in); rotor disc area 78.54 m² (845.42 sq ft)

Payload: up to four passengers or freight carried in the cabin, or 700 kg (1,543 lb) of freight carried as a slung load

Eurocopter EC 135 and EC 635
Multi-role light helicopter

Resulting from a programme launched in the mid-1980s for a technology development helicopter, the **BO 108** first flew in October 1988 with the powerplant of two Allison 250-C20R turboshaft engines. The powerplant drove a dynamic system that included a four-bladed main rotor derived from that of the BO 105 and a conventional tail rotor, although a new all-composite tail rotor of the bearingless type was introduced in 1990. In January 1991 the manufacturer announced that the BO 108 would be used as the basis of a helicopter to succeed the BO 105 in the light utility role with only 75 per cent of the earlier type's operating costs. In January 1992 the type became the **Eurocopter Deutschland EC 135** to reflect the merger of

the helicopter divisions of Aérospatiale and MBB as Eurocopter.

The first true prototype flew on 5 June 1991 with two Turbomeca TM319-1B Arrius turboshafts, and the primary changes effected during the development programme were an increase in the maximum seating capacity to seven persons, and the replacement of the tail rotor by a shrouded multi-bladed rotor of the 'fenestron' type. This was used in conjunction with a bearingless main rotor with composite blades. There followed two pre-production prototypes with different powerplants of the types proposed as alternatives for the production model: the first machine had 435-kW (583-shp) Arrius 2B engines while the second had 463-kW (621-shp)

Pratt & Whitney Canada PW206B engines. A third pre-production prototype was subsequently built, and these three machines undertook the bulk of the development programme. The first production helicopter was delivered in July 1996, and by December 1998 the EC 135 had been cleared for IFR as well as VFR operation. The primary models are the **EC 135P1** with PW206B

engines, the **EC 135T1** with Turbomeca engines in their initial Arrius 2B and later Arrius 2B1 models, the **EC 135 ACT/FHS** (Active Control Technology/Flying Helicopter Simulator) model within the German programme to develop 'fly-by-light' technology, and the **EC 135 Police** with options for different sensor and equipment fits. Police and border patrol versions of the EC 135 are used in Chile, the Czech Republic, Germany, Ireland, Kuwait, Spain, Sweden, the UK and the US.

Military derivative

The almost instant success in the commercial field encouraged Eurocopter to target the EC 135 at the military market. A military mock-up was prepared through the conversion of the first pre-production machine and unveiled in 1998. An offer to the South African Air Force proved unsuccessful, but the new type, designated **EC 635**, was launched with an order for nine machines from the Portuguese army air corps in 1999. This order was cancelled in 2002. In March 2003, the Royal Jordanian Air Force confirmed its acquisition of up to 16 EC 635s.

SPECIFICATION	
Eurocopter EC 635T1 **Type:** multi-role light helicopter **Powerplant:** two Turbomeca Arrius 2B1 turboshaft engines each rated at 500 kW (670 shp) **Performance:** maximum cruising speed 259 km/h (161 mph) at sea level; maximum climb rate 504 m (1,653 ft) per minute at sea level; service ceiling 6095 m (20,000 ft); range 878 km (545 miles) with maximum standard fuel and 675 km (420 miles) with standard fuel	**Weights:** empty 1470 kg (3,240 lb); maximum take-off 2835 kg (6,250 lb) **Dimensions:** rotor diameter 10.2 m (33 ft 5½ in); length 12.16 m (39 ft 10¾ in) with the rotor turning; height 3.62 m (11 ft 10½ in) with the rotor turning; rotor disc area 81.71 m² (879.58 sq ft) **Payload:** maximum mission weight, including fuel and slung external payload, 1380 kg (3,042 lb)

HAL Advanced Light Helicopter/Dhruv
Multi-role helo

In July 1984 Hindustan Aeronautics Ltd signed an agreement with West Germany's MBB for the latter to provide support for the **Advanced Light Helicopter** programme. Design work began in November 1984 and the first runs of a ground vehicle followed in April 1991. The first of five flying prototypes (two basic and one each for the air force/army, navy and civil markets) made its first flight on 30 August 1992.

The fuselage of the **ALH** combines light alloy sandwich material with Kevlar and carbonfibre in its structure. The dynamic system comprises a pair of turboshafts driving four-bladed main and tail rotors. Poor political relations with the US in the aftermath of India's nuclear weapons tests ruled out the use of the 969-kW (1,300-shp) LHTEC CTS 800-4N turboshaft in favour of the Turbomeca TM333-2B2. The rotor hubs and blades are of glassfibre and carbonfibre construction and the main rotor is a hingeless unit. The rotor blade tips are swept on their leading edges.

Landing gear comprises either a pair of fixed skids (air force and army variant) or retractable wheeled gear for maritime and civil models, which have a pair of sponsons on the lower sides of the fuselage to carry the

The first ALHs entered service in March 2002. The payload-carrying section of the type's cabin is accessed by two large rearward-sliding side doors and, at the rear, clamshell doors.

single-wheel main units. However, at least one wheeled example has also been delivered to the air force. The four-axis automatic flight-control system is provided by the SFIM avionics company of France.

Military versions

As an alternative to internal freight, the ALH, known as **Dhruv** (North Star) in its military form, can carry a slung load. The variant for the air force and army has crashworthy fuel tanks, IR and flame suppression and provision for weapons delivered in the day and night attack roles. The naval variant has a harpoon deck-lock, folding tail boom and specialised avionics including mission equipment for the anti-ship and ASW roles. The two armed models can mount pylons on the sides of the fuselage with two hardpoints for weapons such as anti-ship missiles (SS-N-25 'Switchblade' or Sea Eagle are proposed) or

ASW torpedoes in the naval model, or stub wings with four hardpoints for weapons such as eight ATGMs, four rocket pods or four AAMs in the land-based model.

Deliveries of the production ALH helicopters began in 2002 to satisfy initial air force and navy requirements for 200 and 50 helicopters respectively. In the event, the first to adopt the ALH was the coast guard, on 18 March 2002. Following delivery of its first three Dhruvs two days later, the Indian army

is now in the process of raising its first two squadrons of the type.

The Dhruv will initially replace the veteran Chetak in army service, with current orders for 120 examples, of which half will be weapons systems integrated, the unarmed remainder being used in the utility and transport roles. The navy received its first two Dhruvs on 28 March 2002. The first two machines for the air force were then delivered on 30 March 2002.

SPECIFICATION
HAL Dhruv (army version) **Type:** two-crew light military utility helicopter **Powerplant:** two Turbomeca TM333-2B2 turboshaft engines each rated at 825 kW (1,100 shp); the Turbomeca/HAL Ardiden 1H/ Shakti engine is also on order **Performance:** maximum speed 290 km/h (180 mph) at sea level; cruising speed 245 km/h (152 mph) at optimum altitude; initial climb rate 720 m (2,362 ft) per minute; service ceiling 6000 m (19,685 ft); hovering ceiling more than 3000 m (9,845 ft) in ground effect; range 400 km (249 miles) with a 700-kg (1,543-lb) payload; endurance 4 hours **Weights:** empty 2450 kg (5,401 lb); maximum take-off 4000 kg (9,921 lb) **Dimensions:** main rotor diameter 13.2 m (43 ft 3¾ in); length 15.87 m (52 ft ¾ in) with the rotors turning; height 4.98 m (16 ft 4 in); main rotor disc area 136.85 m² (1,473.06 sq ft) **Payload:** up to 14 passengers or freight in the cabin, or up to 1500 kg (3,307 lb) of freight **Armament:** see text

Index